Biological and Chemical Control

of Plant and Animal Pests

A symposium presented by Section O on Agriculture at the Indianapolis meeting of the American Association for the Advancement of Science, December 28-30, 1957

Edited by

L. P. REITZ

Publication No. 61 of the

AMERICAN ASSOCIATION FOR THE ADVANCEMENT OF SCIENCE

Washington, D.C., 1960

Preface

Surely farming, stock-raising, and gardening would be much simpler, and more profitable, if there were no pests. Biologists and conservationists know this pseudo-Utopian state can never quite be achieved; however, they agree with the farmer that severe losses are caused by diseases, insects, weeds, and other pests which persistently harass man's plant and animal food producers.

Some 120 million fewer acres of cropland would have produced the 1942-51 volume of food, feed, and fiber in the United States if all losses in production had been eliminated according to a preliminary report on losses in agriculture published by the U. S. Department of Agriculture. Losses are of several kinds but include the reduction in quantity or quality of products and the deterioration of farm and forest lands. Some losses are preventable by known technology; others presumably will be preventable as research points the way through new discoveries. Still other losses, or wastages, probably are an inevitable part of nature and may never be preventable. For the ten-year period ending with 1951, the reported estimated loss to crops, pastures, ranges, livestock, and products was 32 per cent. Of this, nearly 7 per cent was due to diseases of crops, nearly 5 per cent to crop insects, and nearly 7 per cent to the parasites and diseases of livestock. The vast forest resource of the United States is depleted annually by an equivalent of 226,930,000 acres of annual growth or nearly 1 per cent of the total farm and forest production potential. In terms of annual loss, the acreage equivalent accounted for by diseases was 68,540,000 acres and by insects 53,820,000 acres of production. Fire and wind also cause heavy losses to forests.

Science and scientists have joined battle with these ancient foes, and, through chemical and biological means, have intro-

duced control measures scarcely dreamed of twenty-five years ago. Just how much has been accomplished, some of the consequences of it, and some hint of what more may be done is discussed in this symposium.

DDT and 2,4-D are household words that have come into our vocabulary in one generation. Insect and weed control by these two chemicals is truly revolutionary and miraculous. In addition, agriculture now has available over 200 other basic chemicals for pest control. These in various combinations and formulations number into the thousands of chemical materials available to the public.

What a contrast to forty-five years ago when, on the farm, as I recall, we were limited to salt for stumps, kerosene to control chicken mites, and something called "stock-dip" for all general purposes around the barn and hog lots. On rainy days, or "while we rested" according to father, we boys cut brush, cleaned out the chicken house, or perhaps burned cobs to provide charcoal for the hogs—this was to improve their health. I am not sure that any lasting good came from this activity, but we boys developed big appetites, rain or shine. Now chemicals kill brush and weeds selectively, poultry insects seldom touch a bird from egg to roaster, and pigs get anthelmintics in their daily ration. In college I learned that corn had an odor altogether different from that of chinch bugs—we had these pests practically every year and the odor they imparted to corn seemed normal to me. During World War II we gave up our apple orchard because ten applications of arsenate of lead did not control codling moth and labor was too costly for picking wormy apples.

Part I is concerned largely with the stake every citizen has in pest control. The first paper deals with national policy developed by the United States Department of Agriculture and cooperating state agencies in quarantine and eradication programs in contrast to pest reduction by biological and chemical means. This is followed by two papers dealing with the control of insects and diseases in our national forests and other timbered lands. The proper public relations and the education of users of pesticides, treated in the fourth paper, is a key to getting

public support for control programs, and achieving a reasonable public attitude in the use of chemicals, and a proper assessment of the dangers, as well as the benefits, from their use. Part I closes with a discussion of regulatory control of pesticides, residues considered safe, and explanation of this problem in terms of public safety.

Part II relates recent developments and concepts about chemicals, how they are transported, how they kill, and their potential both for plant and animal health, and for eliminating or reducing undesirable forms of life. The four chapters treat the control of diseases, weeds, insects, and internal animal parasites. The study of chemicals for pest control has evolved through several distinct phases, namely, empirical testing, systematic evaluation of the more promising groups of materials and their analogs, and, finally, studies on what the chemical becomes once it is inside the plant or animal body. The concern about residues within or on the foods from treated plants or animals is not confined to how much of it remains, but also about what the chemical has become. In contrast are the favorable changes for pest control that may occur in some pests when treated with relatively innocuous chemicals. For example, certain phenoxybutyric acids, having little weedicide power, are changed to 2,4-D in some weeds. Chemicals that become systemic in the plant or animal are the most sought at present. These would protect the plant or animal at considerable distance from the point of application. Systemic action has been demonstrated in a number of instances and more will come from this research.

The last paper in this section proves beyond doubt that chemical control for internal parasites of domestic animals is a coming thing. Cited with this one review are 140 papers! In addition to ET-57 recommended for use as a systemic grub killer, USDA now recommends, for control of certain livestock pests, the use of Co-Ral, another systemic grub killer, which is commercially available. With proper precautions it may be used as a spray on cattle for the control of grubs, horn flies, lice, ticks, keds, and screwworms, and on swine for the control

of lice and screwworms. One of this compound's most beneficial uses is for screwworm control. A single treatment de-
stroys existing infestations and usually protects against rein-
festation until the wounds heal, or 7 to 14 days. Higher quality
meat and less waste result from its use.

Part III is on biological control of pests. Basically this mechanism is always operative—too feebly, sometimes, and the pest
overwhelms us. However, always there is some truth in the
jingle, "Big bugs have little bugs upon their backs to bite them,
. . ." except when a pest is introduced into a new area where the
normal enemies do not exist. Numerous examples are reviewed
where such situations have been alleviated by introducing biological counteragents. Antagonists, parasites, predators, the
environment, and management all come into play in biological
control.

Also included in biological control measures are genes for
resistance. Great strides forward have been made through plant
and animal breeding. So many examples of success are known
in plants, especially, that some overenthusiasts see breeding as
the solution to all our problems with pests. Here caution is
needed because good genetic material is not always obtainable,
and pests have genetic mechanisms of their own for adaptation.
One result from breeding resistant varieties is a shift in selection pressure on the pest and a corresponding shift to the genotypes that can survive on the newly bred resistant hosts. This
does not always happen but it is frequent enough to be a continuing challenge to breeders and pathologists.

The nine papers on biological control scarcely do more than
open the subject. Whole books could be and, in fact, have already been written on many of the topics. Although less dramatic, perhaps, than chemical control, biological control is the
ideal way to control pests—no residue problems, no continuing
expense, no further attention by growers. Realization of the
ideal is a long way off for many plant problems; it has scarcely
started in the animal field.

The experts who contributed to the symposium swayed us
first to a viewpoint that ". . . now nothing will be restrained

from them, which they have imagined to do" (Genesis 11:6)
and then to a more sober mood by noting that "he made a
pit . . . and is fallen into the ditch which he made" (Psalms 7:15).
There can be no doubt that much optimism is warranted by
the outstanding achievements and the rapidity with which new
discoveries are adding almost daily to more nearly complete
mastery over our pests. For the most part these advances are
carefully checked out by field tests before being given to the
public. Now and then, however, we get a setback. Recently
a miticide has been recalled (zero tolerance now) because of its
newly discovered carcinogenic properties when fed to dogs and
rats at rates as low as 500 parts per million. In 1950, a new race
of wheat stem rust suddenly occurred in epidemic proportions
and attacked all commercial varieties grown in the United
States. These, however, do not constitute a basis for rejecting
biological and chemical control of plant and animal pests.

L. P. REITZ

U.S. Department of Agriculture
Beltsville, Maryland

Contributors

James A. Beal, Division of Forest Insect Research, Forest Service, United States Department of Agriculture, Washington, D.C.

R. H. Beatty, Amchem Products, Inc., Ambler, Pennsylvania

John D. Briggs, Bioferm Corporation, Wasco, California

John E. Casida, Department of Entomology, College of Agriculture, The University of Wisconsin, Madison, Wisconsin

M. R. Clarkson, Agricultural Research Service, United States Department of Agriculture, Washington, D.C.

E. H. Fisher, Department of Entomology, College of Agriculture, The University of Wisconsin, Madison, Wisconsin

Charles A. Fleschner, Department of Biological Control, Citrus Experiment Station, University of California, Riverside, California

F. O. Gossett, Agricultural Research Center, Eli Lilly and Company, Greenfield, Indiana

J. R. Hansbrough, Division of Forest Disease Research, Forest Service, United States Department of Agriculture, Washington, D.C.

E. F. Knipling, Entomology Research Division, Agricultural Research Service, United States Department of Agriculture, Beltsville, Maryland

George L. McNew, Boyce Thompson Institute for Plant Research, Yonkers, New York

Bernard L. Oser, Food and Drug Research Laboratories, Maspeth, New York

Reginald H. Painter, Department of Entomology, Kansas State University of Agriculture and Applied Science, Manhattan, Kansas

A. D. Pickett, Crop Insect Section, Science Service Laboratory, Canada Department of Agriculture, Kentville, Nova Scotia

J. G. Rodriguez, Department of Entomology and Botany, Agricultural Experiment Station, University of Kentucky, Lexington, Kentucky

J. R. Shay, Department of Botany and Plant Pathology, Purdue University, Lafayette, Indiana

William C. Snyder, Department of Plant Pathology, College of Agriculture, University of California, Berkeley, California

Ernest H. Stanford, Department of Agronomy, College of Agriculture, University of California, Davis, California

Nelson F. Waters, Regional Poultry Research Laboratory, Agricultural Research Service, United States Department of Agriculture, East Lansing, Michigan

Contents

I THE PUBLIC'S STAKE IN PEST CONTROL

Exclusion and Eradication versus Reduction of Plant and Animal Pests

M. R. CLARKSON

Agricultural Research Service, U. S. Department of Agriculture, Washington, D. C.

American farmers are the most efficient and productive in the world. They continually direct their efforts toward this end—toward producing their crops and livestock on fewer acres, with less labor, and at lower cost. And because they do, nineteen out of twenty Americans live and work in towns and cities without a second thought for agriculture. Food, in abundant variety, is as near as the supermarket.

It is important that this is so. In this turbulent age of satellites and missiles, it is comforting to know that most American hands are free for work other than farming. It is vital that agriculture be efficient enough and productive enough to meet any emergency.

There are many reasons why our farmers have gained a high level of production efficiency. But certainly one of them is a positive approach in dealing with foreign agricultural diseases, insects, weeds, and other pests, an approach that has been followed by the Department of Agriculture and the various states for the past seventy years. There can be only one regret—that our forefathers did not recognize this need earlier than they did.

Quarantines

When the colonists came to America, it was a land free of most of the Old World's worst agricultural pests. But by the time Congress passed the first of the Animal Quarantine Acts in 1884, several of these foreign threats had become well established here. By then, other nations were restricting the importation of American livestock, to keep out *our* diseases. And by the

3

time the Plant Quarantine Act became law in 1912, the United States had gained a reputation as "the nursery dumping ground of the world."

We can only conjecture how far advanced American agriculture would be today had there been quarantines from the beginning. But there is no questioning the importance of these quarantines as the first line of defense against agricultural pests. In 1956, for example, livestock quarantine inspectors at American ports and borders turned back more than 4500 head of livestock that were diseased, or had been exposed to disease. Among these were interceptions of cattle carrying tick fever and scabies, two diseases that have been virtually eliminated from the United States.

In that year also, plant quarantine inspectors made more than 290,000 interceptions of prohibited or restricted plant materials at ports of entry. Sixty of these interceptions involved plants infected with citrus canker, a threat to the entire citrus production of this country. Nearly 300 fruit flies were intercepted, including the Mediterranean fruit fly on 62 occasions and the Oriental fruit fly, 17 times. Either of these pests could cause millions of dollars worth of damage annually if they became established here. Other interceptions included the pink bollworm of cotton, 42 times; the golden nematode, a pest of potatoes and tomatoes, 83 times; and the Durra stemborer, a threat to corn, sorghum, and sugar cane production, 10 times. These few examples point up the value of quarantines and the need for keeping them strong in defense of this nation's agriculture.

Nevertheless, it would be misleading to suggest that these quarantine barriers are foolproof; or even that further improving the skill or the total number of inspectors would make them so. The odds against it are too great. Modern high-speed travel that in effect has shrunk the world has also brought tremendous pressure to bear on U. S. quarantines. For example, as one of their duties, quarantine inspectors serving New York City in 1956 checked through 2½ million pieces of baggage from ship's passengers, and another 2½ million pieces carried by passengers of planes arriving from overseas. When inspectors are averaging

nearly 800 interceptions every day of the year, there is good reason to expect a pest occasionally to slip through unnoticed. That is why the United States must be prepared to meet the threat of new diseases and agricultural pests.

The Department, the fifty states and Puerto Rico maintain a cooperative system of detection, survey, and reporting, geared to fast action. This system, which functions routinely and continuously, improves the chances of spotting a new disease or pest quickly. It also provides the means of identifying it and determining the size of the outbreak. The question then is, what to do about it. And invariably the answer is "eradicate, if possible."

Eradication Programs

One reason that the American people think first about eradication is because they have been shown on many occasions that certain diseases and pests *can* be eradicated. Secondly, they have learned that a *practical* eradication campaign is a lot cheaper than living with a pest year after year. Certainly, the good success in eradication efforts from the very beginning has built public confidence in this approach to pest problems.

The Act of 1884, which gave this country its first federal livestock quarantine law, also authorized the Department to assist the various states in their fight against pleuropneumonia of cattle. At the time, the disease was widespread among cattle herds in the East and was known to occur as far west as Missouri and Illinois. Cattlemen with infected herds were hard hit. The cattle industry was suffering because of foreign embargoes placed against American cattle. The Department of Agriculture initiated research on pleuropneumonia and began control activities in cooperation with the states. Within five years, the disease was wiped out, and it has never recurred in the United States. Since then, the eradication philosophy has grown, reinforced by research.

Livestock diseases that have been eradicated for all practical purposes include the cattle fever tick, cattle scabies, dourine and glanders from horses, fowl plague, and the highly fatal

Asiatic form of Newcastle disease of poultry. Six times since 1900 the dread foot-and-mouth disease of cattle has become established in the United States, and six times it has been wiped out. The United States has also cooperated with the governments of Mexico and Canada to eradicate foot-and-mouth disease from these neighboring countries.

The eradication record against plant pests is equally outstanding. The Mediterranean fruit fly was eradicated in 1929;[1] parlatoria date scale in 1936; citrus blackfly in 1938; and citrus canker disease in 1943.

The eradication philosophy—and also the quarantine philosophy—are pretty well implanted here in this country. The two go together. But even so, it is still a philosophy of "eradicate, if possible."

When a new threat is turned up, eradication attempts hinge on the answers to such questions as: How well established is the pest? What is its potential for damage? How much will eradication cost?—and most important: Are there enough facts at hand to get on with the job? Sometimes, it is necessary to settle for a delaying action. The Japanese beetle, for example, was discovered in 1916 in New Jersey, and quickly established itself as a serious threat to American agriculture. New Jersey and other seaboard states fought the beetle as best they could, and in 1919, the Department joined in the fight. The main weapons used against the Japanese beetle have been regulation of commerce out of infested areas to prevent spread by hitchhiking pests and, more recently, the use of modern insecticides to eradicate outlying infestations. As a result of this campaign the pest is still not known to occur west of the Mississippi River, although it could thrive in many of the agricultural areas of the West. On the other hand, living with the Japanese beetle costs the national economy an estimated $10 million a year. In this way, the Department and the states cooperate to control a great many foreign pests that cannot be eradicated, at least for the time being. These include such plant pests as the pink bollworm, white-fringed beetle, and European chafer.

[1] The Mediterranean fruit fly has been eradicated again—in 1957-58.

Livestock diseases that cannot be eradicated now, are generally kept under control by state and federal regulations that cover public stockyards inspection and the regulation of animal shipments within and between states. When a livestock disease breaks out, such as anthrax did in Oklahoma and Kansas in 1957, these regulations prevent movement of animals in or out of the area until the disease can be brought under control.

Still other invasions by foreign pests defy either eradication or a campaign to limit their spread. The spotted alfalfa aphid, first noted in New Mexico in 1954, is an example. By the end of that year, the aphid had spread into at least five other states. In 1955 it was discovered in seven additional states, and today it exists in 31 states—nearly everywhere that alfalfa is grown commercially. The characteristic of this tiny insect to develop tremendous populations almost overnight and its ability to spread quickly over hundreds of square miles on the wind precluded any attempt at eradication. Aided by state and federal research that is developing aphid-resistant varieties, American farmers are learning to live with this pest that has already destroyed an estimated $80 million worth of alfalfa.

Fewer and fewer new pest problems are arising that cannot be dealt with before they become a widespread agricultural problem. The increased knowledge about insects and plant and animal diseases that has been accumulated through nearly a century of research is constantly strengthening this country's abilities to cope with new diseases and pests. Currently, the Department of Agriculture and affected states are cooperating in eradication efforts against such new threats as the parasitic witchweed, a threat to corn production; the soybean cyst nematode; the khapra beetle, an insect that could become our worst stored-grain pest; and the Mediterranean fruit fly, which re-invaded Florida in 1956. New techniques and new scientific knowledge, including the development of an attractant immediately before the fly was discovered in Florida, made possible the rapid approach to eradication of the Medfly.[2] There was close

[2] The last aerial treatment for the Mediterranean fruit fly was applied in February 1958.

correlation of research and regulatory development programs. Although the communities affected were well aware of the spray program, serious dislocations in the industry and drastic measures such as those used in 1929 were not necessary in this campaign. With an expenditure of around $10 million, it was possible to protect two of Florida's major crops, fruits and vegetables, with an annual production worth around $400 million. Also, eradication of the Medfly while still within the bounds of one state was insurance for the growers of soft fruits throughout the Southeast and in all the southern areas of the nation.

The eradication campaign against vesicular exanthema, a virus disease of hogs, is a current effort that is having a great deal of success. VE, as the disease is called, has occurred in California since 1934, but did not become a national problem until June 1952 when it began to appear in other states. By December 1952 diseased or exposed animals had been reported from thirty-one states, and during 1953, ten more states reported herds with VE. The disease was spread in many instances by feeding raw garbage to hogs. State and federal restrictions were devised to cut this line of disease transmission. Today, 95 per cent of the garbage fed to swine in the United States is cooked. And, although quarantines are still in effect in some areas, not one new case of vesicular exanthema has been found in the United States for more than a year.[3]

"Thinking" eradication implies an almost day-to-day reappraisal of old pest problems in terms of new information. For example, the longest continual plant pest control campaign in this country has been directed against the gypsy moth which, uncontrolled, could become one of our worst forest pests. The State of Massachusetts began battling this insect around Boston in 1890. The Department of Agriculture got into the fight in 1900. Since then, all the northeastern states, at one time or another, have fought to reduce the damage and the spread of the gypsy moth. The cooperative maintenance of a barrier zone in

[3] The Secretary of Agriculture announced the eradication of vesicular exanthema from the United States on October 22, 1959.

eastern New York since the early 1920's was eminently successful in preventing the westward and southward spread of the
pest.

After World War II and the advent of modern insecticides,
there was new interest in the possibility of eradicating the gypsy
moth. During the late 1940's, the pest was successfully eradicated from an infestation of 880 square miles in northeastern
Pennsylvania. An equally encouraging success was chalked up
in dealing with the 1954 outbreak of the gypsy moth near
Lansing, Michigan. The known infestation was sprayed with
DDT within twenty days of the first find. In succeeding years,
survey teams discovered new pockets of infestation outside the
treated areas, and these also were sprayed. Trapping and surveying are being continued to determine whether the pest has
been wiped out. Based on these successes, the Department of
Agriculture and affected states have launched a strong program
aimed at the eventual eradication of the gypsy moth from the
United States. In still other cases, re-appraisal becomes necessary to find out why eradication efforts are falling short.

Not so many years ago, tuberculosis was an important disease
of cattle and a threat to human health because it could be
readily transmitted from animals to man. In 1917, when an
eradication campaign was begun, the disease occurred in every
state of the Union. The campaign made excellent progress. By
1940, all states had become accredited tuberculosis-free, which
meant that the infection rate was below ½ per cent. By 1952,
the infection rate had been cut to 0.11 per cent, only 11 of every
10 thousand animals tested were found to be infected. The
infection rate remained the same for three years and then
increased to 0.12 per cent in 1955. In 1956 it had risen to 0.15
per cent, and in 1957, to nearly 0.16 per cent. This is not much
of an increase, but the significance of the trend is that here,
within striking distance of eradication, the campaign has mo-
mentarily stalled. With the incidence of the disease so small, it
has become difficult to track down and destroy the few remaining sources of tuberculosis infection. Careful re-appraisal of the
methods and materials is underway to determine what is needed
to complete the eradication of tuberculosis in this country.

Cooperation All the Way

Currently the Department of Agriculture in cooperation with various states is prosecuting eradication campaigns against about a dozen new and old agricultural pests and diseases. These campaigns, combined with control programs against another thirteen pests and with plant and animal quarantines, are administered as part of the Department's Agricultural Research Service. This has proved to be a sensible and beneficial arrangement.

In many respects, the Department's Agricultural Research Service parallels the research and development organizations of industry. Research is frequently directed toward specific pest control problems, and pest control operations in the field provide practical tests for new research as well as a direction for new research to take. The same kind of men and women are engaged in research and pest control. All are agricultural scientists. Broadly speaking, they have the same educational background; they share common professional interests. Close ties such as these cut through red tape and bring maximum concentration of interest and knowledge on emergency situations such as new pests frequently create.

When witchweed was discovered parasitizing corn plants in North Carolina in 1956, it represented the first occurrence of this pest in the United States. It was a completely unknown quantity In a matter of only days, research plant pathologists and weed specialists brought together much of the world's information about witchweed and not only showed that it could become more devastating than the European corn borer but also established directions for research that would guide effective eradication methods. These studies are now underway. Meanwhile, quarantines have been established to hold this pest within bounds; surveys have pretty well determined the extent of the infestation, which is apparently restricted to the Carolinas; and measures of cooperation for eradication are being worked out.

The developing fight against witchweed points up the value of broad research attacks on new plant pests. These attacks generally begin with a careful evaluation of the world's accumu-

lation of knowledge of the pest, research that has been done in other countries, and the experiences and expert judgment of men who have dealt with it. Then, based on this evaluation, research is initiated in this country. Some of the witchweed research underway here is as basic as determining how and why witchweed seeds germinate and grow in different soil types and under different conditions of moisture and temperature. Other research is directed toward seeking chemical, mechanical, and cultural methods of controlling this pest. It has already been shown, for example, that witchweed can be destroyed by treating the soil with volatile chemical fumigants, but at a relatively high cost per acre. Research has also shown that plowing under two or three host crops a season, say corn, may be another way to eradicate this pest. Still other preliminary research has made scientists hopeful of developing herbicidal treatments of crops, methods of mechanical weed control, and crop rotations that will be effective.[4] From it all will come some one best method or, more likely, a combination of methods that will doom witchweed in the United States.

Chemical Control

It is not surprising that chemicals have become one of the chief plant pest control weapons in recent years, because the agricultural chemical industries have made tremendous strides in the discovery and development of new organic pesticides. The chemical revolution that began with the development of DDT as an insecticide during World War II has provided scores of new, highly effective, and specific pest killers. For example, in grasshopper control operations in the West, just 40 ounces of one of these new insecticides sprayed by plane over a 20-acre area in a matter of minutes killed more than 23,000 pounds of these pests. This is a long step forward from the poison baits of pre-war years that were tediously spread from trucks and wagons.

Chemical fumigants are figuring in current eradication efforts

[4] Many of these methods, growing out of research, have since been used successfully in the early phases of witchweed eradication.

against Hall scale, a fruit and nut tree pest, and against the khapra beetle. Chemical sprays are being used against the Mediterranean fruit fly in Florida and the gypsy moth in New York and New England. Chemical granules are being used in a newly initiated eradication campaign against the imported fire ant in the Southeast.

This amazing progress in pesticidal chemicals is the result of science and industry striving not only for more effectiveness against pests but also for less hazard to man and animals. The wildlife conservationist and the toxicologist have been key men in the development of modern pesticides. The ultimate target is a chemical that is toxic only to the pest under attack and that leaves no contaminating residue in food or animal feed.

Biological Control

One of the great recent research advances is the development of biological methods of eradicating the screwworm fly from the Southeast. Research entomologists have demonstrated that this $10-million-a-year pest of livestock can be eradicated by saturating the natural screwworm population with male flies that have been made sexually sterile by gamma irradiation. Since female screwworm flies mate only once, the repeated release of sterile males increases the chances that females will mate with sterile males. As the natural population drops, but the release of sterile males holds steady, the odds become so overwhelming against the mating of females with natural males that eradication results. This research has been proved in field tests. In 1957, the Department of Agriculture and Florida developed a program for releasing sterile flies at a rate aimed to eradicate the screwworm fly from the Southeast, as many as 50 million a week or more. The campaign is expected to run a minimum of two years. If the campaign is successful—and there is every reason to believe that it will be—it opens up new vistas to the value of mass techniques in biological pest control.[5]

Natural enemies of agricultural pests have been used many times in the past. Entomologists have searched the world over

[5] Dispersal of sterile flies was discontinued in November 1959. No screwworms have been found in Florida since June 17, 1959.

for insects that are predatory or parasitic on certain of our worst agricultural pests. These have been established here, and to varying degrees have effected control. But never have they come close to eradication. In the past they have been allowed to develop populations naturally. But the screwworm fly research suggests that there might be merit in rearing and releasing huge numbers of beneficial insects on a planned schedule directed toward the eradication of a specific pest. There will be well-deserved recognition for the scientists who make this hope a reality.

Basic Research

Other research is promising to broaden eradication efforts against animal diseases. For example, the Animal Disease Laboratory, isolated on Plum Island in Long Island Sound, has given this country's scientists their first opportunity to study such feared foreign diseases as rinderpest, African swine fever, pleuropneumonia, sheep pox, fowl plague, and foot-and-mouth disease. Most of the research is basic. This is as it should be, because although these diseases have received much study through the years in other parts of the world, they are still terrible destroyers. Real improvements in eradication and control methods will come when science achieves major breakthroughs that result in greater understanding of the diseases themselves.

Similarly, another Animal Disease Laboratory, dedicated to the development of new facts about diseases already present in this country, is being constructed at Ames, Iowa. Here scientists will be able to intensify their research on such cattle diseases as those that make up the mucosal complex. Hog cholera, which now costs American farmers nearly $50 million a year, will be another of the many diseases to get greater research attention.

Looking Ahead

There cannot be too much research against diseases and other pests that cost the American economy about nine billion dollars a year. In the years immediately ahead, the goal should be to

maintain and advance the production efficiency of American farmers by reducing these losses. In contemplating the agricultural limitations and the booming population of the world, Dr. James Bonner, Professor of Biology, at the California Institute of Technology, predicts that it will be a necessary step for man to eliminate all agricultural losses to pests within the coming century. Tools for fighting agricultural pests are the best ever, and they are constantly being improved. Research, quarantines, eradication and control, and close working relationships between state and federal pest control agencies, and between government and industry, will take us far. But above all, we have a point of view—a positive philosophy in dealing with these pests—that insures a remarkable record of future achievement.

The historian Toynbee has predicted that in a few hundred years this century will be remembered not for its spectacular achievements like the splitting of the atom. He says that it will be recognized as the first age in which people dared to think it practicable to make the benefits of civilization available to the whole human race. Certainly the twentieth century marks the first time, since the locusts plagued the Egyptians, that man has dared to think it practical to wipe out major pests. We shall continue to think it practical and to make it so, wherever possible, and we shall continue to progress in the years ahead.

Control of Forest Diseases

J. R. Hansbrough

Forest Service, U. S. Department of Agriculture,
Washington, D. C.

The forest disease control problem in the United States cannot be appreciated without an understanding of the total forest resource and the impact of disease losses upon it. The forest area in the United States and coastal Alaska is 664 million acres of which 489 million acres, or approximately 75 per cent, is classified as commercial forest land. The remainder is of primary value for range management, water production, and recreation. On this vast area of commercial forest land, the total volume of timber is estimated to be 517 billion cubic feet, including 2057 billion board feet of sawtimber size. (A "board foot" is the unit of lumber measurement one foot square and one inch thick.)

Losses Due to Diseases

The total annual net growth of wood in trees of sawtimber size is estimated to be 47 billion board feet. Gross growth exceeds this figure by over 9½ billion board feet, which is the estimated annual loss from all injurious agents that kill growing trees in the forest. Of this annual kill, about 2¼ billion board feet, or 18 per cent, is caused by diseases. Of even greater significance, however, is the fact that diseases far outrank all other enemies of the forest in their total adverse effect on productivity. This total growth loss is a measure of reduced forest productivity that takes into account not only outright killing of trees but also reduction of the rate of tree growth, destruction through decay of the heartwood of living trees, understocking of forest land, and other similar factors. The estimated annual growth loss on commercial forest lands from all injurious factors

15

(fire, insects, disease, weather, and animals) amounts to about 44 billion board feet of timber, almost as much as our annual net growth. Of this total annual growth loss about 20 billion board feet, or 45 per cent, is caused by diseases that kill or stunt trees and decay wood already produced.

It is difficult to visualize the enormity of this loss, but perhaps a few examples may make it more easily comprehensible. If the timber destroyed annually by diseases were to be cut into boards one inch thick, it would provide enough lumber to build a wooden sidewalk one-half mile wide from New York to San Francisco. It would build about 2 million new five-room homes—enough to house all the people in 13 cities the size of Indianapolis or in one city a little less than twice the size of Chicago. How to reduce this staggering annual loss is the problem now faced by forest disease research and control agencies in the United States.

There are over a thousand different kinds of forest trees in the United States, including some hundred or more that are commercially important. All these tree species are subject to disease attacks, some of major importance, others less so, but in total they account for the losses previously indicated. It will not be possible to discuss the control of these diseases individually; however, we may profitably consider the general principles by which control may be effectively and economically secured. The methods of control that are being utilized depend upon the kind of disease under consideration—whether it is infectious or noninfectious, and if infectious, whether it is native to this continent or introduced from abroad.

Most noninfectious diseases have been attributed to one or more of several causes, including abnormally high or low temperatures, rapid fluctuations in temperature, moisture deficiency or excess, nutritional deficiency or excess, noxious fumes, or mechanical injuries from wind, snow, hail, lightning, and other climatic irregularities. Most of these factors are inherent to the site or locality. They are subject to alleviation or control through improvement of site quality by protection from fire, erosion, overcropping, or other misuse, and through greater attention to the establishment of the correct species upon the site. Pro-

tection from site deterioration and manipulation of species composition to promote the establishment of wind-resistant species on exposed sites, of snow- and ice-resistant species in areas particularly subject to such storms, of drought-resistant species on dry sites, and of soil-improving species on sites lacking proper nutritional balance, these and many other similar measures will result in a measurable lessening of losses from noninfectious diseases. Particularly in the establishment of plantations is there an enormous opportunity to decrease losses by following such recommendations.

Infectious forest tree diseases are those caused by pathogens which, when introduced into a healthy tree, produce disease symptoms. Most of these pathogens are fungi, but viruses, bacteria, mistletoes, dwarfmistletoes, and nematodes also cause important diseases. All catastrophic forest diseases have been wholly or partially the result of the activity of one or more virulent pathogens, indicating the necessity of suppressing them if we are to reduce disease losses.

Control of Forest Diseases

Control of infectious diseases may be by: (1) direct measures, such as quarantines to deter the spread of domestic diseases and to reduce introductions of new diseases from other continents or to contain them once they become established, eradication of primary and alternate hosts of parasites, and protective chemical sprays; (2) by indirect measures, such as improvement of growing conditions to increase tree vigor or to hinder development of parasites, and selection and hybridization to increase genetic resistance to disease attacks.

Whenever a new infectious disease is discovered, it is of paramount importance to determine as soon as possible whether it is caused by a native organism or by an introduced parasite. If it is an introduced disease, our native forest tree species may be especially susceptible and, in addition, there may be no natural control factors to hold it in check. Such a disease may be capable of practically destroying the species that it attacks. This is exactly what chestnut blight did to the American chestnut when

the causal fungus was brought in from the Orient. Other serious introduced diseases that require expensive control operations are the white pine blister rust and the Dutch elm disease. To lessen the hazard of additional introductions like these, Quarantines 37 and 70 of the U. S. Department of Agriculture were enacted. They prohibit the importation of living trees or parts thereof, excepting seeds, of thirty-six genera of woody plants (other than for experimental or scientific purposes).

To add to our knowledge of important foreign diseases and to permit advance research on effective detection and control methods prior to their possible introduction, we are now engaged in a program that offers much promise. American forest trees have been planted widely around the world in arboreta, in forest plantations, and as ornamentals. Under such conditions they have been exposed to the diseases native to the regions where they have been established. We have searched the literature to determine the susceptibility of our trees to these diseases. At the same time we have evaluated the potential effect on our trees of foreign diseases attacking foreign tree species similar to those in our forests. From these studies we think it will be feasible to point the finger of suspicion directly at certain foreign pathogens and make special efforts to exclude them or to cope with them should they become established here.

Once a disease is established in forest stands, special control measures may be required, such as eradication of infected plants or of alternate host plants. When the European larch canker was found in eastern Massachusetts about thirty years ago, the united efforts of federal and state agencies and private landowners in a program to locate and destroy all infected larch trees in that area resulted in the elimination of that disease on this continent. Oak wilt is being suppressed in eastern states by felling diseased trees, followed by chemical treatment of roots, stumps, and tops to prevent local spread of the pathogen. White pine blister rust is caused by a fungus which must alternate between white pine trees and currant and gooseberry bushes (collectively known as "ribes"). It is controlled by eradicating the ribes to save the pines. The dwarfmistletoes are parasitic

flowering plants that infect many of our important western conifers. Removal of infected trees or of infected branches of trees in the overstory prevents the spread of the parasites to the oncoming generation of young trees in the understory.

Chemical Control Measures

Many forest diseases are amenable to chemical control. In forest nurseries a wide variety of fungicides are successfully used as foliar sprays and soil drenches to prevent disease losses. Nematodes are eliminated from nursery beds by the use of fumigants. Limited tests indicate that selective herbicides may kill dwarfmistletoes without harming the host trees. Application of an antibiotic to blister rust cankers on living western white pine trees has killed the parasite without toxic effect on the trees. Chemical control of insect vectors of tree diseases is effective but has wide application today only in the control of diseases of shade and ornamental trees. The use of chemicals for forest disease control will undoubtedly increase as forestry practices become more intensive.

Indirect control measures are those designed to curtail disease losses by growing the right tree on the right site and giving it adequate space for root and crown development; in other words, practicing good forest management. Such control is based on the theory that a vigorous tree or stand is in far better condition to ward off the attacks of many disease-producing organisms than is a less vigorous tree or stand. This is particularly true for most of our native forest tree diseases.

There are several specific but indirect ways to promote freedom from disease in forest stands. Trees growing on good sites for the species are more vigorous than those on poor sites. In most cases, trees growing in mixtures are more vigorous than those growing in pure stands. Trees growing under optimum stocking conditions according to age and size are more vigorous than those in overdense or too open stands. Trees from the sapling stage to physiological maturity are more vigorous than those that are overmature. Uninjured trees are more vigorous than those that have had to withstand injurious influences. Naturally regenerated stands usually are more vigorous than

planted ones. Native trees adapted to the locality are almost universally more vigorous than exotics. Adherence to these general principles governing forest stand vigor will afford increased freedom from disease.

In addition, there are several specific stand improvement measures that reduce disease losses. Judicious pruning of dead branches removes the infection courts that offer entrance to many heartrot fungi. Reduction of mechanical injuries to roots, stems, and branches is even more effective. Removal of cull trees permits their replacement with sound trees. In all species studied, there is a direct relationship between tree age and the incidence of heartrots. Harvest cuts, therefore, may be scheduled at ages before rot becomes excessive.

It is important to emphasize the fact that there are many interrelationships between disease and insect control problems. Insect attacks weaken trees and make them more vulnerable to some diseases. Disease attacks likewise weaken trees and make them more vulnerable to some insects. Improved control of either insects or diseases yields a considerable dividend in increased resistance to injury from other pests.

Breeding for Resistance

Selecting and breeding forest trees to obtain resistance to disease is the ultimate goal in forest tree disease control. Within our forest trees genetic resistance to disease varies from immunity to very high susceptibility. The investigator can select for resistance or he can hybridize to increase resistance. Significant progress has been made in securing resistance to white pine blister rust, chestnut blight, Dutch elm disease, phloem necrosis of elms, the littleleaf disease of southern pines, and several poplar diseases. Success on these diseases indicates the potential effectiveness of this approach to disease control for other forest tree diseases.

Progress

Now a word as to the present status of forest disease control and what is needed to improve the situation. White pine blister rust is under control on most of the 16 million acres of white

pine timber in thirty-two states. There are a few critical areas in the northern Rocky Mountain and Lake States regions where adequate control has not been secured because environmental conditions are extremely favorable to the development of the rust. Research is underway to improve control in these areas.

Oak wilt is the principal disease affecting oaks in eighteen states in central and eastern United States. Statewide control programs are underway in six states, Michigan, Pennsylvania, Virginia, West Virginia, Kentucky, and North Carolina, and partial control in three states, Ohio, Tennessee, and Arkansas. We are optimistic that natural control factors plus organized control programs in these nine states will prevent any further extension of this disease into our valuable oak-producing areas of the East and South.

The dwarfmistletoes are very destructive pests of western conifers, attacking ponderosa pine, lodgepole pine, Douglas fir, western hemlock, western larch, red fir, and black spruce throughout much of their natural ranges. Effective control measures have been formulated for ponderosa pine in the Southwest but have been applied only on limited areas in a few National Parks and Indian Reservations.

Heartrots collectively are the principal cause of disease losses in North American forests. These losses may be reduced by establishing rotations and cutting cycles that will provide for timber harvesting before heartrot losses are excessive. In addition, most heartrots start through wounds that expose wood to fungus action, indicating the effectiveness of care in forest management to prevent wounds of all kinds: fire scars, logging injuries, broken branches, etc.

These examples show that forest disease control is improving, but there is tremendous room for better methods and more application of present information. There is need for a greatly expanded program of research on the basic causes for the occurrence and intensification of diseases in forest stands. Such a program, along with improved methods of excluding foreign pathogens and of detecting disease outbreaks in their infancy, would put forest disease control on a much sounder basis. At present we are in the position of attempting to reduce losses

in stands already diseased; we need information that will enable us to avoid or prevent disease attacks, to forestall the buildup of diseases to epidemic proportions.

United attack by federal, state, and industrial agencies and private interests is needed to develop better control methods and put them into operation. While we have had significant advances in our knowledge of the behavior of diseases and in the development of control techniques for some of them, our total program, for both research and control, is just beginning to be geared to the magnitude of the problem.

A strong forward step for getting on top of the situation was taken in 1947 when the Congress passed the Forest Pest Control Act. This Act provides a charter for carrying out the measures necessary to a sound national program of forest pest control, both diseases and insects. It prescribes broad policies and principles to be used in carrying out its provisions. It recognizes federal responsibility for controlling pests on federal lands; extends federal aid to control projects on nonfederal lands, in cooperation with the states and other owners of forest lands; provides leadership in conducting surveys to detect and evaluate pest outbreaks on all classes of forest ownership; and makes provisions for planning, organizing, directing, and carrying out needed control projects. A number of states have enacted legislation somewhat paralleling federal legislation. These state laws permit the state agencies to enter into cooperative agreements with the federal government and with landowners in a share-the-cost joint attack on forest protection problems that must be handled cooperatively.

In the long run there is no forest disease that cannot be prevented or suppressed in one way or another, but there are no short cuts to that goal. It will require the united efforts of everyone interested in natural resource conservation. A good start has been made. A few diseases are under control. A few more await an action program. Research to formulate controls is underway for most of our remaining serious diseases. It is not unreasonable to expect that with continued adherence to the course we have charted, the present enormous drain on forest production from diseases can be and will be sharply reduced.

Control of Forest Insects

James A. Beal

Forest Service, U. S. Department of Agriculture,
Washington, D. C.

The forests of our country constitute one of our major natural, renewable resources. They supply 90 per cent of the nation's needs for timber, wood, and wood products. They serve as the storage basins for a large part of its usable water. They likewise serve as the habitat for an abundance of fish and game, the summer range for vast herds of livestock, and the outdoor playground for millions of people throughout the year. Forest industries comprise a major portion of the economy of many of the states. In addition, many other business activities are largely dependent for their existence upon the forests and their resources of wood, water, and forage. In fact, about one person in eight in the United States is dependent for his livelihood on the nation's forests.

A recent survey indicates that total timber growth is slightly in excess of timber drain. Unfortunately, however, the same survey also revealed that much of this growth is on inferior species and trees of low quality. It further showed that we are using our better quality wood faster than it is being replaced. In other words, wood quality is falling off. This may become a serious problem unless we grow a larger volume of high-quality trees.

The loss in wood quality may become serious because potential demands for timber products, based on population increase and prospective economic growth, are definitely upward. For example, it is estimated that timber requirements by 1975 will increase by about 30 per cent and by about 80 per cent by the year 2000. In order to keep pace with this growing demand, it

is obvious that we are going to have to do a better job of re-generating, managing, and utilizing the nation's timber crop.

Losses Caused by Insects

Adequate protection against insects is becoming more and more a vital part of successful forestry programs. This stems from the fact that insects affect forests and forest products adversely in many ways and often to a serious extent. They attack trees of all ages and of all sizes and species. Epidemics of certain bark beetles and defoliators kill extensive stands of timber outright. Other insects reduce the volume and lower the quality of wood in many ways. For example, attacked trees that survive may be distorted or deformed; their growth rates may be reduced; or their trunks may be shot full of worm holes, resulting in serious timber degrade. Site, stocking, and stand conditions are altered by insects, and often result in the replacement of high-quality material with that of low quality. These things are going on in our forests at all times.

Insects rank first among the causes of timber mortality. Among trees of sawtimber size, for example, in 1952, a typical year, insects were responsible for 40 per cent of the total mortality and for 28 per cent of the mortality of all timber large enough for commercial use. At this rate of destruction, insects outrank fire by a ratio of 7 to 1. According to recent estimates, they kill about 6 billion board feet of sawtimber each year. This includes catastrophic losses resulting from widespread epidemics which, over the past 50 years, have averaged more than 1 billion board feet annually. In addition to this, insects are causing an estimated loss in pole-size timber of more than 2 million cords annually.

It is not easy for one to visualize either 6 billion board feet of timber or 2 million cords of pulpwood. It might be more meaningful, therefore, to say that this represents enough lumber to build 600,000 average-size homes, or 60 per cent of those constructed in the United States in 1956. The additional losses in pole-size timber is the equivalent of nearly one-fourth of the

amount of pulpwood currently consumed annually in the manufacture of this country's newsprint.

Changing Attitudes

Interest in the control of forest insects has increased markedly
during the past few years. As a result, timber owners are no
longer willing to accept insect-caused losses as inevitable, but
are willing and anxious to do something about them. No doubt
this change in attitude has been brought about by a better
understanding of the magnitude of forest insect-caused losses.
Other contributing factors have been improvements in survey
techniques, which provide earlier detection and more accurate
appraisals of existing outbreaks, the development of more
efficient and more effective control methods for many species,
and, last but far from least, the increased value of existing
timber supplies.

The desire to get on top of the forest insect problem has been
reflected through increased attention during the past few years
to this subject by industry and government alike. The federal
government, because of its responsibility in protecting the
timber on the National Forests and other public lands and its
role in advising private citizens and industry on forest insect
control has substantially increased its efforts not only in insect
research but also in insect surveys and control. Many of the state
forestry offices have shown increased interest by adding forest
entomologists to their staffs. Some have also formed survey
organizations in an effort to keep abreast of insect conditions
within their states. An ever increasing number of private forestry
companies are utilizing the services of trained forest entomologists, a few to conduct research, but more often to conduct or
direct surveys and control operations on company-owned lands.
Some states, as well as some timber companies, are cooperating
on aerial surveys by providing planes, pilots, and observers to
work with federal personnel. Forest pest control action com-
mittees also have been formed in many parts of the country for
the purpose of stimulating concerted action by all timberland
owners in forest pest control.

Surveys

Detection and appraisal surveys are the first steps in forest insect control. They are the first steps because infestations not only must be found but also must be accurately located and evaluated before decisions regarding control can be made. They are conducted both from the ground and the air, largely from the latter.

Airplanes, usually of the small single engine type, are being used increasingly in this work. Aerial surveys are being used as extensively as possible because they can be conducted at comparatively low cost. Their use also insures early detection, even in remote areas, simplifies and reduces the cost of follow-up ground surveys, and provides for the orderly planning of control measures or salvage operations. They have been used on a random sampling basis over spruce-fir forests, lightly infested by spruce budworm, and have provided adequate detection coverage at a rate of 84,000 acres per hour of flight time. Satisfactory appraisals of tree-killing by bark beetles also have been made by line-strip visual surveys at the rate of about 400,000 acres per hour of flight time. In other words, extensive areas can be surveyed from the air at a cost of only a fraction of a penny per acre.

Airplanes likewise are used in the photographic sampling of forest insect damage from the air. In this work, high-speed color film is being used to best advantage. Through its use with high-speed rotary shutters, extremely sharp and detailed images are produced at relatively low flight levels. Sketch mapping also is done from airplanes. Here, viewing filters comprised of a combination of magenta and cyan are used to improve the detection of reds and browns, normally associated with insect infestations, without upsetting the balance of other colors. Additional aids to improve the accuracy and effectiveness of aerial survey operations have been developed, such as special Plexiglas doors on the planes to afford maximum lateral visibility, a map-rolling device to simplify the job of handling the maps in the cockpit, and stripviewers to aid in identifying acreage of area sampled.

It is not always possible, however, for aerial observers to identify the species of insect responsible for tree killing. Therefore, it usually is necessary to conduct ground surveys as a complement, or supplement, to aerial observations. This is true particularly where more specific and detailed information is needed on such items as incidence and degree of insect parasitization and disease in making an appraisal of an infestation

Chemical Control

Control of forest insects through the application of insecticides is by far the most common method of direct control in use today. The synthesis of more effective chemicals and the development and improvement in equipment and methods of applying them are largely responsible for their widespread use. Among the more important recent advances in this type of control of forest insects has been the use of the airplane for the distribution of concentrated sprays such as DDT from the air. During the past ten years, research has gathered considerable information on dosages and formulations, and on the atomization, distribution, and application of aerial sprays. Furthermore, it has helped develop effective guide lines for operational procedures. Today, as a result, aerial spraying to control many forest insect defoliators is widely practiced in both the United States and Canada. In fact, nearly 15 million acres of spruce budworm infested forests have been treated from the air in the United States and Canada during recent years. Outbreaks of the Douglas fir tussock moth, white pine butterfly, hemlock looper, pine looper, gypsy moth, forest tent caterpillar, Saratoga spittlebug, the walkingstick, some sawflies and other defoliators have also been controlled by aerial spraying.

Some of the newer chemicals are also being widely used in the control of bark beetles, insects not amenable to control from the air, particularly in the West and in the South. Ethylene dibromide emulsions, for example, are largely replacing older insecticides for the control of the Engelmann spruce beetle, the Black Hills beetle, and the mountain pine beetle. The habit of the Engelmann spruce beetle in concentrating its attack on the

lower portion of the trunk also led to the successful use of stirrup pumps and the spraying of standing trees from the ground for control of this pest of spruce in Colorado. Where beetle infestations extend high up on the trunks of trees, felling prior to treatment is necessary. The usual presence of water in forested areas and its place in the emulsion have greatly reduced the cost of this type of control. By using the emulsion instead of oil solutions, it is no longer necessary to transport large quantities of oil to infested stands, many of which are in remote and more or less inaccessible areas.

Benzene hexachloride (BHC) is another of the newer insecticides that is being used extensively for the control of some forest insects, especially in the South. It has greatly increased the possibilities of preventing damage to logs, lumber, and pulpwood by wood-boring insects. For example, by spraying benzene hexachloride solution onto freshly cut logs, the latter are kept relatively free from attack by bark beetles and borers for a period of three to four months during the period of greatest beetle activity. This solution can also be used to spray green stacks of lumber to prevent attack by ambrosia beetles. As a matter of fact, BHC is proving useful not only for controlling insects which attack trees after they are cut, but also for the control of certain beetles which attack standing trees. An example is its increasing use to control or prevent turpentine beetle attacks on seed trees left after cutting and on gum-producing pines in turpentine orchards. In this connection, BHC is likewise highly effective as a residual spray against the southern pine beetle. Here the infested trees are felled, the unsalvaged portions sprayed, and the emerging beetles killed as they individually gnaw their way through the outer bark.

Some of the insecticides already mentioned, as well as a number of others, are also useful in the control of insects that damage wood products. For example, chlordane, dieldrin, benzene hexachloride, and DDT when used as soil poisons under and around dwellings, are giving good protection from termites. Also, by dipping wood for a few seconds in solutions containing lindane, toxaphene, DDT, or chlordane, protection

from *Lyctus* beetles can be assured for at least five years. Finally, pressure treatment of wood with creosote, pentachlorophenol, and other materials has long been and is still being used to protect wood from both insects and decay when it is subject to severe conditions of exposure.

Silvicultural and Management Control

Forest insect control is not, however, dependent entirely on the use of chemicals. There is much, in fact, that can be done toward minimizing certain types of insect losses through the application of silvicultural and management practices. A few of the examples where research has demonstrated this fact will serve to illustrate this point.

Studies, initiated in the West several years ago to determine and define the characteristics of trees susceptible to attack by bark beetles, are continuing to pay off in terms of new information and wider application of their results in control practices. This work led to the development of the sanitation-salvage logging method of controlling the western pine beetle. This method, which involves the selective removal from the stand of trees that are in such poor current health that they are highly susceptible to this beetle, has proved successful beyond expectations. Through the cutting of trees of immediate risk to beetle attack, or only about 15 to 20 per cent of the merchantable green stand volume, pine mortality has been reduced in test areas by some 70 per cent for a period of ten years. In other areas, treated from eight to ten years ago, losses have been reduced by about 90 per cent. Sanitation-salvage logging is now being widely used to control the western pine beetle. It is likewise being used to control the Jeffrey pine beetle, and work is underway to extend its use to still other bark beetle pests.

It appears likely that the use of hybrid trees or insect-resistant strains also may have, in the not too distant future, an important place in preventing damage by certain forest insects. It is now known, for example, that the pine reproduction weevil, a species that does not survive in Coulter pine but which is a serious pest of planted Jeffrey and ponderosa pines in California brushfield

areas, will not survive in a hybrid of Coulter and Jeffrey pines that has been developed by the Institute of Forest Genetics. Certain strains of ponderosa pine, moreover, have shown equally good resistance to the reproduction weevil.

With increased emphasis on forest tree genetics and additional knowledge of what constitutes resistance to insects, we can expect further advances in this phase of silvicultural control.

Logging as a means of controlling many species of bark beetles is being practiced on a scale that was not anticipated ten years ago. This has resulted from increased timber values and the development of more effective logging equipment. In numerous instances the most carefully prepared management plans are being ignored or drastically changed in order to salvage beetle-killed timber and to remove the infested trees from the forests in order to prevent further losses. Literally thousands of miles of access roads and secondary feeder roads are being built for the purpose of better coping with beetle epidemics. Logging equipment is being adapted for this special use, and small units are being organized to salvage-log small groups or even single infested trees before the beetles can emerge from them. Control through logging is being supplemented in most instances by chemical treatment of infested portions or cull trees that are left in the woods.

Salvage-logging of infested trees is an effective and feasible method of western pine beetle control where conditions are favorable for the rapid removal of light volumes. An infestation of this sort was controlled on a 6000-acre area on the Lassen National Forest by this method. Sale of the infested stumpage plus salvageable timber resulted in a net cash return of $14,000.

On a current Engelmann spruce beetle control project in Montana, most of the emphasis is being placed on logging. In some areas the beetles are concentrated by felling trap trees in strategic locations in early summer. During flight the beetles are attracted to these trap trees in large numbers, and the broods are later removed with the logs.

Many of the management practices outlined above are being used by both the federal government and private industry in their attempts to cope with the Engelmann spruce beetle in

the Rocky Mountain States, the western pine bettle and the Douglas fir beetle in the Pacific Northwest, and the southern pine beetle and other bark beetles in the South.

Biological Control

Probably no type of forest insect control is more efficient or more effective than is biological control that results from the work of parasites, predators, and diseases. The importance of one or all of these natural control factors in preventing or terminating outbreaks of a variety of forest insects frequently has been noted and recorded. Unfortunately, we have not yet progressed very far in our knowledge of how to manipulate them so that they can be used to replace other control methods.

One of the most successful of recent developments in the biological control of a forest pest is the use of a virus disease organism to control the introduced European pine sawfly. Research workers in Canada first isolated and cultured this virus. It has since been thoroughly tested against this species and, where applied by both ground and aerial spraying equipment, has been found to be highly effective. A water suspension of the virus is made from the bodies of diseased larvae. It persists in treated plantations and infects subsequent sawfly populations. It also has the advantage of being highly specific to the European pine sawfly. In addition to its use in Canada, this virus disease is being used in the eastern and central states to control European pine sawfly infestations in red pine plantations.

In tests conducted jointly by the Agricultural Research Service and the Forest Service, the Virginia pine sawfly, a pest of pines in the eastern and central states, also has been controlled in localized areas with a spray made from a native virus disease.

The most important single factor in controlling a recent outbreak of the white fir sawfly in California was a polyhedrosis-type virus isolated and identified by the Department of Biological Control, University of California. This virus became evident among the fourth and fifth instar larvae in mid-July, and within ten days caused mortality in excess of 90 per cent throughout the entire population.

Although no such spectacular use has yet been made of par-

asites and predators, they may well be equally important. In any event, it is probable that many control projects could be delayed or eliminated if we but had complete enough information on the parasite-host relationship. The possibilities of this was amply demonstrated recently in connection with an epidemic of the spruce budworm in Maine. Entomologists had been keeping track of the parasites in the infestation for several years prior to the development of epidemic conditions. Through application of the knowledge gained during these studies on the distribution, abundance, and identity of parasites throughout the infested area, it was possible to limit the control effort to a single spraying of one 20,000-acre area. There is little doubt but that much larger acreages would have been treated had we not known precisely what the parasites were doing in the epidemic areas.

The same type of information on the parasite-budworm relationship was a major factor in arriving at a recent decision against control of a 600 thousand-acre epidemic of the spruce budworm in Oregon. Thus, it is evident that knowledge of parasites can often be used to good advantage in determining direct control needs, especially when enough information is available on their year-to-year activities in specific outbreaks. The cost of obtaining such information would be but a fraction of the cost of a single large spraying project.

Conclusions

Fortunately, there is increasing public recognition of the extensive losses caused by insects to the forests of the United States. There are increasing demands for coordinated control action, for more intensive surveys, and for additional research to improve and develop more efficient and more effective control measures. In the light of our present knowledge, it is probable that in the control of forest insects we shall have to continue to rely heavily on the use of chemicals for a long time in the future. Greater use of silvicultural, biological, or other preventive control measures will come only as rapidly as research can discover them, demonstrate their value, and develop methods for their effective application.

Education in the Use of Pesticides

E. H. Fisher

University of Wisconsin, Madison

Pesticides are a boon to mankind. The record points to economic, esthetic, and life- and health-saving gains achieved by proper pesticide usage, as opposed to only occasional adversities from misuse.

As new pesticides become available, the public desires to know how to use them. A nationwide survey in 1954 showed that about 17 per cent of all requests for information from county agricultural agents (and their counterparts) concerned insects, and during the crop-growing season 36 per cent. The figure for Wisconsin were 12 and 30 per cent, respectively. Add to this the questions on weeds, plant diseases, rodents, and other pests, and the agricultural advisor has little time for other work.

Promotional and Directional Education

Education in the use of pesticides involves developing skill in the appraisal of their necessity, efficiency, economy, timeliness, and safety. Proof that they are necessary, economical, and safe are the selling points. These along with ways to reduce the per-unit cost of production and to protect health and property constitute the major responsibilities of educators in the use of pesticides.

Large-scale adoption of research-proven practice is commonly slow; without such knowledge, adoption of improved practices lags. For example, a 1957 survey in Wisconsin revealed that only 24 per cent of the farmers interviewed understood the pH scale for soil acidity, and only 60 per cent had a desirable understanding of the three figures commonly used to represent a fertilizer analysis; yet these expressions have been in common usage for two generations. Between grower aware-

ness and the adoption of improved practice, there are intermediate stages of interest, evaluation, and trial. Guidance to
conduct a successful trial brings satisfaction to the grower and
more rapid adoption.

It is generally agreed by agricultural specialists that we presently have the know-how (without further research) to produce
agricultural products adequate for the predicted vastly greater
human population of twenty years hence. However, this assumes
rather complete adoption of improved practices. Increased
efficiency can offset much agricultural commodity price support
and in turn bring about increased conservation of natural resources. By comparison, most industry production is geared to
demand, not to the near productive potential as is more common
in agriculture.

Although education is essentially factual, it may also be promotional and directional. Promotional education is primarily
with the farmer, householder, and urban or other area group,
inciting action in recommended pest control programs. Directional education covers these groups also, but it starts with the
manufacturers of pesticides and application equipment, formulators, dealers, and custom control services. The consuming
public must know or have access to the recommended types of
pesticides, application equipment, and control services.

Program planning and coordination are commonly enhanced
by cooperation with grower and industry associations, and
federal, state, or smaller governmental units. County agricultural
extension personnel use local leaders to extend educational
efforts. In 1952 it was estimated that the 1,200,000 local leaders
in the United States devoted an average of eleven days annually
to some aspect of the extension program—a total effort equal to
more than 50,000 persons employed for 260 work days a year.

Package Programs

Farmers can learn more about how to grow corn when the
educational program involves all phases of production, not just
the importance of fertilizer, for example. A Pacemaker Corn
Program in Wisconsin has proved that coordinated guidance

by specialists in soils, agronomy, agricultural engineering, plant pathology, and entomology is needed. Similarly, "grassland farming" is better understood owing to combining its several aspects into a unit approach. Members of 4-H clubs are taught that pest control is an integral part of most projects. The youngster who takes a dairy cattle project learns that control of flies, lice, and grubs is a step to successful dairying. A unified story on pest control is desirable.

The pesticide industry, dealers, custom sprayers, and the general public need to be informed of recommended types of control materials and methods. This may be done through conferences where university research and extension personnel may report on recent findings on the control of insects, weeds, and diseases, and give recommendations for the forthcoming season. Legal and health aspects involving the Federal Food and Drug Administration, Civil Aeronautics Administration, State Aeronautics Commission, the State Department of Agriculture, and Board of Health should be discussed. It is likewise important to publish booklets summarizing the recommendations, precautions, etc., and to keep these up to date.

Urban pest control activities also demand educational attention. These include well-organized area control programs as well as pest control for the individual household or business establishment. The area programs are primarily tailor-made and require considerable planning with city officials and residents to avoid unwarranted criticism and unnecessary inconvenience or damage.

The media of "Sprayer Service Letter," newspapers, magazines, circulars, demonstrations, general meetings, radio, television, movies, slides, and personal interviews are employed to educate. When possible the package program technique is employed; it is a time-saving, fruitful method of education.

Wisconsin was probably the first state to recommend parathion, a hazardous chemical, for insect control. From the beginning there have been efforts to lessen the hazards in its use. These include: working with the State Medical Association to make sure that doctors had information about parathion poison-

ing symptoms and treatment; having canners and aerial applicators adopt a safety program; and encouraging the State Board
of Health to maintain a cholinesterase activity laboratory service
for canners and aerial applicators as a check on overdosage and
carelessness. More recently, simple kits for cholinesterase activity determination have been used by canners and aerial
applicators. There have been no deaths from parathion in
Wisconsin.

General Considerations

The recent Miller Bill and resultant Federal Public Law 518
were the basis for an orderly procedure for pesticide research,
recommendation, and use. However, the actions of federal
agencies concerned with establishing pesticidal tolerances,
labeling pesticides, and recommending them are not always
coordinated. This creates need for local judgment.

Frequently we are confronted with "convenient diagnoses"
and improperly qualified public statements. The public is greatly
influenced by sensational information, occasionally to its dis-
advantage. A few examples will explain the problem.

1. In a perplexing case of illness in a Wisconsin farm family
a few years ago, one medical specialist wrote the family doctor
that DDT poisoning would be a "convenient diagnosis." Agricultural Extension initiated an investigation which resulted in
the factual answer that a bad water supply was the cause of the
family's trouble. If this problem had remained improperly
answered, unjust condemnation of pest control would have
spread through antagonism.

2. Leptospirosis in two dairy herds was first diagnosed by
individual veterinary doctors as poisoning by insecticides. In
one instance the blame was placed on a quick knockdown fly
spray; the other was attributed to grain fumigant contamination of feed. Again Agricultural Extension sought and obtained
the answer to the true cause, much to the satisfaction of the herd
owners.

3. A recent publication referred to the rodenticides strych-

nine, 1080, Pival, and warfarin as "the most deadly compounds in commercial use today." Such inaccurate generalizations impede the use of effective and safe materials; the American Medical Association recommends the use of anticoagulants like warfarin as relatively safe. The New York City Poison Control Center (with records for about five years) reported an average of about twelve cases per month of accidental ingestion of anticoagulant rodenticides by humans without any resulting cases of hemorrhage. Furthermore, since warfarin first appeared on the market in 1950, there has not been an authentic case in the United States of human death due to its being ingested, and it is by far the most widely used rodenticide. We know of fifteen human deaths due to rat poisons in the United States this year, but none was caused by warfarin or any other anticoagulant rodenticide.

The skull and crossbones is not required on some common materials which cause the most accidental poisonings. Incorrect use can make most pesticides hazardous. An example of a pesticide used in human therapy is warfarin. One form of it is the most widely used rat and mouse killer, yet another has saved and prolonged the lives of many when used as a therapeutic agent for certain circulatory conditions.

Many stories call attention to the hazards of insecticides. On the other hand, some records show that drugs are responsible for nearly half of all cases of accidental poisoning and that aspirin lures the most victims. Possibly the reason for so few actual cases of pesticide poisoning lies in the success of educational programs.

Some achievements from education in the use of pesticides are:

1. Closer working relationship with other phases of agricultural work, with grower and industry groups, and concerned federal and state agencies.

2. Greater efficiency in crop and livestock production.

3. Protection of property, health, and well-being.

4. A record of safety in spite of more hazardous materials.

5. Better supplies of recommended pesticides.

6. More power sprayers on farms.

Regulatory Control of Pesticides

BERNARD L. OSER

Food and Drug Research Laboratories, Inc.,
Maspeth, New York

Regulatory control of the use of pesticides in agriculture, as we understand it today, can be said to date from the adoption of the Federal Insecticide, Fungicide, and Rodenticide Act of 1947 and the Miller Amendment to the Federal Food, Drug, and Cosmetic Act which was enacted in 1954. Considered together, these laws constitute an acknowledgment of the tremendous expansion in the number and use of pesticides to meet the needs for increased agricultural production and an improved food supply. Authoritative predictions of a 35 per cent increase in the American population during the present quarter century, and of a simultaneous annual loss of one million arable acres to highways, airports, and industries, portend increased attention to any and all means of expanding and protecting farm crops and produce. In the past twenty-five years the yield per acre of certain food crops has increased as much as threefold, owing in no small measure to the judicious use of pesticides. Yet a survey published in *Chemical Week* places the loss in value of food and fiber harvests attributable to insects, fungi, and other animal and plant pests at $11 billion per year. No one can place a dollar estimate on the cost of diseases like malaria, yellow fever, murine typhus, and bubonic plague, which are transmitted by insects or rodents, but the U. S. Public Health Service has estimated that, since 1942, 5 million human lives have been spared and 100 million cases of illness prevented by the use of insecticides alone.

Law Extended to Pesticides

Up to World War II, agricultural insecticides and fungicides were relatively few in number and consisted mainly of arsenic

and lead compounds, nicotine, pyrethrum, and rotenone. The Food, Drug, and Cosmetic Act of 1938 provided that the addition of a poisonous or deleterious substance to a food could be permitted only if it could be established to be required in its production or unavoidable in accordance with good manufacturing practice, and then only if the amount so required or unavoidable did not exceed a safe tolerance limit established for each substance by regulation. This section of the law has proved to be impractical and very few tolerances have been established under it. The growing realization that pesticides, which by their very nature are poisons, could not be demonstrated to be necessary or unavoidable, no matter how useful or beneficial they might be, led to the enactment of the Miller Amendment, a more realistic adaptation to the present situation.

The law now provides for the promulgation of "regulations establishing tolerances with respect to the use in or on raw agricultural commodities" of pesticidal chemicals "to the extent necessary to protect the public health." It recognizes the necessity for the use of pesticides "for the production of an adequate, wholesome, and economical food supply." However, it specifies that the Secretary of Agriculture shall certify as to the usefulness of the pesticide chemical. Thereafter the Secretary of Health, Education, and Welfare considers the toxicological and other data submitted in the petition and issues a regulation either establishing a tolerance for the petitioned use or exempting the chemical from the necessity for a tolerance. It is interesting to note the limitations under this law embodied in the definition of "pesticide chemical" and of "raw agricultural commodity." A pesticide chemical is an economic poison under the Insecticide, Fungicide, and Rodenticide Act, and is broadly defined as "any substance or mixture of substances intended for preventing, destroying, repelling, or mitigating any insects, rodents [or any other vertebrate animal], fungi, weeds, or *other forms of plant or animal life* or viruses, except viruses on or in living man or other animals, which the Secretary of Agriculture shall declare to be a pest." Raw agricultural commodities include "*among other things,* fresh fruits, whether or not they have been washed and colored or otherwise treated in their

unpeeled natural form; vegetables in their raw or natural state, whether or not they have been stripped of their outer leaves, waxed, prepared into fresh green salads, etc.; grains, nuts, eggs, raw milk, meats, and *similar agricultural produce.*" The italics (supplied) emphasize the great breadth accorded these definitions; however, "raw agricultural commodities" specifically exclude "foods that have been processed, fabricated, or manufactured by cooking, freezing, dehydrating, or milling." This definition has been construed as broad enough to include uncooked poultry, despite the fact that it is processed to the extent of defeathering and evisceration.

Establishing Tolerances

The data needed for evaluating the usefulness and safety of a pesticide chemical include:

"(A) the name, chemical identity, and composition of the pesticide chemical;

(B) the amount, frequency, and time of application of the pesticide chemical;

(C) full reports of investigations made with respect to the safety of the pesticide chemical;

(D) the results of tests on the amount of residue remaining, including a description of the analytical methods used;

(E) practicable methods for removing residue which exceeds any proposed tolerance;

(F) proposed tolerances for the pesticide chemical if tolerances are proposed; and

(G) reasonable grounds in support of the petition."

To be considered useful or suitable for use, a pesticide must not only be shown by laboratory or field tests to be effective against the particular pest or pests when used in the manner proposed, but it also should not adversely affect the growth or maturation of the plant (unless it is a herbicide); it should not adversely affect the productivity of the soil either through direct chemical action or through the destruction of beneficial microorganisms or nematodes; it should not adversely affect the

quality of the edible product in respect to palatability, appearance, or nutritive value. Although there is little experimental evidence on the effect of pesticides on the vitamin or mineral content of food crops, the fact that the quality of fruits and vegetables is preserved by protecting them from insect or fungus attack would suggest that the proper use of pesticides prevents rather than promotes loss of nutritional values. Questions have arisen concerning the effect of insecticides on the flavor of vegetables. A paper from the University of Wisconsin (1) describes organoleptic evaluations of a series of raw, cooked, and canned vegetables treated with chlorinated hydrocarbon insecticides (aldrin, dieldrin, endrin, chlordan, heptochlor, lindane, and toxaphene). Of these, lindane showed the most pronounced effect on flavor, especially in canned vegetables. It is interesting to note that in these four-year studies a buildup in the soil was not reflected in a perceptible increase in off-flavor. Color was significantly augmented in the case of canned beets as a result of the use of endrin, and to a lesser extent in squash, pumpkin, carrots, and rutabagas. While effects on flavor, color, or culinary properties may raise esthetic rather than health questions, they nevertheless are considered important by the Department of Agriculture, which zealously seeks to maintain a high quality of farm produce.

Official tolerances have been established for some sixty chemicals (mostly insecticides) as used in the production of one or more among eighty-six groups of plant products and three groups of animal products (2). There is a continuing need for expanding the list and for maintaining regulatory supervision. This protects both the public and the manufacturers who strive to provide safe, yet effective, pesticides for agricultural use.

Bioassay the Final Test

Besides the question of residue tolerances, other aspects of safety of pesticide chemicals must be taken into account. The chemicals themselves are generally sold to formulators who manufacture the products that in turn are applied by operators. In California alone over 900 firms manufacture about 12,000

formulations which are applied by 1300 licensed pest control operators. (This state, incidentally, used about one-fifth of the estimated $290 million dollars worth of pesticides sold in the United States in 1956.) Experiments with animals must be conducted to ascertain the conditions for safe handling of these poisonous chemicals. Observations are generally made of the effects on the skin and eyes of exposure to the chemicals or to formulations thereof, of inhalation toxicity of vapors, mists, or dusts, and of acute oral toxicity. Industrial experience in the production of the chemical often provides useful information with regard to human exposure.

In addition, consideration must be given to the possible effects of pesticidal applications on farm and domestic animals, birds, fish, and wildlife generally. In fact birds are reported to be more sensitive to DDT than warmblooded mammals, and fish even more so.

Residues

After the usefulness of a pesticide chemical is certified by the Secretary of Agriculture, the problem of safety of its residues must be considered. This presupposes that appropriate steps have been taken to minimize the residue such as by controlling the interval between the last application of the pesticide and the harvesting of the crop. It also presupposes the determination, by accurate chemical analysis, of the amount of residue remaining on the product as sold in interstate commerce. The methodological research needed to insure sufficiently sensitive and reliable analytical methods has proved to be one of the most costly features of a pesticide development program. One recent appraisal placed the cost of analytical development for a single insecticide at $130,000, compared with $75,000 for the toxicological work. In this case the total cost of developing the product, aside from capital expenditures, was $1.5 million. This example may not be typical but it is certainly not uncommon.

Numerous analyses must be conducted to estimate the quantity of residue not only in the crops on which the pesticide is to be used, but, if it is a forage crop, also in meat, milk, or

eggs. A major difficulty in applying microanalytical methods has been the requirement that residue data be furnished for each agricultural product for which a proposed tolerance is requested. By virtue of their chemical complexity, natural products introduce interferences with the analytical procedures which are at times exceedingly difficult to overcome. For this reason it has been proposed to divide products of plant origin into categories so that analytical data for any one product in a given category may be considered applicable to all the others. Adoption of this principle would facilitate extension of tolerances as experience dictates, without requiring repeated official processing.

A prime requisite for official consideration of proposed tolerance levels is a sufficient body of reliable toxicological information. Recommended procedures have been outlined by the Division of Pharmacology of the Food and Drug Administration and by the Food Protection Committee. As a minimum these toxicological programs embody acute, subacute, and chronic studies on a rodent species, generally the rat, and subacute feeding studies on a non-rodent species, generally the dog or monkey. Observations are made of growth, food utilization, blood and urine changes, reproduction, lactation, general appearance and behavior, and physiological reactions. Where possible, metabolic or biochemical studies are performed to determine the fate of the ingested toxicant or its mode of action. Necropsies, with gross and microscopic examinations of the major organs, constitute an essential feature of these investigations.

Toxicology: A Hybrid Science

It is apparent that a wide variety of scientific disciplines is called into play. Toxicology is in fact a hybrid science whose ancestry includes pharmacology, physiology, nutrition, chemistry, pathology, biometrics, and perhaps a few less clearly identified progenitors. Notwithstanding the application of objective and statistical criteria, a strong element of human judgment enters into the design and especially the interpretation of tox-

icological experiments. Evaluations for safety involve working in the region of minimal or marginal response where pathological effects may be subtle and their incidence low. Under these circumstances a causal connection to dosage is often difficult to establish, and the estimation of a "no-effect" level may require educated guesswork. In the final analysis, extrapolations of dosage response from experimental to practical dietary conditions and from animal species to man are necessary. In setting tolerance limits for a pesticide chemical, account must be taken not only of the toxicological data and the proposed usage but of the possibility of non-permitted extension of its use, and of the chemical and pharmacological relationship to other chemical components of the diet. Since decisions must be based on animal feeding tests rather than on lifetime experience in man, absolute assurance of safety for all population groups is never possible. Honest differences of opinion among competent scientists are inevitable in any area of value judgment.

Fortunately, the National Academy of Sciences and National Research Council offer the means whereby these perplexing questions may be studied by experts and recommendations made to the parties concerned. Reports have been rendered on specific topics such as "The Safety of Artificial Sweeteners for Use in Foods," "The Relation of Surface Activity to the Safety of Surfactants in Foods," and "The Safety of Polyoxyethylene Stearates for Use as Intentional Food Additives." Moreover the Miller Amendment makes possible the referral of controversial issues to an ad hoc scientific advisory committee appointed by the Secretary of Health, Education, and Welfare from a panel of experts selected by the National Academy of Sciences for their competence in the particular subject in question. This procedure, which has already been invoked both by industry and by the government, offers a logical basis for resolving scientific issues at the scientific level, without depriving either the Food and Drug Administration of its responsibility and authority or industry of its right to judicial appeal.

Reference was made above to the mounting costs of introducing new pesticidal chemicals, what with the cost of meeting

rigid regulatory requirements added to that of the usual chemical, entomological, and agricultural development work. A serious question has arisen as to whether these costs will tend to direct interest of the chemical industry away from pesticides to products whose development require less capital investment with less risk. At any rate, it can be said with assurance that pesticidal chemicals are for big business, not for the small entrepreneur. New pesticides will replace old ones only on the basis of proven better efficiency, lower cost, or greater safety. In the course of time, existing tolerances may be modified or withdrawn on the basis of further knowledge. Occasional accidents may be expected to occur from the misuse of pesticides as from any other substance or device. However, the extreme care presently exercised in regulating usage levels should provide assurance of the safety of pesticides for the consuming public along with their direct and indirect benefits.

REFERENCES

1. Birdsall, J. J., K. G. Weckel, and R. K. Chapman. *J. Agr. Food Chem.* 5:523 (1957).
2. Official FDA Tolerances. *Natl. Agr. Chemicals Assoc. News and Pesticide Rev.* 16:4-14 (1958).

II   RECENT ADVANCES IN CHEMICAL CONTROL

Fungicides and Bactericides for Controlling Plant Diseases

GEORGE L. McNEW

Boyce Thompson Institute for Plant Research, Inc.,
Yonkers, New York

More progress has been made in the control of plant diseases during the past twenty-five years than in all the preceding history of scientific agriculture. One of the larger contributing forces has been the development of new fungicides, bactericides, and nematocides that could be used safely on crops without serious hazard to man or domestic animals.

The progress may be attributed to two tremendous developments. The discovery of organic chemicals as fungicides, starting with the announcement of the alkyl dithiocarbamates as fungicides in 1934, launched this new era. This group was not exploited commercially until after the quinone fungicides (chloranil) were introduced in 1940. However, the possibilities of designing organic molecules with superior fungitoxicity, greater margin of safety for use on crops, and less hazard to consumers of agricultural products were clearly established as soon as the dithiocarbamates were discovered.

The second great step forward came with the development of antibiotics to control bacterial diseases of crops. The ordinary surface protectants had failed to control the bacteria since they invade through stomata, wounds, or other natural openings where they escape destruction by superficial deposits. Streptomycin was found to have a limited systemic effect so it could prevent establishment of infection.

Most of this progress has been made by empirical testing and fortuitous observation. It is only within the past half dozen years that substantial basic knowledge has begun to accumulate as to the mode of action of these new plant therapeutants. There

49

is slowly evolving a science of fungus toxicology which will be invaluable both in the development of new chemicals by the industrial research teams and the wise application of chemicals to crops by the agricultural scientists.

The effective microbicide on crops must have four attributes in addition to relative safety to the crop and low hazard to the consumer of the produce. (1) The material must be able to penetrate the fungus membrane or change these membranes to establish itself as a site of operation. (2) It must enter into reaction with cell metabolites to disrupt the biochemical processes of the cell essential to its growth and functioning. (3) The toxicant must be selective so it will not enter into extraneous reactions and become detoxified or become attached to relatively inert cell structures such as a spore wall. (4) The molecule must be sufficiently stable to permit its effective use as a spray deposit, chemotherapeutant or, as occurs in at least two or three examples, to generate fungitoxic decomposition products as required.

This paper deals with the design of organic molecules to attain these four attributes. Examples from the literature have been selected to illustrate how each attribute can be enhanced by the design of an organic molecule even while the material is being rendered safe for use on a plant tissue. Finally, we shall examine some of the recent developments with antibiotics to gain an insight into the potentialities of chemotherapy and the use of synergistic forces to accentuate the toxicology of microbicides.

Membranes of Fungus Spores and Their Penetration

Probably 95 per cent of all fungicides are applied as protective deposits so they will be in position to destroy the fungus spore when it reaches the susceptible tissue. The primary function of the protective deposit is to release molecules that will penetrate the spore when it arrives. If one assumes that the molecule is designed to inactivate cell metabolites such as an enzyme, it must find its way into the spore. To do this it conceivably must penetrate the lipid or waxy layer that surrounds

the spore cell and prevents its desiccation, proceed through the wall proper (possibly via the oily materials impregnated in the chitinous structure) to the cell membrane, find its way through the lipoprotein structure of the membrane into the cytoplasm, and then remain mobile in the cytoplasm until it can establish contact with lipid layers in the mitochondria or other sites of enzyme activity.

A molecule that can do these things must have a very delicate balance between lipid solubility and hydrophilic properties. Conceivably, if it is not soluble in lipoidal phase it could never reach the cell membrane, and if it has no hydrophilic properties, it could not transfer from the cell membrane to the cytoplasm. If it is too soluble in free oils, it could easily be dissolved in the numerous oil droplets in the cytoplasm of some spores so it would never be able to contact enzymes or other metabolites. Although there is good reason to believe that spore walls and membranes may not be the rigid barriers they are ordinarily considered to be (34), they obviously give form to cells and regulate the movement of ions and molecules into and out of the cell and therefore the above concept of penetrating a membrane probably has reasonable validity.

When Miller, McCallan, and Weed (37) began to study the uptake of 2-heptadecyl-2-imidazoline (glyodin base), they found this material had tremendous ability to penetrate spores. Spores of *Monilinia fructicola* placed in a suspension of 2 p.p.m. took up 6700 p.p.m. of chemical in half a minute from a total dose of 10,160 p.p.m. Apparently most of this material was inside the spore since it could not be removed by washing. Studies of the spore tissues by Owens and Miller (46) revealed that very little of the material had become fixed in the cell wall or cuticular layers, and about 75 per cent was absorbed to very fine particulate matter that could be removed from spore brei by centrifugation at 80,000 g for one hour. This excellent fungicide has a low innate toxicity (36) since 6500 p.p.m. have to be taken up before 50 per cent of the spores are inactivated. Its efficacy depends upon its ability to penetrate the spore so readily.

In the course of developing glyodin, Wellman and McCallan

(62) tested many related imidazoline compounds. They found that both fungitoxicity and phytotoxicity increased as the carbon side chain in the 2 position was increased up to 11 carbon atoms. Further elongation of the chain yielded compounds that were relatively less phytotoxic and progressively more fungitoxic up to the 17-carbon compound. Both fungitoxicity and phytotoxicity diminished as the chain was lengthened beyond 17 carbons. Since the 2-heptadecyl derivative was optimal in fungicidal ability for a given degree of phytotoxicity, it was chosen for commercial development. It has been a very successful commercial product for use on apple and cherry because it provides excellent disease control without blemishing the fruit as many apple spray materials do.

In retrospect, we see that these studies on the carbon chain were merely a move to regulate the lipid solubility of the imidazoline compound so it would penetrate the fungus spore without penetrating the cuticle of fruit and foliage. Rich and Horsfall (48) have demonstrated that the length of side chain regulates the coefficient of partition in an olive oil-aqueous medium.

The length of an alkyl group has been used to regulate fungitoxicity in various other series such as the quaternary ammonium compounds and the N-n-alkylethylenethioureas. In the latter series Ross and Ludwig (50) found that fungitoxicity increased as the chain was increased in length up to 8 carbons. This was accompanied by a progressive decrease in water solubility and an increase in the oil-water partition coefficient. The length of alkyl side chains has been observed to affect fungitoxicity in other series such as ethylenethioureas (49) and tetrahydropyrimidines (47).

The p-chlorophenyl group has been used to increase fungitoxicity in some classes such as the nitrosopyrazoles (33) and the s-triazines (52, 65). This group changes the partition coefficient of pyrazoles in oil-water phase according to Rich and Horsfall (48) and increases spore permeation by the s-triazines according to Burchfield and Storrs (9).

One of the large areas for future investigation is the effect

of fungicides on the membrane itself. Lipid-soluble materials are certain to create surface strain by the attractiveness of the molecule for the lipid phase of two members of a system. If the two lipid surfaces are attached to a protein, the two protein molecules could be drawn closer together and thereby cause imperfections in a layered structure.

One is stimulated to consider this possibility by recent data of Miller, McCallan, and Weed (38) on uptake of silver and mercury ions. Pretreatment of spores with silver makes them more susceptible to uptake of mercury even after the spores are incapable of growth. The silver affects the spore membrane so it is more susceptible to penetration from without or within. Even though the intact fungus spores lose substantial quantities of material when washed (34), the loss of labeled phosphorus and sulfur compounds is increased substantially by silver ions. An analogous situation was observed by Burchfield and Storrs (9) for the substituted s-triazines. The fungicides altered the permeability of the membranes but this did not appear to be a lethal effect.

Reaction with Cell Metabolites

The preponderance of evidence obtained from use of labeled compounds is that most of the fungicides do pentrate the fungus cell and operate internally by reaction with normal cell constituents. The one possible exception is sulfur. Miller, McCallan, and Weed (35) found that sulfur is reduced almost immediately after coming into contact with the spore and is released as hydrogen sulfide. Apparently very little of the exogenous sulfur is retained in the cell, and the cell yields very little of its endogenous sulfur as hydrogen sulfide. It is probable that the exogenous sulfur is reduced at the spore membrane by an electron transfer. This is associated with a disruption of the oxidative forces in the cell so that a molecule of carbon dioxide is released for every mole of sulfur reduced (31). The biochemical site of the decarboxylation has not been established but may very well be responsible for inactivation of the spore.

Other fungicides have been found internally in spores dis-

integrated by sonic waves, which are capable of rupturing the cell walls without macerating them. Substantial amounts of the glyodin, dichlone, silver, zinc, and mercury reached the particulate matter of the cell. Since Owens and Miller (46) could not release these materials with lipid solvents except for glyodin extracted by acetone, they apparently had entered into reaction with groups on the mitochondria. The natural assumption is that they have reacted with sulfhydryl and amino groups of enzymatic proteins or other receptive sites of these tissues.

Apparently there is considerable independence of choice in site of action of unrelated compounds since glyodin, mercury, silver, and cerium do not interfere with each other when applied jointly or separately in binary mixtures (38). As a matter of fact, spores killed by one of these materials will take up about the same amount of the other fungicides as normal functioning spores. In addition to the rather dubious idea that fungicides destroy the spore by physical means such as those discussed in the preceding section, five potential reactions have come to be considered with favor. These are: reaction with sulfhydryl or amino groups of enzymatic proteins to destroy their activity, the chelation of cations such as the metallic component of enzyme systems, changes in the oxidation potential of the cell, and competition with metabolic intermediates so as to block a vital pathway of metabolism without necessarily interfering with enzymes and uncoupling of phosphate bonds.

The interference with energy transfers through the phosphate bond may be one of the more important mechanisms of fungicide action. Attention is directed toward this possibility because many phenolic substances are fungicidal, and the nitrophenols are the classic example of materials capable of causing uncoupling of high-energy bonds. Likewise, any interference with the synthesis of phosphate into organic compounds would be fatal to energy transfers of the fungus. Owens (45) of our laboratory has found substantial evidence that certain fungicides do affect phosphate metabolism of Neurospora sitophila spores. These data should be sufficiently complete for publication within the coming year. [Added in proof: Contribs. Boyce Thompson Inst. 19(6): 463-482 (1958).]

On the surface, the possibility of interfering with the oxidation reduction potential of a cell appears very attractive. Copper and sulfur are oxidizing materials. Reasoning from this fact, W. P. ter Horst decided (personal communication) that oxidizing agents for rubber should be fungicidal. This is true to a surprising extent and has directed interest toward materials with high oxidation potentials such as chloranil (tetrachloro-p-benzoquinone), dichlone (2,3-dichloro-1,4-naphthoquinone), and thiuram (tetramethylthiuram disulfide) (51). Unfortunately, the theory has found very little support from experimentation. There is no direct evidence that these materials do change the electron status of the cell appreciably, and there are other mechanisms that explain their effects as will be discussed below. Their highly oxidized state probably is significant in that they are highly reactive materials, but its significance beyond this point remains to be proved.

The antimetabolite or competitive theory has been considered ever since Woods (67) established the idea of a competitive role of sulfanilamide with p-aminobenzoic acid. The theory has been extended and amplified by the brilliant deductions of Woolley (68). However, there has not been enough effort spent on analyzing the injured cells to be certain how far theory is substantiated by reaction in the cells, but the idea certainly is a valid working hypothesis. The quinones and phenol fungicides may very well be antimetabolites because it is well known (29) that their analogues are normal constituents of fungus cells and probably are vitally important to their functioning. The numerous heterocyclic nitrogen and sulfur compounds which are being used or have recently been discovered might have a comparable function, particularly in the synthesis of proteins, pyrroles, and pyrimidines. Full data are not available on this type of reaction, but there is substantial evidence that heptadecylimidazoline may serve as a competitive analogue of guanine (63).

A substantial number of the organic fungicides have ability to react with sulfhydryl and amino compounds. It is probably a common reaction with all those materials that can serve as alkylating agents. The reaction of quinones with these groups is well known (54), and a variety of enzymes with such groups

is immobilized by both benzoquinones and naphthoquinones (18, 32). As shown by Owens (42, 43), the quinones react with either group on enzymes when experimental conditions are suitable. We are not certain whether the conditions in a cell are satisfactory for reaction since the reaction products have not been isolated and identified.

The substituted *s*-triazines readily react with sulfhydryl and amino groups according to Burchfield and Storrs (8, 9). Cysteine, glutathione, and glycine react through the nuclear halogens of 2,4-dichloro-6-(anilino)-*s*-triazine. Reactivity is enhanced by substitution of chlorine on the anilino group with ortho > meta > para > unsubstituted. Although the ortho derivative is more effective than the other isomers against *Alternaria solani* and *Phytophthora infestans* (52), the para isomer is more effective against *Neurospora sitophila* (9). The reason for these specific differences has not been established, but it is suspected that penetration of the cell walls of *N. sitophila* may be a dominant consideration, and the *p*-chloroanilino isomer is the more capable penetrant.

Those enzymes that are dependent upon metallic moieties for their activity should be destroyed as readily by removal of the metal as by blocking the reactive group on the protein. Because of this, the chelation of metals has been advanced as a mechanism of action (72). A very heated debate has revolved around the mechanism of action of 8-hydroxyquinoline in the past fifteen years since Zentmyer (71) first proposed that its ability to chelate metals such as zinc might explain its action. Albert *et al.* (1) substantiated the chelation hypothesis and demonstrated that the quinoline compounds with substituents placed so there could be no chelation were much less active bactericides.

The chelation hypothesis is considerably confused by the fact that copper 8-hydroxyquinolinate has been found to be more active than 8-hydroxyquinoline. Since the receptor sites for bivalent cations are fully occupied, one must assume that either the copper is released preferentially in favor of some metallic cofactor for a vitally important enzyme system. This could be

achieved by displacement with a metal farther down the series, by removal of the copper to a stronger chelating agent such as histidine or ethylenediaminetetraacetic acid (10), or by enzymatic hydrolysis (57) of the copper quinolinate into 8-hydroxyquinoline and copper ions. The removal of copper has been demonstrated by Zentmyer and Rich (73) for L-histidine and L-cysteine at concentrations of 0.5 per cent in culture media. These chelators reverse the fungitoxicity of both copper quinolinate and 8-hydroxyquinoline presumably by keeping copper away from 8-hydroxyquinoline or removing copper from the already formed copper 8-hydroxyquinoline. Horsfall and Rich (22) had previously suggested that 8-hydroxyquinoline released from copper quinolinate might be toxic for certain species of fungi because of its acidic nature.

No one knows exactly what goes on inside the fungus cell when it is exposed to 8-hydroxyquinoline. These studies on chemical structure have provided provocative hypotheses, but the final answer awaits some data on the products formed inside the cell. Much of the differences in fungitoxicity may depend upon physical properties rather than chelating ability or chemical reactivity of various molecular substituents. For example, Anderson and Swaby (2) and Block (6) have shown that because the solubility properties of the copper chelate and 8-hydroxyquinoline differ they may penetrate the cell tissues at different rates. Additional ideas on the chelation of various compounds may be found in the very good reviews by Horsfall (19–21).

The chelation mechanism finds support in data on inhibition of specific enzymes of fungus systems. Such metallic-dependent enzymes as polyphenoloxidase and catalase are affected by many fungicides (42). Nearly all the derivatives of dithiocarbamic acid tested by Owens (44), except the copper-containing members, inhibited polyphenoloxidase (a copper-dependent enzyme). A very close correlation between relative stabilities of these complexes and fungitoxicity (23) for *Aspergillus niger* was observed, but the correlation did not extend to three other species. The ethylenebisdithiocarbamates were

more effective inhibitors than the alkyl dithiocarbamates. Various other materials with a $NH_2C{=}S$ group such as bisthiocarbamyl disulfide, phenylthiourea, dithiooxamide, and dithiobiuret were also active inhibitors of the enzyme. The ability of the dithiocarbamates to inhibit metal-dependent enzymes probably is only one factor in their fungitoxicity since they also affect sulfhydryl-dependent enzymes (42, 53).

Detoxification Mechanism

Very few of the fungicides now used are efficient. Minimum effective dosages (ED_{50}) range from about 80 p.p.m. for silver ions to about 20,000 p.p.m. for sulfur (30, 36) on a spore weight basis. This indicates a low order of specificity. Most of the fungicides probably enter into miscellaneous reactions that dissipate their effectiveness without seriously injuring the fungus tissues. This undoubtedly has led to many misinterpretations of chemical structure in relation to fungitoxicity where attempts have been made to deduce what may happen inside the fungus cell.

Attempts to correlate fungitoxicity with innate reactivity of a series of homologous compounds will reveal many such errors. Such studies were made by Owens (43) on ability of twenty-seven quinoid and benzenoid compounds to react with two amylases that were dependent upon sulfhydryl and amino groups, respectively. Benzene compounds were neither fungicidal nor enzyme inhibitory as a general rule. The phenolic materials ranged from inactive to very active, and activity was closely associated with ability to inhibit the two enzymes. Most of the benzoquinones were highly active enzyme inhibitors and were fungicidal, with a very close correlation between the two attributes. The naphthoquinones were extremely fungicidal but only moderately active as enzyme inhibitors. This confirms the general observation (32, 51) that dichlone is many times as fungitoxic as chloranil. It is innately less reactive with enzymes as would be postulated from its oxidation potential and general structure. Although the cyclic structure may enhance penetration of cells by the naphthoquinones, there is another possible

explanation for the greater activity than their benzoquinone analogues. The naphthoquinones are much less reactive with secretions, particularly those from dark-colored spores. To a large measure it is suspected that chloranil loses much of its potential effectiveness by detoxifying reactions with amino groups or by hydrolysis to chloranilic acid and other compounds that are relatively poor fungicides. The chlorines are readily replaced by hydrolysis in alkaline media or by exposure to amino and sulfhydryl groups.

Detoxification mechanisms undoubtedly exist for many other fungicides. The copper ion, for example, is so readily chelated by nitrogen compounds that it can be detoxified. As shown by Yoder (69) cysteine can reverse the activity of this material in the cell. Undoubtedly the flat slope of the dosage-response curve of this material is attributable to its reactivity with many cell constituents, so these reactions must be satisfied en masse before the cell succumbs.

Stability of Fungicides

The old concept that fungicides operate in the form in which they are deposited is gradually disappearing. For many years Bordeaux mixture has been known to carbonate on exposure to air and to lose calcium when exposed to rainfall. Sulfur volatilizes and is reduced to hydrogen sulfide before the fungus is destroyed. Chloranil applied to beet seed may be converted into phytotoxic materials, presumably amine derivatives and, in alkaline mineral soils, to chloranilic acid. In general, a loss of fungicidal ability may be anticipated from reactions of this sort, but there are exceptions where fungitoxicity is enhanced.

The outstanding example of increased potency is with the alkylenebisdithiocarbamates. These materials were screened out on glass slides and proved to be valuable foliage protectants in 1942 (5, 12). Disodium ethylenebisdithiocarbamate (nabam), however, gave erratic results when used commercially. When the addition of zinc sulfate and lime improved its field performance, attention was directed toward the zinc salt (zineb) which proved to be remarkably successful on potatoes

and many other crops. Eventually the manganese salt (maneb) was developed and has been used extensively. This sequence of evolutionary changes was made in commercial practice without understanding too well what factors were involved.

The instability of dithiocarbamates (60) probably explains these developments. Nabam and probably the other salts are not fungicidal per se since McCallan (30) has shown that a 10 per cent solution of nabam will not destroy spores when they are immersed in a closed container protected from oxidation. When nabam is applied to foliage it rapidly disappears as shown by Ludwig, Thorn, and Miller (26, 27) and is replaced by substantial quantities of ethylenethiurammonosulfide and its polyethylene derivative. This sulfide provides a generating plant for ethylenediisothiocyanate which, although evanescent, is highly fungitoxic. Thus an isothiocyanate is the fungitoxicant (28) as originally surmised by Klöpping and van der Kerk (24, 56). The isothiocyanate apparently operates as a fungicide by poisoning sulfhydryl-bearing enzymes (53). Zineb is more stable than nabam so that it persists longer and generates the thiurammonosulfide over a sufficient period of time to give effective protection.

Appreciable evidence is at hand that some of the organic sulfur fungicides such as Mylone (3,5-dimethyltetrahydro-1,3,-5,2H-thiadiazine-2-thione) may hydrolyze or otherwise decompose into fungitoxic substances. The methyl isothiocyanate identified by Torgeson, Yoder, and Johnson (55) does not seem to be the primary fungitoxicant so the exact fungicide remains to be identified.

Use of Antibiotics

The forces of antibiosis have been exploited by plant pathologists for many decades (66). Diseases of the root such as Texas root rot, the take-all of wheat, strawberry root rot, and potato scab can be suppressed substantially by encouraging the growth of competitive microorganisms, primarily bacteria, by adding organic matter to the soil. As early as 1932, Weindling (61) demonstrated that *Trichoderma viride* secreted a ma-

terial, later identified as gliotoxin, that would inhibit damping-off of citrus.

Antibiotic preparations were tested against many bacterial and fungus diseases with moderate to indifferent success until 1951. After Murneek (41) had shown that fireblight of apples could be controlled by very low concentrations of streptomycin, interest in the use of antibiotics to control bacterial diseases of plants gained momentum. The observations on fireblight were confirmed and expanded (15, 17, 64), and the material was shown to be effective against halo and common blights of bean (70), bacterial spot of tomato and pepper (11), walnut blight (3), and other bacterial induced diseases (7).

The success of streptomycin where the ordinary protective fungicides had given indifferent results apparently was due to a local systemic effect. Mitchell *et al.* (39, 40) found the material inside bean leaves where it was capable of being translocated upward from the stem and from the proximal to distal parts of leaves but not from the leaves to the stem. Streptomycin does penetrate bean from dusted leaves (4) and will move in pear and apple (13). By means of laboratory tests English and Van Halsema (14) were able to show that several cultures of *Erwinia amylovora* and *Xanthomonas vesicatoria* acquired appreciable tolerance for streptomycin after eight to fifteen transfers on culture media containing sublethal doses. This tendency was suppressed when 10 per cent of tetracycline (Terramycin) was incorporated into the streptomycin so a mixture of the two materials was formulated. This combination has been used commercially since 1952 under the trade name of Agrimycin.

In the course of evaluating Agrimycin, the material was found to be synergized by certain insoluble copper compounds such as copper oxychloride sulfate, cuprous oxide, and tribasic copper sulfate (58). The synergistic effect depends upon the mechanism of action of copper and streptomycin, but the exact mechanism has not been established. The synergism extends to the control of phycomycetous fungi such as *Phytophthora infestans*, the cause of late blight of potatoes.

This synergism might be due to stimulation of polyphenol-

oxidase activity according to Vörös, Kiraly, and Farkas (59). They noted that enzymatic activity both in the fungus and host tissue was accentuated by streptomycin and deduced that supplementary supplies of copper might enhance this effect since the enzyme is copper dependent. Their hypothesis is intriguing because resistance to the late blight fungus in some varieties of potatoes has been correlated with ability of the polyphenoloxidases to produce oxidized phenolic substances.

There has been considerable effort expended on the development of antibiotics to control fungous diseases of plants (25). A number of very effective materials have been discovered but have not been reduced to commercial use. Among these are materials such as phytoactin and phytostreptin (74), and anisomycin, which have been studied in our own laboratories. They are exceedingly effective against rust (Uredinales) and powdery mildew (Erysiphales) fungi. The major question is whether they can be produced economically enough to find a place in agriculture. One of the interesting possibilities is to react these materials with chemicals to modify their properties. By this means a whole class of effective compounds related to anisomycin has been produced and evaluated in cooperation with Chas. Pfizer & Co.

One of the more interesting fungitoxic antibiotics is cycloheximide (Actidione). The material is extremely potent against many fungi but has been so phytotoxic that it has found very limited use. There is good evidence that it may be made safe by conversion into the semicarbazone or oxime. On the basis of limited field trials, these materials appeared to have appreciable promise as eradicants for black stem rust of wheat, according to Hacker and Vaughn (16).

From our present vantage point, it is obvious that exceptionally effective fungicides and bactericides from antibiotic sources are available. Many of them are much more active than the synthetic organic chemicals. They have a tendency toward being phytotoxic, but they can be used at such nominal dosages that most of them will not be eliminated from use because of crop injury. They are certain to find uses in agriculture, if they can be produced economically.

The antibiotics are exceptionally interesting from a basic research viewpoint. They are organic molecules, but they have come from living cells where they existed in substantial concentrations without causing injury or being detoxified. The living cells have placed the substituent groups where they ought to be. Therefore they are the logical models to study in developing chemotherapeutants. The door to this fascinating realm has been opened just enough to know it is not a dream. Encouragement is offered by the examples of streptomycin for bacteria, cycloheximide for rust control, eradication of bean rust by anisomycin derivatives applied after infection had caused subepidermal pustules in our experiments, and the eradication of powdery mildews from bean and rose in a fashion that is not matched by any other materials now available.

Summary

The outline of a new science has begun to emerge from the studies on fungicides in this decade. Fungus toxicology is in its infancy, but it has begun to take shape. It has grown since the interest in organic fungicides began to develop, because it is essential to the design of better molecules. It is possible to design these molecules to attain almost any degree of reactivity, penetrability, or selective toxicity, if we know how they are to operate and what role each change in chemical configuration is expected to play.

The pattern that has been followed is very logical. First, there was extensive empirical testing of materials from the shelves of chemical companies and from the supply houses. Then there was a systematic study of the more promising nuclei to see how minor changes in their substituents would affect fungitoxicity and phytotoxicity. Finally, there was a rather extensive effort to design analogues and members of homologous series to see if related compounds were active.

Next followed a period of wild speculation as to what these materials might be doing inside the cell. Since the reasoning was largely based on analogy, the deductions rarely can be accepted as factual. All too often we have forgotten that the change of a single substituent may alter the physical attributes

of a particular molecule as much as it does its chemistry. No change in a homologous series or from one analog to another can be explained until its effects on each of the four major attributes reviewed above have been carefully evaluated. For example, if a halogen ortho to the nitrogen in the anilino group of 2,4-dichloro-6-(o-chloroanilino)-s-triazine accentuates chemical reactivity with sulfhydryl groups (9) while the same halogen placed in the para position exerts its influence primarily upon spore penetration, what validity does reasoning by analogy hold for the effect of halogen isomerism? Empirical reasoning and conjecture have no more place in this new science than empirical experimentation except to serve as tools in orienting the design of experiments.

Enough data have been acquired to make certain reasonable deductions as to why substituent groups may affect fungitoxicity. Already some compounds are being designed for testing by deductive reasoning from performance of a group in one structure to possible value in other classes of compounds. Unfortunately the data on the fungitoxicity of such materials are rarely interpreted in light of the changes in physical properties of the molecule, chemical stability in the test environment, and capacity for electron transfer.

The next era that must follow our present status is to study chemical changes in the fungus cell. The molecules now in use are extremely inefficient since they must penetrate the spore in concentrations of hundreds to many thousands of parts per million of weight before they destroy a vital function. As Miller, McCallan, and Weed (38) have pointed out, this is a very poor performance compared to an antibiotic against a bacterium, a herbicidal plant hormone, or botulinum toxin in warm-blooded animals where < 1 to 10 p.p.m. is usually fatal. Undoubtedly the modern fungicides are not so selectively efficient as they should be and probably enter into many detoxifying reactions.

The need for analyses of spore constituents should not discourage the investigator of today because by wise use of paper chromatography, column chromatography, and radioisotope

techniques he should be able to separate the reaction products and identify them. It is only by so doing that we can separate the chaff from the kernels of knowledge and develop a sound understanding of what goes on inside the cell. We already know (38, 46) that the silver ion is readily displaced, dichlone apparently enters into chemical reaction so it is fixed in the cell, and glyodin becomes attached to mitochondria or other small particulate matter of the cell. The next step is to find out why these things are so.

A substantial contribution both in practical progress and in theory is to be made from a study of the antibiotics. Undoubtedly, one of the great areas for development is with systemic therapeutants, and many of the antibiotics have abilities of this sort. It is logical that they should have these attributes more than man-made molecules because they were created in the living cytoplasm of a cell and were immune to detoxification reactions while in this aqueous medium. The synthetics, developed as protective fungicides on the other hand, are too reactive, too nonspecific and too well designed for lipid solubility to remain mobile in an aqueous medium without being detoxified. Again man should turn to the living cell for knowledge and guidance when his own inventiveness has failed him. New concepts are needed if chemotherapy is to make progress.

The implied need for better fungicides, bactericides, and nematocides in the preceding discussion is a real one. In spite of all the progress of the past twenty-five years, we have merely opened the door to the future. It is true that the nabam family of fungicides has played a heavy role in helping to increase the yield of potatoes 90 per cent in the decade following World War II. Likewise, ferbam and dichlone have brought the anthracnoses and rusts under control better than had been previously considered possible. Glyodin will control apple scab without blemishing fruits, and Karathane suppresses the powdery mildews very effectively. The antibiotics control bacteria on beans, pear, apple, tomato, pepper, and tobacco when we had despaired of preventing their damage.

As great as these achievements may be, the harsh fact re-

mains that plant diseases take a toll of about three billion dollars annually from the crops grown in the United States. It is analogous to plowing, sowing, and seeding almost 30 million acres from which no crop will be harvested. Unfortunately many of them even increase the cost of harvesting what remains and continue to take their toll of produce in transit to market or in storage.

Every resource of the agricultural scientist will be called upon to reduce these losses, and one of those resources is the help that may come from the agricultural chemicals industry. This help will come sooner and more surely if the new science of fungus toxicology can be established more firmly on a sound basis of fact. These facts will come from understanding the nature of the chemical reactions going on inside the cells of the pathogens.

REFERENCES

1. Albert, A., S. D. Rubbo, R. J. Goldacre, and B. G. Balfour. The influence of chemical constitution on antibacterial activity. Pt. III. A study of 8-hydroxyquinoline (oxine) and related compounds. *Brit. J. Exptl. Pathol.* 28:69-87 (1947); *C. A.* 41:7436^f (1947).

2. Anderson, Beverley I., and R. J. Swaby. Factors influencing the fungistatic action of 8-hydroxyquinoline (oxine) and its metal complexes. *Australian J. Sci. Research B4*:275-282 (1951).

3. Ark, P. A. Experiments with streptomycin for walnut blight control. *Diamond Walnut News* 35(3):6 (1953).

4. Ark, Peter A., and Eugene M. Wilson. Movement of streptomycin into plant tissues from streptomycin-pyrophyllite formulations. *Phytopathology* 46:634 (1956) (Abstract).

5. Barratt, Raymond W., and James G. Horsfall. Fungicidal action of metallic alkyl bis-dithiocarbamates. *Conn. Agr. Expt. Sta. Bull. 508*, 1947.

6. Block, S. S. Fungitoxicity of the 8-quinolinols. *J. Agr. Food Chem. 3*:229-234 (1955).

7. Bonde, Reiner. Preliminary studies on the control of bacterial decay of the potato with antibiotics. *Am. Potato J. 30*:143-147 (1953).

8. Burchfield, H. P., and Eleanor E. Storrs. Chemical structures and dissociation constants of amino acids, peptides, and proteins in relation to their reaction rates with 2,4-dichloro-6-

(o-chloroanilino)-s-triazine. *Contribs. Boyce Thompson Inst.* *18*:395-418 (1956).

9. ———. Effects of chlorine substitution and isomerism on the interactions of s-triazine derivatives with conidia of *Neurospora sitophila*. *Contribs. Boyce Thompson Inst. 18*:429-452 (1957).

10. Byrde, R. J. W., and D. Woodcock. Effect of the interaction between chelating agents on their fungitoxicity. *Nature 179*:539 (1957).

11. Cox, R. S., W. R. Comegys, and J. W. Heuberger. Preliminary tests with antibiotics for the control of bacterial leafspot of pepper. *Trans. Peninsula Hort. Soc. 67*:24-28 (1953) (*Bull. Delaware State Board Agr. 43*).

12. Dimond, Albert E., John W. Heuberger, and James G. Horsfall. A water soluble protectant fungicide with tenacity. *Phytopathology 33*:1095-1097 (1943).

13. Dunegan, John C., and R. A. Wilson. Preliminary note on the downward movement of streptomycin in apple and pear tissues. *Plant Disease Reptr. 40*:478 (1956).

14. English, Arthur R., and G. Van Halsema. A note on the delay in the emergence of resistant *Xanthomonas* and *Erwinia* strains by the use of streptomycin plus terramycin combinations. Mimeographed lab. rept. Chas. Pfizer & Co., Inc., 1954.

15. Goodman, Robert N. Antibiotics: a new weapon for fire blight control. *Am. Fruit Grower 73*(11):7, 16-17 (1953).

16. Hacker, Robert G., and John R. Vaughn. Cycloheximide analogues cause preinfection resistance to *Puccinia graminis* var. *tritici* in spring wheat. *Phytopathology 47*:14 (1957) (Abstract).

17. Heuberger, J. W., and P. L. Poulos. Control of fire blight and frog-eye leaf spot (black rot) diseases of apples in Delaware in 1952. *Plant Disease Reptr. 37*:81-83 (1953).

18. Hochstein, P. E., and Carroll E. Cox. Effect of tetrachloro-*p*-benzoquinone on certain fermentative enzyme systems in fungi. *Phytopathology 42*:11 (1952).

19. Horsfall, James G. *Fungicides and Their Action*. Chronica Botanica, Waltham, Mass., 1945.

20. ———. *Principles of Fungicidal Action*. Chronica Botanica, Waltham, Mass., 1956.

21. ———. Mechanisms of fungitoxicity. *Advances in Pest Control Research 1*:193-218 (1957).

22. Horsfall, James G., and Saul Rich. Fungitoxicity of heterocyclic nitrogen compounds. *Contribs. Boyce Thompson Inst. 16*:313-347 (1951).

23. Klöpping, Hein Louis. *Chemical Constitution and Antifungal Action of Sulfur Compounds.* Schotanus & Jens, Utrecht, 1951.
24. Klöpping, H. L., and G. J. M. van der Kerk. Investigations on organic fungicides. V. Chemical constitution and fungistatic activity of aliphatic bisdithiocarbamates and isothiocyanates. *Rec. trav. chim.* 70:949-961 (1951) (Abstract) *in R.A.M.* 33: 308 (1954).
25. Leben, Curt, and G. W. Keitt. Antibiotics and plant disease. Effect of antibiotics in control of plant diseases. *J. Agr. Food Chem.* 2:234-239 (1954).
26. Ludwig, R. A., and G. D. Thorn. Studies of the breakdown of disodium ethylene bisdithiocarbamate (nabam). *Plant Disease Reptr.* 37:127-129 (1953).
27. Ludwig, R. A., G. D. Thorn, and D. M. Miller. Studies on the mechanism of fungicidal action of disodium ethylene bisdithiocarbamate (nabam). *Can. J. Botany* 32:48-54 (1954).
28. Ludwig, R. A., G. D. Thorn, and C. H. Unwin. Studies on the mechanism of fungicidal action of metallic ethylenebisdithiocarbamates. *Can. J. Botany* 33:42-59 (1955).
29. Mayer, Fritz. *The Chemistry of Natural Coloring Matters.* (Trans. and rev. by A. H. Cook) Reinhold Publishing Corporation, New York, 1943.
30. McCallan, S. E. A. Mechanisms of fungitoxicity with special reference to fungicides. *Proc. 2nd International Plant Prot. Conf.* Fernhurst, England, June 20, 1956, 1957. Pages 77-95.
31. McCallan, S. E. A., and Lawrence P. Miller. Equimolar formation of carbon dioxide and hydrogen sulfide when fungus tissue reduces sulfur. *Contribs. Boyce Thompson Inst.* 18: 497-506 (1957).
32. McNew, George L., and Harry P. Burchfield. Fungitoxicity and biological activity of quinones. *Contribs. Boyce Thompson Inst.* 16:357-374 (1951).
33. McNew, George L., and Norman K. Sundholm. The fungicidal activity of substituted pyrazoles and related compounds. *Phytopathology* 39:721-751 (1949).
34. Miller, Lawrence P., and S. E. A. McCallan. Movement of ions and compounds into and out of fungus spores. *Science* 126: 1233 (1957) (Abstract).
35. Miller, Lawrence P., S. E. A. McCallan, and Richard M. Weed. Quantitative studies on the role of hydrogen sulfide formation in the toxic action of sulfur to fungus spores. *Contribs. Boyce Thompson Inst.* 17:151-171 (1953).
36. ———. Rate of uptake and toxic dose on a spore weight basis of

various fungicides. *Contribs. Boyce Thompson Inst.* 17:173-195 (1953).

37. ———. Accumulation of 2-heptadecyl-2-imidazoline, silver, and cerium by fungus spores in mixed and consecutive treatments. *Contribs. Boyce Thompson Inst.* 17:283-298 (1953).

38. ———. The use of radioisotopes in studying the affinity of various toxicants for spores. Proc. 2nd Radioisotope Conference, Oxford. *Med. & Physiol.* 1:381-389 (1954).

39. Mitchell, John W., William J. Zaumeyer, and W. Powell Andersen. Translocation of streptomycin in bean plants and its effect on bacterial blights. *Science* 115:114-115 (1952).

40. Mitchell, John W., William J. Zaumeyer, and William H. Preston, Jr. Movement of streptomycin in bean plants. *Phytopathology* 43:480 (1953) (Abstract).

41. Murneek, A. E. Thiolutin as a possible inhibitor of fire blight. *Phytopathology* 42:57 (1952).

42. Owens, Robert G. Studies on the nature of fungicidal action. I. Inhibition of sulfhydryl-, amino-, iron-, and copper-dependent enzymes *in vitro* by fungicides and related compounds. *Contribs. Boyce Thompson Inst.* 17:221-242 (1953).

43. ———. Studies on the nature of fungicidal action. II. Chemical constitution of benzenoid and quinonoid compounds in relation to fungitoxicity and inhibition of amino- and sulfhydryl-dependent enzymes. *Contribs. Boyce Thompson Inst.* 17:273-282 (1953).

44. ———. Studies on the nature of fungicidal action. III. Effects of fungicides on polyphenol oxidase *in vitro*. *Contribs. Boyce Thompson Inst.* 17:473-487 (1954).

45. ———. Effects of fungicides on levels of adenosine polyphosphates, inorganic phosphate, and phosphate esters contained in fungus spores. *Phytopathology* 46:23 (1956) (Abstract).

46. Owens, Robert G., and Lawrence P. Miller. Intracellular distribution of radioactive fungicides and metal ions in fungus spores. *Phytopathology* 47:531 (1957) (Abstract).

47. Rader, Wm. E., C. M. Monroe, and R. R. Whetstone. Tetrahydropyrimidine derivatives as potential foliage fungicides. *Science* 115:124-125 (1952).

48. Rich, Saul, and James G. Horsfall. The relation between fungitoxicity, permeation, and lipid solubility. *Phytopathology* 42:457-460 (1952).

49. ———. Fungitoxicity of ethylenethiourea derivatives. *Science* 120:122-123 (1954).

50. Ross, R. G., and R. A. Ludwig. A comparative study of fungi-

toxicity and phytotoxicity in a homologous series of *N-n*-alkylethylenethioureas. *Can. J. Botany* 35:65-95 (1957).

51. Schoene, D. L., H. Douglas Tate, and T. W. Brasfield. Use of quinones as fungicides. *Agr. Chem.* 4(11):24-27, 73, 75-77 (1949).

52. Schuldt, Paul H., and Calvin N. Wolf. Fungitoxicity of substituted *s*-triazines. *Contribs. Boyce Thompson Inst.* 18:377-393 (1956).

53. Sijpesteyn, A. Kaars, and G. J. M. van der Kerk. Investigations on organic fungicides. VIII. The biochemical mode of action of bisdithiocarbamates and diisothiocyanates. *Biochem. et Biophys. Acta* 13:545-552 (1954).

54. Snell, J. M., and A. Weissberger. The reaction of thiol compounds with quinones. *Jour. Am. Chem. Soc.* 61:450-453 (1939).

55. Torgeson, D. C., D. M. Yoder, and J. B. Johnson. Biological activity of Mylone breakdown products. *Phytopathology* 47:536 (1957) (Abstract).

56. van der Kerk, G. J. M., and H. L. Klöpping. Investigations on organic fungicides. VII. Further considerations regarding the relations between chemical structure and antifungal action of dithiocarbamate and bisdithiocarbamate derivatives. *Rec. trav. chim.* 71:1179-1197 (1952). (Abstract in *Rev. Appl. Mycol.* 34:47.)

57. Vicklund, Richard E., Milton Manowitz, and Vincent J. Bagdon. Mechanism of action of copper 8-quinolinolate. *Mycologia* 46:133-142 (1954).

58. Visor, Frederick C., George L. McNew, Geo. Koch, and Alvaro Goenaga. Composition and method for combating bacterial and fungal infections in plants. U. S. Patent No. 2,777,791 (Appl. June 4, 1954) Jan. 15, 1957.

59. Vörös, J., Z. Király, and G. L. Farkas. Role of polyphenolase in streptomycin-induced resistance to *Phytophthora* in potato. *Science* 126:1178 (1957).

60. Weed, Richard M., S. E. A. McCallan, and Lawrence P. Miller. Factors associated with the fungitoxicity of ferbam and nabam. *Contribs. Boyce Thompson Inst.* 17:299-315 (1953).

61. Weindling, R. *Trichoderma lignorum* as a parasite of other soil fungi. *Phytopathology* 22:837-845 (1932).

62. Wellman, R. H., and S. E. A. McCallan. Glyoxalidine derivative as foliage fungicides. I. Laboratory studies. *Contribs. Boyce Thompson Inst.* 14:151-160 (1946).

63. West, B., and F. T. Wolf. The mechanism of action of the fungi-

cide, 2-heptadecyl-2-imidazoline. *J. Gen. Microbiol. 12*:401 (1955).
64. Winter, H. F., and H. C. Young. Fireblight control may be achieved by antibiotics. *Ohio Farm and Home Research 38*(284):84-85, 94 (1953).
65. Wolf, Calvin N., Paul H. Schuldt, and M. M. Baldwin, s-Triazine derivatives—a new class of fungicides. *Science 121*:61-62 (1955).
66. Wood, R. K. S., and M. Tveit. Control of plant diseases by use of antagonistic organisms. *Botan. Rev. 21*:441-492 (1955).
67. Woods, D. D. The relation of p-aminobenzoic acid to the mechanism of the action of sulfanilamide. *Brit. J. Exptl. Pathol. 21*:74-90 (1940) C. A. *34*:7408[5] (1940).
68. Woolley, D. W. Recent advances in the study of biological competition between structurally related compounds. *Physiol. Revs. 27*:308-333 (1947).
69. Yoder, Donald M. Reversibility of copper toxicity to conidia of *Sclerotinia fructicola. Phytopathology 41*:39 (1951) (Abstract).
70. Zaumeyer, W. J., H. Rex Thomas, and J. W. Mitchell. Streptomycin controls halo blight. *Am. Veg. Grower 1*:5, 16-17 (Nov. 1953).
71. Zentmyer, George A. Mechanism of action of 8-hydroxyquinoline. *Phytopathology 33*:1121 (1943) (Abstract).
72. ———. Inhibition of metal catalysis as a fungistatic mechanism. *Science 100*:294-295 (1944).
73. Zentmyer, George, and Saul Rich. Reversal of fungitoxicity of 8-quinolinol and copper-8-quinolinolate by other chelators. *Phytopathology 46*:33 (1956) (Abstract).
74. Ziffer, Jack, S. J. Ishihara, T. J. Cairney, and A. W. Chow. Phytoactin and phytostreptin, two new antibiotics for plant disease control. *Phytopathology 47*:539 (1957) (Abstract).

Chemical Weed Control

R. H. BEATTY

*Amchem Products, Inc.,
Ambler, Pennsylvania*

Certain undesirable plants have been referred to as weeds since Biblical times, but many people do not fully realize the importance of weed control. In 1954, the U. S. Department of Agriculture estimated the losses caused by weeds on farms in this country to be around $4 billion annually. This equals the combined losses caused by insects and diseases and is surpassed only by losses from soil erosion. The problem is an enormous one and the urgency of solving it often makes us impatient with our progress until we realize that the greatest advances have occurred within the last twelve to fifteen years.

Chemicals that control weeds have been known for sixty years or more. Herbicides such as sodium arsenite, borates, chlorates, pentachlorophenol, and the dinitro compounds are still used for specific purposes, but each of these has definite limitations. Unknowingly, an entirely new approach began to evolve in 1880, when Charles Darwin published *The Power of Movement in Plants.* His observations were the first in a chain of independent investigations which finally led to the isolation and positive identification of a naturally occurring hormone (indoleacetic acid) by Kögl and his co-workers (9, 10).

The discovery of a plant growth regulator was revolutionary. Many workers found practical uses for it, and also synthesized hormone-like substances such as naphthaleneacetic acid. The new concept was largely responsible for the discovery of the value of 2,4-dichlorophenoxyacetic acid (2,4-D). Pokorney (13) found 2,4-D ineffective as a fungicide or insecticide when he synthesized it in 1940; later its hormone-like configuration led to its successful testing as a herbicide.

Advances are often camouflaged and recognized slowly. Those of us who deal primarily in applied science must never allow ourselves to forget the importance of basic studies in pure science, and must constantly be alert to keep our vision fresh.

2,4-D Leads the Way

Realization of the outstanding characteristics of 2,4-D of selectivity, translocation, and extreme activity led to a radical change in ideas on weed control. For the first time, it became possible to kill dicotyledonous plants without killing monocotyledonous species. It became practical for farmers to kill most broadleaf weeds without killing grain crops.

Today, it is estimated that one man manufacturing herbicides equals in effectiveness 800 people hoeing to kill weeds. Only ¼ pound of 2,4-D applied to an acre of wheat will control most broadleaf weeds, thereby often increasing wheat yields. One-third of a pound of 2,4,5-trichlorophenoxyacetic acid (2,4,5-T) applied to an acre of Texas pastureland will kill mesquite without injury to native grasses and will actually increase them by eliminating competition for the water that is so scarce in that area. By 1952, herbicides were being applied to over 30 million acres of cultivated land in the United States, including 17 million acres of small grains, 9 million acres of corn, 2 million acres of other crops, and 3 million acres of pastureland. It is estimated that over 85 million pounds of herbicides were used—about $48 million worth.

The introduction of herbicides readily translocated in plants prompted the development of a new science, one requiring men with intensive training in plant physiology, chemistry, agronomy, horticulture, and related fields.

Progress made with 2,4-D in the last few years includes the introduction of low-volatile esters and the very recent invert emulsion formulations of 2,4-D which promise to reduce the hazard of drift to susceptible plants. Much of the research work has consisted of fundamental studies of absorption, translocation, mode of action, and biological activity as related to chemical configuration.

Absorption and Translocation Must Occur

As a result of Blackman's (2) extensive work with radioactive isotopes, it first appeared that C^{14}-labeled 2,4-D entered a plant primarily in the undissociated molecular form. Orgell and Weintraub (12) found indications that the proportion of various cations present determined primarily the rate at which 2,4-D was absorbed by the leaf, and perhaps the amount that was absorbed.

Weintraub (22) and his colleagues suggested that the most important and possibly the exclusive influence of pH was upon the membranes of the plant tissues, not upon the compound.

Johnson and Bonner (8) have recognized three separate phases of radioactive 2,4-D entry into oat coleoptiles. First, there appears to be a rapid adsorption of the herbicide to the oat. This is simultaneous with another rapid uptake through which the auxin is adsorbed more tightly by the oat and can be taken off only by exchange with other molecules of the herbicides. The third process lasts several hours and is clearly dependent upon respiration. Which of these processes is involved in producing the toxic reaction or the growth reaction is not clear.

Adequate translocation of a herbicide is essential if the roots are to be affected by foliar sprays. Crafts (4) demonstrated with tagged 2,4-D that translocation into stems and roots of cotton and cucumber plants was greatest from cotyledons, and proportionately less from higher leaves. No 2,4-D was transported from young leaves that were still importing food from more mature plant parts.

The extent of translocation after entry may be at least part of the key to herbicide specificity. With the use of radioactive 2,4-D material, Butt (5) clearly demonstrated the lack of absorption and translocation by grasses. In an extension of this work, Weintraub and others (23) found that the difference between the export of 2,4-D from leaves of various broadleaf species and from cereal crops is even more striking.

The fluorophenoxyacetic acids, which are generally more active on grasses than the chlorophenoxyacetic acids, appear

unique with regard to translocation. When fluorine is substituted for chlorine in the ring, selectivity is reduced and effectiveness on grasses is increased, particularly with regard to
flowering. This could be useful in controlling annual grasses.
Weintraub (23) found that C^{14}-labeled 2,4-difluorophenoxyace-
tic acid was translocated more rapidly than 2,4-D in corn. Also,
4-fluorophenoxyacetic acid was translocated in corn, whereas
the chloro analogue moved very little from the site of application. 4-Fluorophenoxyacetic acid shows promise of controlling
annual bluegrass and crabgrass.[1] Some mixed chlorofluorophe-
noxyacetic acids are very active herbicides and may find a place
in weed control or as growth regulators.

Concerted efforts have been made to determine the precise
fate of 2,4-D within the plant. A few days after application of
small quantities of 2,4-D to buds, both side chain carbon atoms
can be found distributed among a wide variety of plant fractions including acids, sugars, starches, proteins, and cell wall
materials (24). Weintraub (22) has recently isolated amino
acid–2,4-D complexes with two of the five amino acids involved
being common to all fractions. These complexes may be products of the 2,4-D that does not play a part in the reaction which
produces a visible response.

The application of herbicides to soil for absorption by roots
presents a new set of problems involving such soil properties
as chemical composition, partical size, distribution, colloidal
content, reaction, organic matter, and microflora. Hill's report (7)
on his CMU soil-fixation studies gives some idea of the scope
of the problem. He found that 150 times as much soluble CMU
was adsorbed on bentonite, a clay of high exchange capacity,
as on kaolinite, a clay of low exchange capacity. When organic
matter was removed from a sandy soil, adsorption was reduced
approximately 85 per cent.

Our understanding of the mode of action of herbicides is
increasing, although slowly. As fundamental knowledge of
plants increases with respect to adsorption, translocation, and
enzyme action, we should be able to make significant advances
in the applied science of weed control.

More knowledge of screening techniques and of weeds themselves is being acquired. Shaw (17) and his co-workers devised the equipment and many of the methods now generally used by industrial organizations for screening thousands of chemicals each year for biological activity. Originally, screening consisted of spray applications to one or two species, generally tomato and bean, as a basis for deciding herbicidal activity. Now that we realize the almost unpredictable selectivity of chemicals within plant families and even within a single species, more sensitive screening procedures have been developed. For instance, a commercial organization may use sixteen or more representative weed and crop species for primary screening. Steinbauer and Grigsby's work (18) testing dormant and non-dormant seed of fifty-four weed species from fifteen families under a variety of temperature, soil, moisture, and other factors is giving us a better comprehension of the conditions under which weed seeds germinate best and those under which they can be grown. Switzer (19), Buchholtz (3), and Seely (16) worked with wild carrot, quackgrass, and wild oats respectively, and found that different varieties of each of these species reacted quite differently to a given chemical. Through the choice of a minor rather than a major variety for screening, much valuable information could be lost. In spite of these and many other problems, it is remarkable how many worth-while herbicides have been introduced during the past five years.

New Herbicides

Let us now consider some of these new materials. 2,2-Dichloropropionic acid (dalapon) and 3-amino-1,2,4-triazole (aminotriazole) are helping fill the need for chemicals capable of better translocation in deep-rooted perennials. Dalapon is essentially a grass killer; aminotriazole kills broadleaf weeds and several perennial grasses.

Dalapon is superseding the unreliable trichloroacetic acid formerly used for removing Johnson grass seedlings from sugar cane fields. Recent research indicates that repeated treatments with dalapon at lower rates are more effective than single treat-

ments at higher rates, and that dalapon can be used safely to control grass in apple and pear orchards, and in plantings of asparagus and potatoes. Two interesting new combinations are possible with dalapon. Mixing it with 2,4-D or aminotriazole gives us, for the first time, a combination of chemicals to remove both grassy and broadleaf weeds through foliar absorption and translocation into the roots. A combination with gamma-(2,4-dichlorophenoxy) butyric acid [4-(2,4-DB)] will remove annual grassy and broadleaf weeds from new or established stands of legumes, a major contribution in this field.

The outstanding characteristics of aminotriazole are rapidity of absorption and translocation, its unique ability to inhibit chlorophyll formation, and its apparent persistence which results in delayed or prolonged reaction. Basic studies with radioactive aminotriazole indicate that it is translocated throughout the plant in several forms. Besides pure 3-amino-1,2,4-triazole, a large fraction of the material seems to be a glucose-aminotriazole complex, and several unknown forms remain to be identified. Hall (6) has evidence that aminotriazole is not active in the chelation of metal ions such as magnesium. Rogers' work (15) indicates that sublethal doses of aminotriazole inhibit the development of plastids from proplastids; without plastids, chlorophyll cannot form in higher plants.

Aminotriazole is the most effective herbicide ever discovered for controlling such noxious perennial weeds as Canada thistle, whitetop, and cattails. Its effects on the extensive root system and rhizomes of these weeds are remarkable and clearly show that a herbicide must not only translocate into the root system but also must affect those parts of the plant from which regeneration can occur. Aminotriazole will kill poison ivy and poison oak without injury to dogwood, oak, hickory and many other woody plants. It will kill Bermuda grass without injury to citrus, or control quackgrass and leave the soil residue-free for planting corn safely seven to ten days later. At suitable rates, cranberries and oats are resistant to this chemical. Combining relatively low amounts of aminotriazole with other herbicides such as the substituted ureas, trichloroacetic acid (TCA) or dalapon is

producing interesting results, especially regarding the regrowth of perennial weeds.

The substituted urea herbicides are a versatile group of compounds. 3-(p-Chlorophenyl)-1,1-dimethylurea (monuron) and 3-(3,4-dichlorophenyl)-1,1-dimethylurea (diuron) are used for soil sterilant purposes and selective weed control in crops.

3-(3,4-Dichlorophenyl)-1-methyl-1-n-butylurea (neburon) has a low order of solubility and affects emerging seedlings and shallow-rooted perennials. It is used for controlling annual weeds and grasses in commercial plantings of certain ornamental evergreens in the eastern states. The introduction of 3-(phenyl)-1,1-dimethylurea (fenuron) makes possible a new approach to brush control, that of root absorption from pelleted material applied by airplane. Fenuron's selectivity is based on great solubility and movement through the soil. The chemical has been used to remove blackjack oak and post oak selectively from Texas rangeland without serious injury to the native grasses.

Two herbicides representing a new group of chemicals and novel modes of selectivity have been introduced recently. α-Chloro-N,N-diallylacetamide (Randox) and 2-chloroallyldiethyldithiocarbamate (Vegadex) kill only germinating seeds and are markedly toxic to most annual grasses and some broadleaf weeds. They are being used commercially in soybeans, onions, mustard grass, spinach, and several other crops.

One of the most outstanding pre-emergence herbicides was introduced in 1956: 2-chloro-4,6-bis(ethylamino)-s-triazine (simazin). In removing both annual grasses and broadleaf weeds from corn it has exhibited great selectivity and consistent results under a wide range of soil types, moisture conditions, and other factors which affect a pre-emergence herbicide.

Unfortunately, soybeans are very sensitive to simazin and in corn-belt areas, which use a corn-soybean rotation, application of this chemical to the corn will have to be adjusted so there will not be a residue toxic to the succeeding soybean crop. Other promising agronomic uses for this chemical are weed control in grapes, sugar cane, asparagus, fruit trees, pineapples, and ornamentals.

When used at higher rates, simazin is most effective as a temporary soil sterilant and will control a large number of annual and perennial weeds. This is a most interesting chemical and several related compounds such as 2-methoxy-4,6-bis(ethyl-amino)-s-triazine are worthy of further study.

The polychlorinated benzoic acids were investigated thoroughly in 1955, 1956, and 1957. Biologically, in pre-emergence field research, 2,3,6-trichlorobenzoic acid has generally been the most active isomer. The 2,3,5-tri- and 2,3,5,6-tetrachlorobenzoic isomers are also quite active, and in some cases show a wider range of selectivity. Recently field observations in Oregon, Kansas, California, Nebraska, and Texas have shown that 2,3,6-trichlorobenzoic acid and the polychlorinated benzoic acids have outstanding ability to kill field bindweed (*Convolvulus arvensis* L.), a deep-rooted noxious perennial that has previously responded satisfactorily only to high sterilizing rates of chlorates.

An interesting phenomenon observed and studied recently by Linder and his co-workers (11) concerns the movement of 2,3,6-trichloro- and 2,3,5,6-tetrachlorobenzoic acids from one plant to another through their root systems, and not by evaporation or movement through the air. Acid placed on stems or leaves of bean plants was adsorbed and translocated throughout the plants, and produced growth modification. Apparently the compound moved downward and out through the roots into surrounding soil. Then it was adsorbed by the roots of adjacent plants and translocated upward, producing growth modification in the untreated plants. Movement from the roots of plants of other genera was apparent. This is not the first compound to exhibit this characteristic, for Preston, Mitchell, and Reeve (14) reported the movement of alpha-methoxyphenylacetic acid in this way and further research may open the door to practical application.

Foliage sprays of 4 to 5 pounds of polychlorinated benzoic acids per acre kill woody evergreens. Used to control quackgrass, they permit planting corn a few days after the sprayed area is plowed. There is indication that it is chemical residue

in the soil rather than a translocated and accumulated chemical which keeps dormant quackgrass buds from sprouting.

Another recent advance concerns the gamma-substituted phenoxy n-butyric acids. In 1947, Synerholm and Zimmerman (20) observed that in a homologous series of substituted phenoxy alkyl acids, alternate compounds were biologically active. They proposed that these chemicals were being degraded to the active acetic acid form by beta oxidation. Careful studies by Wain and his associates suggested that some plants may lack the necessary oxidation enzyme system to degrade the inactive homologues to the active acetic acid compound. Wain (21) reasoned that it might be possible to use some of the butyrics as selective herbicides in certain crops.

Field testing has shown that 4-(2,4-DB) and gamma-(2-methyl-4-chlorophenoxy) butyric acids are quite selective. They are tolerated by many legumes, including crops sensitive to most herbicides, but lethal to many broadleaf weeds. This work may open new fields in herbicide research. The concept of differing enzyme systems suggests other possibilities with regard to the selectivity of herbicides and emphasizes the delicacy and complications of adequate screening. If 4-(2,4-DB) had been tested on only beans, a biologist would have eliminated it from further screening on the basis of low activity. It had to be screened on alfalfa, peas, and annual broadleaf weeds to show its full potential.

Chloropicrin, carbon disulfide, and methyl bromide have been used successfully as soil fumigants to kill weed seeds and perennial roots in the soil before planting. Excessive cost per acre, need for special equipment, and poisonous qualities have limited their use. Progress has been made with the introduction of sodium methyldithiocarbamate (Vapam) and 3,5-dimethyltetrahydro-1,3,5,2H thiadiazine-2-thione (Mylone). These two chemicals are quite effective as a preplanting treatment to control annual and perennial broadleaf weeds and grasses, and will find use in tobacco seed beds, nursery and ornamental plantings. Rates used for weed control also control nematodes and certain soil fungi.

In 1956, ethyl-N,N-di-n-propylthiolcarbamate (EPTC) was introduced. This chemical performs satisfactorily as a pre-emergence herbicide, and its effectiveness is increased when it is incorporated with the soil and used as a preplanting treatment. At a moderate rate, it controls many annual broadleaf weeds in such crops as alfalfa, birdsfoot trefoil, corn, sugar beets, and flax. A slightly higher rate worked into the soil is quite effective on nutgrass (*Cyperus* sp.), a serious weed for which no suitable control had yet been found. The influence on EPTC of factors such as soil type, soil temperature, soil moisture, and volume of spray were studied. Soil moisture is apparently the primary one influencing field performance, EPTC was relatively ineffective when applied to wet soils.

1,2,4,5-Tetrachlorobenzene, a herbicide introduced in 1957, depends on its vapors to kill wild oats, a serious weed in some wheat-growing areas. It must be incorporated in the soil for best results.

Progress is being made with chemicals whose vapors can kill germinating and dormant seeds. Chemicals which reduce costs because only a few pounds per acre are required, chemicals which do not require special equipment, chemicals which are less toxic, and chemicals with selectivity to certain crops are being found.

No doubt it has been noted that many of the chemicals mentioned as promising herbicides are unrelated structurally. So far, no practical theory of the relationship between biological activity and chemical structure has been developed; experience over the years has shown that all theories have become practically meaningless. Specific activity must be tested. Many theories will be formulated and discarded. This is a fundamental part of learning and progress. At the present time, practice has outdistanced theory. Ultimately, an Albert Einstein or a Willard Gibbs may appear, correlate the chemical with the enzymatic and spatial relationships involved, and produce a simple equation to cover all the facts. In the meantime, careful screening remains the most important source of chemical advances.

REFERENCES

1. Anderson, B. R., and S. R. McLane. *Weeds 6*, 52 (1958).
2. Blackman, G. E., and R. C. Robertson-Cunninghame. *New Phytologist 52*, 71 (1953).
3. Buchholtz, K. P. Personal communication.
4. Crafts, A. S. *Hilgardia 26*, 287 (1956).
5. Englund, K. L. *J. Agr. Food Chem. 3*, 826 (1955).
6. Hall, W. C., S. P. Johnson, and C. L. Leinweber. *Texas Agr. Expt. Sta. Bull. 789*, 1954.
7. Hill, G. D. Unpublished paper presented before Weed Society of America meetings, New York City, 1956.
8. Johnson, M. P., and J. Bonner. *Physiol. Plantarum 9*, 102 (1956).
9. Kögl, F., H. Erxleben, and A. J. Haagen-Smit. *Physiol. Chem. 225*, 215 (1934).
10. Kögl, F., A. J. Haagen-Smit, and H. Erxleben. *Physiol. Chem. 228*, 90 (1934).
11. Linder, P. J., J. C. Craig, Jr., F. E. Cooper, and J. W. Mitchell. Personal communication.
12. Orgell, W. H., and R. L. Weintraub. Unpublished paper presented before American Institute of Biological Societies meetings, Storrs, Conn., 1956.
13. Pokorny, R. *J. Am. Chem. Soc. 63*, 1768 (1941).
14. Preston, W. H., Jr., J. W. Mitchell, and W. Reeve. *Science 119*, 437 (1954).
15. Rogers, B. J. *Hormolog 1*, 12 (1957).
16. Seely, C. I. Personal communication.
17. Shaw, W. C., and C. R. Swanson. *Weeds 1*, 352 (1952).
18. Steinbauer, G. P., and B. H. Grigsby. *North Central Weed Control Conf. Research Rept. 13*, 186, 187 (1956).
19. Switzer, C. M. *Proc. Northeastern Weed Control Conf. 11*, 319 (1957).
20. Synerholm, M. E., and P. W. Zimmerman. *Contribs. Boyce Thomp. Inst. 14*, 369 (1947).
21. Wain, R. L. *Ann. Appl. Biol. 42*, 151 (1955).
22. Weintraub, R. L. Personal communication.
23. Weintraub, R. L., J. H. Reinhart, and R. A. Scherff. U. S. Atomic Energy Commission Report No. TID-7512, 1957.
24. Weintraub, R. L., J. N. Yeatman, J. A. Lockhart, J. H. Reinhart, and M. Fields. *Arch. Biochem. Biophys. 40*, 227 (1952).

Organophosphorus Systemic Insecticides

John E. Casida

*Department of Entomology,
University of Wisconsin, Madison*

Systemic insecticides are well established for the control of plant-feeding insects and have been used on a limited scale as antimyiatic agents for cattle. From the thousands of chemicals screened for systemic control of insects infesting plants and mammals, one chemical type has almost invariably displayed the best activity, esters and anhydrides of phosphoric and phosphorothioic acids. Pioneering studies by Dr. Gerhard Schrader and co-workers of Farbenfabriken Bayer and thorough investigations by thousands of other research workers converted the laboratory observations of the 1940's into practical chemicals for field usage in the 1950's. The rate of progress in developing new systemic insecticides is as yet undiminished. Many excellent reviews are available on systemic insecticides (1–12) and no attempt will be made here at an exhaustive treatment of the available literature. The effectiveness of certain systemic organophosphates will be discussed in relation to the mode of action and toxic hazards associated with their use.

General Considerations

Organophosphates are toxic to insects and mammals because of their ability to inhibit the cholinesterase in nervous tissues. Plants do not contain cholinesterase or other enzymes of known physiological importance that are inhibited by low levels of organophosphates. Most of the organophosphates are nonphytotoxic at insecticidal concentrations. A few highly insecticidal organophosphates are of relatively low toxicity to mammals. These are the compounds that have been investigated as possible antimyiatic agents.

A plant systemic insecticide must be absorbed and translocated by the plant in amounts lethal to insects feeding thereon. Systemic activity is a matter of degree rather than a specific property since almost all phosphorus insecticides are capable of penetrating into plant foliage but few are then translocated and stored in insecticidal concentrations. Systemic action therefore depends upon: (a) ability to penetrate into the plant through roots, stems, or leaves; (b) sufficient water solubility to enable the movement of the compound or an active metabolite in the plant sap; (c) sufficient stability to hydrolytic detoxification within the plant to enable the systemic compound to exert the required degree of residual insecticidal action; and (d) decomposition within the plant tissues to nontoxic products within a reasonable period of time so that no residues toxic to mammals are present at harvest. Most of the systemics for phytophagous insects yield no phytotoxicity or off-flavors at insecticidal dosages. Precautionary measures are necessary in the application of most organophosphate systemics to plants because of their high toxicity to mammals. Yet this can be safely accomplished as demonstrated by the wide scale use of parathion, an organophosphate contact insecticide of high mammalian toxicity. Adequate microanalytical methods are available for determining the magnitude of persisting residues and a wealth of toxicological information is available on each compound to evaluate the hazards associated with small amounts of residues when present.

For use as an antimyiatic agent, selective toxicity to insects is essential so that control may be obtained without harming the mammalian host. The compound must be sufficiently stable after absorption through the skin or digestive tract or after injection to reach the internal insect parasite in a toxic form. For compounds fed to cattle this implies stability to attack by the rumen microorganisms. The lipoid-water partitioning property for the organophosphate is important as this and the stability to hydrolysis determine persistence of residues and possible secretion into the milk. Several chlorinated hydrocarbon insecticides are effective antimyiatic agents, but they are not

considered satisfactory because large amounts are stored in the fat and secreted in milk.

Plant Systemic Insecticides

DIMETHYLPHOSPHORAMIDES

Schradan (octamethylpyrophosphoramide) and dimefox (tetramethylphosphorodiamidic fluoride) were the first practical plant systemics. These chemicals are absorbed readily through both the roots and foliage of plants and offer prolonged protection against aphids, mites, and certain other sucking forms without great hazard to insect predators, parasites, and pollinators. Both are quite toxic to mammals on acute and chronic administration, and as such their use has been restricted primarily to nonedible crops. Small amounts of these dimethylphosphoramides are oxidized in the plant, insect, or mammal to very potent and unstable anticholinesterase agents which consist of N-oxides and isomerization products thereof. Residue analysis is accomplished by colorimetric determination of the orthophosphate or dimethylamine formed on hydrolysis of the insecticide.

THIOETHER-CONTAINING PHOSPHOROTHIOATES

Both phosphorothioate and phosphorodithioates with thioether groupings have been developed as plant systemic insecticides. Demeton (O,O-diethyl O-ethylthioethyl phosphorothioate and its phosphorothiolate isomer) and methyl demeton (O,O-dimethyl O-ethylthioethyl phosphorothioate and its phosphorothiolate isomer) have been widely used as foliar sprays to control mites, aphids, and other sucking forms. Long residual action is achieved for mites and aphids without hazard to the predators and parasites of the plant pests. The thiol isomers of these insecticides are the most effective forms and are readily absorbed after foliar treatment. Methyl demeton is the safer of the two compounds to mammals while demeton approximates the acute toxic hazard of parathion. Both materials when absorbed by plants are quickly oxidized to the O,O-dialkyl S-ethylsulfinyl-

ethyl and S-ethylsulfonylethyl phosphorothiolate derivatives which are potent anticholinesterase agents. Residue analysis is made by anticholinesterase determinations on treated crops for the O,O-dialkyl S-ethylsulfonylethyl phosphorothiolate metabolites.

Thimet (O,O-diethyl S-ethylthiomethyl phosphorodithioate) and Disyston (O,O-diethyl S-ethylthioethyl phosphorodithioate) have been most effective when used as seed treatments or by application to the soil for uptake by the plant roots. Residual action for mites and aphids may last more than a month. The use of Thimet and charcoal in the coating of cotton seeds is an established practice in many areas. Thimet and Disyston constitute a greater hazard to mammals than parathion as they are more toxic by both acute and chronic administration. When absorbed by plants, both materials are very rapidly oxidized to form the O,O-diethyl S-ethylsulfinylalkyl and S-ethylsulfonylalkyl phosphorodithioates, which then serve as precurosors for the gradual accumulation of the sulfinyl and sulfonyl phosphorothiolates. The fully oxidized plant metabolites, the O,O-diethyl S-ethylsulfonylalkyl phosphorothiolates, are the most potent anticholinesterase agents formed and afford the method of residue analysis through inhibition of this enzyme.

SUBSTITUTED VINYL PHOSPHATES

Phosdrin (O,O-dimethyl 1-methoxycarbonyl-1-propen-2-yl phosphate) has filled the need for a systemic that can be used close to harvest time without danger of hazardous residues. The cis is the most toxic and least persistent of the geometrical isomers. The use of Phosdrin as a foliar spray will control a wide variety of insects through action as a contact, systemic and fumigant type insecticide. The acute and chronic toxicity to mammals is similar to that of parathion. Residues on plants are dissipated within a few days by volatilization and through hydrolysis of the vinyl phosphate bond and the carbomethoxy group. Residue analysis is by anticholinesterase methods for the potent cis isomer.

CARBAMOYL PHOSPHORODITHIOATES

American Cyanamid CL 12,880 or Rogor (*O,O*-dimethyl S(*N*-methylcarbamoylmethyl) phosphorodithioate) has shown promise as a foliar systemic of reduced mammalian toxicity. The acute toxicity to mammals is less than one-tenth that of parathion. Relatively little information is available on field effectiveness of 12,880 but it appears to afford long residual protection of plants to mites, aphids, and certain other insects. Metabolism within the plant occurs by oxidation of the phosphorothioate grouping and hydrolysis at several sites within the molecule. Residue analysis is by determination of monomethylamine or orthophosphate following hydrolysis or by insect bioassay.

DIETHYLAMINOETHYL PHOSPHOROTHIOLATES

Chipman R 6199 or tetram (*O,O*-diethyl S-(2-diethylaminoethyl) phosphorothiolate hydrogen oxalate) was proposed as a foliar spray for scales and mites. This material can be formulated as a variety of salts, but the systemic action appears to be due to the penetration of the free tertiary amine base. R 6199 is more toxic to mammals than parathion, and extreme care must be used in its application. Residual persistence is among the greatest for the systemics and breakdown in the plant is probably due only to hydrolysis of the phosphorothiolate grouping. Anticholinesterase assays form a very sensitive method of residue analysis.

Animal Systemic Insecticides

DIPTEREX AND DIAZINON

Dipterex or L 13/59 (*O,O*-dimethyl 2,2,2-trichloro-1-hydroxyethyl phosphonate) is effective in controlling cattle grubs when administered orally at 100 mg./kg. Very little Dipterex is secreted into the milk following oral administration and no information is available on tissue residues. Diazinon (*O,O*-diethyl *O*-(2-isopropyl-6-methyl-4-pyrimidinyl) phosphorothioate) will control cattle grubs when fed or injected at between 5 and 50

mg./kg. Small amounts of Diazinon are secreted in the milk shortly after treatment. Grubs in cattle treated with Dipterex and Diazinon generally emerged from the backs of the animals but failed to survive pupation. These compounds are less effective antimyiatic agents than Trolene, Co-Ral, and Dimethoate.

TROLENE

Trolene or Dow ET-57 (O,O-dimethyl O-(2,4,5-trichlorophenyl) phosphorothioate) administered orally at 100 mg./kg. not only kills larvae present in the backs of cattle but also completely prevents the encystment of new larvae. The recommended 100-mg./kg. dose results in some blood cholinesterase depression and rarely produces symptoms of organophosphate poisoning in the cattle, and these are of a mild, transient nature. Trolene is now available for limited field usage. Large amounts of Trolene appear in the milk of lactating cows shortly after administration, and residues in the tissues persist for several weeks, particularly in the fat. Metabolic attack on the compound occurs by oxidation to O,O-dimethyl O-(2,4,5-trichlorophenyl) phosphate and by hydrolysis of this derivative and the original phosphorothioate at both the phosphorus-oxygen-methyl and phosphorus-oxygen-phenyl bonds. Residue analysis is by colorimetric determination of 2,4,5-trichlorophenol after hydrolysis.

CO-RAL

Co-Ral or Bayer 21/199 (O,O-diethyl O-(3-chloro-4-methylumbelliferone) phosphorothioate), when applied as a spray, gives effective control of cattle grubs, screwworm, hornfly, ticks, and lice. The epidermal dose commonly applied to cattle is about 30–50 mg./kg. body weight. Penetration of the skin and systemic action is definitely involved in cattle grub control. A very small percentage of the applied dose actually penetrates, and the residue on the hide persists many weeks. Very small amounts of Co-Ral or its oxygen analog are secreted in the milk and by two months after treatment the tissue residues in cattle are at a very low level. Metabolism of Co-Ral occurs by the same pathway as with Trolene; by oxidation of the phosphoro-

thioate grouping and hydrolysis of the phosphorus-oxygen-ethyl and the phosphorus-oxygen-chloroumbelliferone groupings. Residue analysis is by a fluorometric method.

DIMETHOATE

Dimethoate or American Cyanamid CL 12,880 (*O,O*-dimethyl S-(*N*-methylcarbamoylmethyl) phosphorodithioate) is effective against the later instars of the cattle grub when administered orally at 10 to 15 mg./kg. body weight. Dimethoate is readily absorbed from the intestine into the blood and then within a few hours partitions into and out of the body fat. A small amount of Dimethoate is secreted into the milk during the first thirty-six hours following treatment but is not detectable thereafter. Tissue residues are essentially dissipated within two to three weeks following administration. Metabolism within the cow of Dimethoate occurs primarily by hydrolysis of the alkoxyl-phosphate, phosphorothiolate, and carbamoyl groupings.

REFERENCES

1. Bennett, S. H. The behaviour of systemic insecticides applied to plants. *Ann. Rev. Entomol.* 2:279-296 (1957).
2. Dahm, P. A. Uses of radioisotopes in pesticide research. *Advances in Pest Control Research* 1:81-146 (1957).
3. Giang, P. A. A bibliography of systemic insecticides. U.S.D.A. Agricultural Research Service, Ent. Research Branch, E-874 (1954).
4. Lindquist, A. W., and E. F. Knipling. Recent advances in veterinary entomology. *Ann. Rev. Entomol.* 2:181-202 (1957).
5. McGregor, W. S., and R. C. Bushland. Research on the use of systemic insecticides for the control of livestock pests. *J. Econ. Entomol.* 49:86-88 (1956).
6. Metcalf, R. L. *Organic Insecticides.* Interscience Publishers, New York, 1955.
7. Radeleff, R. D., and G. T. Woodard. Toxicological problems in the use of systemic insecticides for livestock. *J. Econ. Entomol.* 49:89-91 (1956).
8. Ripper, W. E. The status of systemic insecticides in pest control practices. *Advances in Pest Control Research* 1:305-352 (1957).

9. Saunders, B. C. *Some Aspects of the Chemistry and Toxic Action of Organic Compounds Containing Phosphorus and Fluorine.* Cambridge University Press, New York, 1957.

10. Schrader, G. The development of systemic insecticides based on organic phosphorus compounds. *Höfchen-Briefe* 5:161-171 (1952).

11. Spencer, E. Y., and R. D. O'Brien. Chemistry and mode of action of organophosphorus insecticides. *Ann. Rev. Entomol.* 2:261-278 (1957).

12. Spindler, M. Systemic insecticides, a review. *Z. Pflanzenkrankh. u. Pflanzenschutz* 62:97-165 (1955).

Chemical Control of Internal Parasites of Domestic Animals

F. O. GOSSETT

Eli Lilly and Co.,
Indianapolis, Indiana

The importance of animal parasites cannot be accurately determined because of the complex nature of animal disease. Recent estimates (95) indicate animal parasites cause an annual loss of more than $400 million. Losses resulting from parasites of swine alone are probably in excess of $275 million annually.

The need for satisfactory parasite control measures, such as good sanitation combined with prophylactic or therapeutic chemical agents, is obvious. The primary requisites for an ideal antiparasitic agent are nontoxicity to the host, ease of administration, low cost, and effectiveness (9). Furthermore, anthelmintics should be sufficiently nontoxic to be fed as a continuous supplement in the feed, being sufficiently palatable and effective to attack all the species present, although not necessarily entirely parasiticidal (52). It is also important that drugs used for these purposes be unabsorbed or, if absorbed into the blood stream, be excreted rapidly without storage in edible tissues of the treated animal to avoid adulteration of human foods.

This paper presents a discussion of chemicals useful in the control of certain helminths and protozoa considered of substantial economic importance. Greatest emphasis is placed on compounds which are of recent interest. For those desirous of more complete information, references are cited. The review by Enzie, Colglazier, and Wilkens (40) is quite comprehensive and has been useful in preparation of this paper.

Anthelmintic Agents

PHENOTHIAZINE

Phenothiazine may be regarded as a prototype anthelmintic. It can be administered as a drench or in a capsule, or the divided dose can be added to feed, salt, or mineral mixtures. It is relatively nontoxic, inexpensive, and effective against adults, larvae, and embryonating eggs of some nematodes of ruminants. Because of these advantages, this drug has been widely used for the past decade.

The value of low-level phenothiazine therapy for the control of gastrointestinal nematodes of cattle has been demonstrated by Andrews, Muniz, and Orihuela (3), Mayhew (85), and Cauthen (16). These workers demonstrated that the treatment reduced pasture contamination with infective larvae by lowering egg production and interfering with embryonation. Habermann and Shorb (63) reported that the feeding of 0.5 gram of phenothiazine in salt to sheep arrested larval development within 48 hours. Ratios of 1 plus 9 and 1 plus 14 (phenothiazine to salt) were consumed in sufficient quantities to attain an average dose of 0.615 and 0.879 gram per day respectively.

Brock, Pearson, and Kliewer (10) in 1952 reported that continuous low-level medication for cattle was effective in controlling the lungworm *Dictyocaulus viviparus*. Results of field trials emphasized the need for initial therapeutic dosings followed by 2 grams daily for greatest effect on intestinal nematodes. In a herd of 500 calves, losses from lungworms ceased after the animals were started on a regimen of 2 grams of phenothiazine daily per calf. The possible mode of action of phenothiazine in the control of lungworm infections was suggested in the review of Enzie *et al.* (40). In a single trial a calf was infected experimentally with lungworms and started on a low-level regimen a few days after infection was established. While larvae continued to be produced during the experiment, the treatment somehow rendered them incapable of developing to the infective stage. In 1954 Jarrett, McIntyre, and Urquhart (69) reported that phenothiazine given orally or intratracheally

was lethal to the first stage of lungworm larvae, either during their passage through the gut or within a few days after their elimination in the fecal material. A 15-gram dose given to a two-year-old heifer was sufficient to kill almost all the larvae for several days.

Herlich and Porter (65) obtained satisfactory control of *Haemonchus contortus* and *Oesophagostomum radiatum* in calves with mixtures containing 10 per cent phenothiazine in salt or mineral mixtures. The salt mixture appeared to be less palatable. Consumption ranged from 0 to 3 grams phenothiazine per head per day. The drug did not control four other species of nematodes. Pelleted feeds containing molasses would seem to make a satisfactory vehicle to assure uniform dosing in that the molasses tends to mask the flavor of the drug and improve its palatability. The stability of phenothiazine in the presence of molasses was satisfactory as reported by Alicata and Koshi (1). Britton (8) was very favorably impressed by the use of a single therapeutic dose of phenothiazine for parasitized calves that had not responded to several previous treatments with copper sulfate and nicotine sulfate solutions. He recommended doses of 12 grams for calves, 25 grams for cattle 12 to 16 months old, and 40 grams for older cattle.

Foster (45, 46) suggested that 0.5 gram of phenothiazine daily per 100 pounds of body weight up to a total dose of 2 to 5 grams per head daily for animals over 400 or 500 pounds should successfully control gastrointestinal nematodes of cattle. Adequate dosage was obtained in some instances when the chemical was added to salt or to various mineral mixtures, but these methods have not been applicable in all instances. The reasons for occasional failure have not been definitely established, although Foster thought it to be a result of inadequate consumption of the feed, salt, or mineral mix containing the drug.

The effect of phenothiazine on *Nematodirus* infections in cattle has not been adequately established, but in studies by Turner and Colglazier (21, 132) excellent control of this nematode was obtained in sheep with 1 part of phenothiazine plus 9 parts of salt. The continuous treatment appeared to reduce

recontamination of pastures. Combined with the elements of nature, phenothiazine contributes to progressive decontamination of pasture. The trials with sheep reviewed by Enzie *et al.* (40, II) indicate that as with cattle, the beneficial effects of low-level medication with phenothiazine may be attributed to the destruction of preinfective larvae and to an interference with the establishment in the host. In this species, the chemical appears to be most effective against *Haemonchus, Bunostomum,* and *Oesophagostomum,* somewhat less effective against *Trichostrongylus* and *Ostertagia,* and without significant effect on *Cooperia* and *Strongyloides.*

Todd *et al.* (128) demonstrated the practical value of this drug in the control of some intestinal nematodes of horses. Four groups of three horses each was fed 0.5, 1.0, 2.0, or 4.0 grams of phenothiazine daily for a period of 52 weeks to determine the effect of continuous low-level phenothiazine therapy on the intestinal parasite fauna and on the physical well-being of the horses. A direct relation was found between the amount of phenothiazine fed, the reduction of strongyle infection, and prevention of reinfection, as evidenced by the number of strongyle eggs passed. The fertility of worm eggs decreased as the amounts of phenothiazine fed was increased. At post-mortem examination of one horse from each of the four groups a reduction was found to have occurred in the number of immature *Strongylus vulgaris* present in the anterior mesenteric artery.

Douglas *et al.* (28) administered a 25-gram dose of phenothiazine to lambs over periods of one, three, five, and seven days. They found that anthelmintic efficacy was decreased in an essentially linear relationship, dropping from 65 per cent when the dose was given at one time, to zero when it was given in equal daily doses over a period of seven days. These results were contrary to the findings of most other investigators. Dennis (25) found that the daily consumption of feed by cattle containing sufficient phenothiazine to give 0.5 gram per 100 pounds of body weight was effective in reducing pasture contamination by reducing parasite ova production as well as larval development.

Shelton *et al.* (118) reported unsatisfactory control of nematodes of sheep running on irrigated pastures. A phenothiazine salt mixture was fed continuously, and therapeutic doses of phenothiazine were given biweekly. Twenty per cent of the lambs and 11 per cent of the ewes were lost because of parasites. Signs of severe gastrointestinal parasitism were observed in most of the animals at some time during the study. It was suggested that the high humidity and high moisture content of the forage crops resulting from irrigation encouraged the development of the larval forms to the extent that an overwhelming inoculum was consumed by the sheep. Another possible cause of the occasional failure of phenothiazine treatment may be due to the emergence of forms resistant to the chemical. Drudge *et al.* (31, 32, 81) suggest that the continuous administration of phenothiazine over a period of years may have permitted the development of strains of nematodes of sheep which are tolerant to the drug. The repeated drenching of sheep with phenothiazine over a 10-year period had been effective in the control of nematodes, but with the passage of time became less effective.

Ellison and Todd (37) have studied the distribution of phenothiazine in the digestive tract, blood serum, bile, urine, liver, kidney, spleen, and mesenteric lymph nodes after the administration of single doses to cattle. No drug was detectable in any of the excreta or tissues assayed 120 hours after the administration of the drug.

It appears that phenothiazine is still a drug of considerable value in the control of intestinal nematodes of ruminants, providing sufficient dosage can be maintained; however, certain findings indicate that resistant strains of parasites may develop.

PIPERAZINE COMPOUNDS

Hewitt *et al.* (66) have been credited by Worley *et al.* (139) as the first workers to demonstrate efficacy against intestinal helminths in dogs with a piperazine compound (diethylcarbamazine). Kanegis (72) obtained comparable results in both dogs and cats treated for ascariasis. For example, 25 milligrams

per pound of body weight removed 97 per cent of the ascarids from kittens. No intoxication was noted in cats given doses up to 50 milligrams per kilogram. In this species, Colglazier and Enzie (20) found the compound was ineffective against hookworms.

Diethylcarbamazine has been used with some success by Foley (43) and Ziegler (140) in the control of heartworm infection of dogs when a dose of 10 milligrams per pound was given daily for seven to 21 days. It had some action against adult worms but it had greater effect on the microfilariae. Garnier (50) also reported diethylcarbamazine effective as a preventive of canine filariasis. Complete control of heartworm infection was achieved in 44 dogs that received a dose of 25 milligrams per pound of body weight on each of three successive days and repeated at intervals of six months. Blood of these animals remained free of microfilariae throughout the test period; four dogs in this group that were autopsied for one reason or another during the test period were free of heartworms. All five control dogs became positive for microfilariae during the 18-month period of observations, and all had heartworms when autopsied.

Piperazine adipate gave encouraging anthelmintic results in dogs, cats, pigs, horses, and poultry when tested by Sloan, Kingsbury, and Jolly (122). The chemical was given to 13 dogs at dose rates ranging from 25 to 200 milligrams per kilogram. A total of 193 ascarids were eliminated after treatment, and no ascarid eggs were found in subsequent fecal examinations over a period of several weeks. No ascarids were found in one of the dogs that was autopsied after treatment. The chemical was ineffective against tapeworms and exhibited little action against *Ancylostoma caninum* in single doses up to 300 milligrams per kilogram, and repeated treatment failed to achieve complete removal of this species. These authors observed several advantages of the piperazine compounds such as low toxicity, absence of irritation to the gastrointestinal tract, adaptability to feed or water administration, and absence of coloring in the excreta.

Several piperazine compounds [piperazine adipate (39, 73,

122), piperazine hexahydrate (39, 60), piperazine sulfate (73), and betaine of 1-piperazine carbodiothioic acid (73, 80, 114)] have controlled immature as well as mature *Ascaris* and nodular worms of swine. They have a wide margin of safety in the pig and are well tolerated by humans; therefore, possible tissue residues, if they did occur in rare instances, would not be dangerous. The efficacy of these compounds for the individual treatment of swine is well established (60, 80, 114, 122). In these trials, therapeutic dosages of several piperazine derivatives removed 96 per cent of the ascarids from 70 pigs and 99 per cent of the nodular worms from 12 pigs. Enzie *et al.* (40, II) noted that little critical data appear to have been obtained on the performance of various piperazines when given to groups of pigs. In this connection it may be noted that in limited trials by Leiper (80) efficacy against both ascarids and nodular worms was lower in group trials than in animals treated individually. Piperazines may be given conveniently in feed or drinking water. Dosages are calculated on the basis of body weight and should be consumed within a reasonably short period of time.

Reidel (114) found that Parvex (piperazine-carbon disulfide complex) when given to swine at a rate of 110 to 125 milligrams per kilogram was 95 to 100 per cent effective against *Ascaris*. The drug was inactive against the "thorny-headed worms." Lindquist (82) found that piperazine had no effect on the migrating larvae of *Ascaris lumbricoides*. Enzie, Wilkens, and Colglazier (41) in a recent report confirm the anthelmintic value of piperazines against *Ascaris* and *Oesophagostomum* while they were essentially ineffective against *Trichuris* and *Hyostrongylus.* Of the six piperazine forms tested piperazine citrate seemed most satisfactory. There appeared to be some variation in the palatability of those tested; therefore, efficacy under field conditions could vary considerably.

Piperazine adipate showed effective anthelmintic action against ascarids, pinworms, and small strongyles of ponies in trials reported by Sloan, Kingsbury, and Jolly (122). Yearling ponies received a dose of 250 to 400 milligrams per kilogram

followed by massive doses of 1250 to 1500 milligrams per kilogram one week later. There was no indications of toxicity. Anthelmintic action was also exhibited against pinworms, *Oxyuris equi*, and small strongyles, the *Trichonema* species. Reports by Poynter (108, 109), Downing, Kingsbury, and Sloan (29) indicate that piperazine adipate is effective against adult *Trichonema* species against mature and immature *Ascaris* and *Oxyuris equi* when given at a dose rate of 220 milligrams per kilogram. This dosage was also effective against *Strongylus vulgaris*, but there was little or no action against S. *edentatus* and S. *equinus*. Critical tests with piperazine adipate showed that the chemical had no effect on the stomach bot larvae in the equine stomach.

Poynter (110, 111) reported that piperazine 1-carbodithioic acid exhibited marked action against *Ascaris* and in small strongyles of horses, but showed negligible effect on *Strongylus* species. He found no demonstrable differences in anthelmintic effect of the piperazine adipate, citrate, phosphate, and 1-carbodithioic acid when given to horses in dosages of comparable piperazine content (200 milligrams per kilogram). In an experiment by Drudge *et al.* (33) involving 197 sucklings, weanlings, yearlings, and mares, the piperazine-carbon disulfide complex at 37.5 milligrams per pound of body weight resulted in the removal of immature and mature ascarids as well as small strongyles. This dose showed no action against *Strongylus vulgaris* and *Strongyloides westeri*.

In limited trials by Lee (79) all the *Neoascaris vitularum* were removed from two calves that were given piperazine adipate as a drench at a rate of 1 gram per 10 pounds of body weight. The drug was effective against both mature and immature worms, but it had no effect on the development of eggs. In eleven other calves, dosages of 1 or 2 grams per 10 pounds of body weight resulted in the removal of numerous worms and a complete disappearance of *Ascaris* eggs from the feces. The chemical was well tolerated, and in specific toxicity trials, no unfavorable reactions were observed in animals that received dosages of 10 to 30 grams per hundredweight.

In Australia, Gordon (54) used piperazine salts and the complex piperazine 1-carbodithioic betaine effectively against *Oesophagostomum* species, but with less success on other nematodes in the large intestine in sheep. When injected directly into the abomasum, the salts were not effective against *Haemonchus contortus* or *Trichostrongylus colubriforms,* but the complex which yields carbon disulfide in an acid medium was effective against *H. contortus.* The action of the salts and the complex on *Oesophagostomum* was rapid, 99 per cent of the parasites being passed within 24 hours.

Piperazine adipate exhibited marked anthelmintic action in poultry against the large roundworm, *Ascaridia galli,* in trials reported by Sloan, Kingsbury, and Jolly (122). The chemical was given in single doses or in various feed mixtures at dose rates ranging from 100 to 440 milligrams per kilogram body weight. The drug removed 97 per cent of the Ascaridia from seventy birds.

Piperazine citrate in preliminary trials described by Shumard and Eveleth (120), exhibited marked anthelmintic action against the large roundworm, but was somewhat less effective against the cecal worm *Heterakis gallinae.* In a field trial, the chemical appeared to be completely effective against ascarids when given at a rate of 10 grams per gallon in drinking water for three days but was not effective against cecal worms. The drug was apparently well tolerated, although there was the suggestion of a temporary deleterious effect on egg production. Bradley (7) reported marked ascaricidal action in broilers that were given the chemical at a rate of 6 grams or 8 grams per gallon of drinking water. The treatment was well tolerated.

Edgar, Davis, and Frazier (35) found that 250 and 500 grams of piperazine hexahydrate and half that amount of pure piperazine per bird in capsule form or at a concentration of 0.4 per cent or 0.8 per cent in drinking water eliminated 95 to 100 per cent of the mature *A. galli* and 75 to 100 per cent of the immature form. Shumard (119) found that 125 milligrams of a carbon disulfide and piperazine complex per kilogram of body weight removed 90 per cent of the *A. galli* from chickens, while

950 milligrams per kilogram failed to remove *H. gallinae*. Worley *et al.* (139) reported neither diethylcarbamazine, compound 180-C (1-carbethoxy-4-methylpiperazine hydrochloride), nor carbon disulfide-piperazine complex reduced the number of lumen larvae of *A. galli* in experimental infections of chickens.

HALOGEN COMPOUNDS

Habermann, Foster, and Enzie (62) stated that at least 250 halogenated compounds have been studied as anthelmintics, but the most useful and best known are certain chlorinated hydrocarbons. They reported also on activity of certain metal fluorides.

Fluorides. In the tests cited above (62) barium fluoride, sodium aluminum fluoride, and sodium fluoride were found to be of value in the control of swine parasites. One per cent sodium fluoride in the feed for three days appeared to be of greatest value. Monnig (91) reported sodium fluoride, sodium silicofluoride, calcium fluoride, and sodium aluminum fluoride to be of value for the treatment of oesophagostomiasis in sheep. Turk and Hale (131) found in a test that sodium fluoride removed more adult ascarids than did either cadmium oxide or cadmium anthranilate; however, weight losses during the treatment period were greater with sodium fluoride than with the other compounds. In a field experiment, Clore and Wille (19) observed that one per cent sodium silicofluoride added to swine feed (2 to 5 pounds of feed per pig) was effective in the removal of whipworms.

Sodium fluoride is a very effective ascaricide for swine, but the undesirable side effects which accompany its use have caused its popularity to decrease greatly in recent years.

Todd, Kelley, and Hansen (129) found that 2.5 grams of sodium fluoride per 100 pounds of body weight as a drench was effective against both mature and immature *Parascaris equorum* in ten horses. At necropsy, 24 hours after treatment, this dose was found to be 99.8 per cent effective. A smaller dose of 1.5 grams per hundredweight was only 61 per cent effective. Gastroenteritis, hemoconcentration, leucocytosis, and hemolysis were observed as undesirable side effects of the drug.

Chlorinated Hydrocarbons. Dichlorophen was effective against the common and fringed tapeworms of sheep (*Moniezia expansa* and *Thysanosoma actinioides*), in trials reported by Ryff *et al.* (115, 116). A dose of 0.04 gram per pound of body weight was sufficient to remove the common species and 0.25 gram per pound was effective against the fringed tapeworm. Subsequent reports by Olsen (97), Allen and Jackson (2), and Price and Hardy (113) on the use of the chemical against the fringed tapeworm indicated, however, that the safety, efficacy, and economy of the treatment have not been adequately established. After trials with the drug, Enzie *et al.* (42) concluded that dichlorophen was not so reliable as other available teniacides for removal of *Moniezia*.

Douglas *et al.* (27) found that bis(5-chloro-2-hydroxyphenyl) methane (Diphenthane-70), when administered at the rate of 6 grams per 50-pound lamb, did not reduce the number of nematodes in the abomasum or small intestine. It also failed to effect the reduction in the number of eggs produced by the female worm. Craige and Kleckner (23) found that this compound in doses of 200 milligrams per kilogram was a good teniacide for dogs while 2 grams in a single dose did not produce serious toxic effects. Blair (5) reported that 0.1 gram of this compound and 0.1 milliliter of methylbenzene per pound of body weight was very effective against ascaris, hookworms, and tapeworms of dogs.

Olsen (96) credits Thienel with the introduction of hexachloroethane as a fasciolicide in 1926. Olsen and Wade (98) and Olsen (96) found hexachloroethane bentonite suspension to be very effective against *Fasciola hepatica* of cattle, the common liver fluke of sheep, and the stomach worm *Haemonchus contortus* when a 15- to 30-gram oral dose was given. It was less effective against seven other nematodes of sheep.

n-Butyl chloride and tetrachloroethylene have been used by Whitney and Whitney (137) with some degree of success for elimination of common nematodes of dogs. They (138) reported on the specific action of *n*-butyl chloride on whipworms of dogs. Emesis was so frequent that the drug was undependable; however, Whitney (136) has suggested a regimen which

was more satisfactory. Dogs were fasted for 24 hours and then were given five oral doses (1 milliliter of *n*-butyl chloride per 10 or 12 pounds) at one-hour intervals followed by feeding two hours later. Since these were pets, critical examinations were not possible; however, fecal flotation checks indicated this method of treatment was of practical value.

Cadmium Oxide. This (0.01 and 0.02 per cent in the feed for two or three days) was first described as an ascaricide for swine by Bunde *et al.* (13) in 1954, and additional findings were published by Burch and Blair (15). The treatment that gave the best results consisted of a three-day schedule in which the only source of feed contained 0.015 per cent of cadmium oxide. In critical trials the treatment was 98 per cent effective, and this procedure gave a satisfactory result in the field. Feed mixtures containing this concentration of cadmium oxide were well tolerated in various types of feeds, which could be fed either wet or dry. Concentrations of 0.03 per cent reduced feed consumption and produced vomiting and diarrhea. After the administration of cadmium oxide in feed for three days, tissue residues were found in liver, kidney, and spleen. Elimination of the drug required 30 days after medication.

Cadmium Anthranilate. This was first reported to have ascaricidal action in swine by Guthrie (58) in 1954. The most consistent results were obtained when the chemical was given for three consecutive days at a concentration of 0.066 per cent of the regular ration. It was palatable, well tolerated, and re-moved 98 per cent of the ascarids in twelve pigs. It was not possible to determine the acute toxicity of the chemical because feed containing large concentrations of cadmium anthranilate were promptly vomited. Tissue analysis revealed that small amounts of cadmium were retained in the kidney, liver, spleen, and lungs of treated swine, thus confirming the report of Burch and Blair (15). Guthrie (59) in further trials with cadmium anthranilate, found that the ascaridical action of the chemical was not materially impaired when the concentration was re-

duced to 0.044 per cent. The administration of this level for three days removed 93 per cent of the ascarids from fifty-four pigs. This lower concentration is the one recommended for general use. Enzie and Colglazier (39), in feeding trials using 0.044 per cent cadmium anthranilate in the ration for three days, found that the drug removed 81 per cent of the ascarids from nine pigs.

Enzie and Colglazier (39) compared cadmium oxide, cadmium anthranilate, cadmium fumarate, piperazine hydrate, piperazine-carbon disulfide complex, and piperazine adipate. The piperazine compounds had a broader spectrum and were essentially nontoxic to pigs. Kelley, Olsen, and Garwood (73) found a 21-day treatment with cadmium anthranilate to be quite efficient in the removal of ascarids from swine. However, the treatment did not increase their subsequent gains and ability to utilize feed when compared to parasitized, untreated, control animals.

Arsenic-Containing Compounds. According to Otto (103), thiacetarsamide is probably the most effective drug available for the destruction of adult heartworms of dogs, but it has no significant effect on the microfilariae. It was given intravenously daily for 15 days at a dose rate of 1.0 milliliter of a 1 per cent solution for each 10 pounds of body weight. The dog should be closely confined during treatment and for a month or two thereafter, until resolution of the dead worms occurs. Since microfilariae may exist for prolonged periods following the treatment for destruction of adult forms, a microfilariacide should be administered three weeks following this treatment. Soltys (125) suggests the possible use of a proteolytic enzyme to assist in the digestion of the dead adult worms. Other results indicating the value of some arsenicals are reported by Drudge (30), Otto and Maren (104, 105).

Kume and Oishi (78) and Kume (77) found that 94 per cent of the adult worms are destroyed within ten days by dichlorophenarsine hydrochloride given intravenously at the rate of 1.0 milligram of arsenic per kilogram of body weight daily for three days. Thiacetarsamide accomplished the same result

(destruction of 97 per cent of the adult worms) when given at the same dosage and in the same manner; however, the action was slower. A minimum of ten days must elapse before the full value of the arsenical can be determined.

Compounds Containing Antimony. Kume (77) reemphasized his previous findings that the action of antimony compounds are effective against microfilariae of dogs; however, these agents have little or no effect on the adult *Dirofilaria immitus.* Otto (101, 102) and Otto and Maren (106) present a very comprehensive review of the chemotherapy of filariasis with antimony compounds and arsenic compounds.

Arsenates. Foster and Habermann (47) indicated that lead arsenate was a safe and effective treatment for removing the common tapeworm *M. expansa* from sheep. In investigations discussed by Enzie *et al.* (40, II), it has been demonstrated that teniacidal action of lead arsenate is not dependent upon the objectionable element lead. In preliminary trials the arsenate of calcium, cobalt, copper, and iron were well tolerated and quite effective in the removal of this parasite from lambs.

Tin. Di-*n*-butyltin dilaurate, a tetravalent tin compound, has been shown by Kerr (76) to be a safe and effective treatment for the removal of cestodes from chickens. The suggested dose is about 75 milligrams per kilogram body weight. Unlike hexachloroephane it does not adversely affect egg production. The chemical is compatible in the following mixture: nicotine sulfate, 6.785 per cent; phenothiazine, 28.5 per cent; di-*n*-butyltin dilaurate, 8.62 per cent. The compound is generally given to birds in combination with these drugs in the feed (final concentration of 1 per cent in feed). Such a mixture was 30 to 86 per cent effective against large roundworms.

Mercury. Guthrie and Harwood (61) found that 50-milligram doses of phenyl mercuric phthalate, phenyl mercuric borate, and phenyl mercuric benzoate was 92 to 96 per cent effective in the removal of tapeworms from chickens.

MISCELLANEOUS COMPOUNDS

Cyanacethydrazide as reported by Walley (134, 135) was active against the most important species of lungworms known

in domestic animals. It is effective against *D. filaria* in sheep and goats, *D. viviparus* in cattle, *Prostrongylus rufescens* in sheep, and *Metastrongylus apri* in swine. It was effective against those worms normally living in the air passages, but it had no action against *Muellerium capillaris* and *Neostrongylus linearis* in the lung tissue. Preliminary results suggest some action against *Syngamus trachea*. It had no action against migrating larvae. The compound was active when given orally or parenterally. This drug appears to have a rather narrow margin of safety and considerable testing of it under field conditions will be necessary to establish its practical value. It is of exceptional interest since it represents an approach to the systemic treatment of this condition. It is not parasiticidal but stimulates the expulsion of the worms.

Emetine Hydrochloride. Durbin (34) found that emetine hydrochloride was reasonably safe and effective against *Protostrongylus rufescens* and *Muellerium capillaris* in sheep and *M. capillaris* in goats. A 1 per cent aqueous solution of the chemical was given intramuscularly at a rate of 0.15 milliliter per pound of body weight, followed by a second injection two days later. Güiralp *et al.* (51) also found the drug to be effective against *M. capillaris.*

Quinacrin Hydrochloride. In trials reported by Link and Smith (83), quinacrin hydrochloride was found to be effective against *Taenia* and *Dipylidium* of dogs. The chemicals were given in capsules at a rate of 10 to 20 milligrams per pound of body weight. Tapeworms were expelled within 10 hours after treatment. It appeared to be about 90 per cent effective against both parasites. Aside from vomiting, no other serious side effects were apparent.

Phthalofyne (3-methyl-1-pentyne-3-yl sodium phthalate). This has shown considerable promise as a trichuricide for dogs. Ehrenford (36) found that 200 milligrams phthalofyne per kilogram of body weight removed all the whipworms from eight of nine dogs. Burch (14) found that 250 milligrams per kilogram of body weight removed all the whipworms from 40 to 42 dogs that retained the drug. Eight of the treated dogs vomited the drug; therefore, no action was apparent in these animals. In

another group of 50 dogs, two doses of 200 milligrams per kilogram eight hours apart following feeding removed all whipworms from the 44 which retained the drug.

Jordan (70), Magrane (84), and Green and Gruesser (56) have reported good results in field cases. Enzie *et al.* (40, III) did not find the drug nearly so effective when given in a single dose of 200 milligrams; however, two doses 8 hours apart removed 87 per cent of whipworms from 10 dogs. Hoekenga (67) reported that the oral dose of this drug is equally as effective when given to dogs intravenously. Oral doses of 100 to 200 milligrams per kilogram in human patients were 50 per cent effective against whipworms, but a disturbing number of these patients developed keratitis, conjunctivitis, and in some cases, lens changes and deafness.

Toluene. Oral doses of 1 milliliter toluene per pound of body weight to horses on a full feed removed 99 per cent of 419 ascarids present in eight animals when tested by Todd and Brown (127). Sinclair and Enzie (121) suggested that 10 milliliters per hundredweight may be adequate if the animal is fasted prior to treatment. Smith (123) confirmed Todd's findings, and the drug in this case was well tolerated in sucklings, weanlings, yearlings, and mares. It was found to be effective against mature and immature ascarids but ineffective against strongyles. Enzie and Colglazier (38) found that 0.1 milliliter per pound of body weight is a safe and effective treatment for the removal of ascarids and hookworms from dogs and cats, but it was not effective against whipworms. The drugs were found to be more desirable than *n*-butyl chloride.

Todd (126) and Todd and Stone (130) reported that 15 milligrams of penicillin, neomycin, and streptomycin per pound of feed reduced the growth rate of *Ascaridia galli* and permitted fewer worms to develop; however, 30 milligrams of penicillin was no better than 15 milligrams per pound of feed. The birds receiving the antibiotics made better weight gains. Brown *et al.* (12) reported that five-day administration of 1 gram of Aureomycin, 1 gram of Terramycin, 1 gram of streptomycin, 10,000 units of bacitracin, or 400,000 units and 2,000,000 units of penicillin exhibited limited ascaricidal action in cats. How-

ever, they were ineffective against *Ancylostoma caninum, Dipylidium species,* and *Taenia taeniaeformis.*

McCowen *et al.* (86) reported that an antibiotic, produced by a strain of *Streptomyces hygroscopicus,* demonstrated effective anthelmintic properties. Goldsby and Todd (53) confirmed the anthelmintic effectiveness of the fermentation product of the microorganism by tests in swine. McCowen *et al.* (87) and McCowen, Gossett, and Downing (88) reported the principal anthelmintic agent to be the antibiotic hygromycin B, and showed experimentally that 10, 20, 40, and 80 million units of hygromycin B per ton of complete feed fed to pigs for a period of 35 days was effective in the removal of ascaris, strongyles, and whipworms. The 10- and 20-million-unit levels were slightly less effective against the whipworm than the higher concentrations.

Gossett and Callender (55) found that a dried broth product mixed in a complete feed to give a final concentration of 12 million units of hygromycin B per ton, fed for a period of six weeks, was very effective in the elimination of ascaris, nodular worms, and to a lesser degree, whipworms of swine. Kelley *et al.* (74) found that 12 million units of hygromycin contained in Hygromix (*S. hygroscopicus* Fermentation Products, Lilly) per ton of complete feed was effective in the control of ascarids of swine. Smith (124) found the same concentration in complete feed to be effective against ascaris and nodular worms of swine.

The continuous feeding of Hygromix containing 12 million units of hygromycin B per ton of complete feed to swine of all ages is valuable in the control of ascaris, nodular worms, and whipworms of swine. Hygromix is the first broad-spectrum anthelmintic for swine that can be fed on a continuous basis for the control of these intestinal nematodes. It can also be fed to breeding stock without toxic side effects.

Anti-Protozoan Agents

Sulfa drugs have been valuable for the control of coccidiosis, particularly of poultry, in the past ten years. Sulfaquinoxaline became widely accepted because it was economical to use and

easily administered either in drinking water or mash for both the prevention and treatment of coccidiosis. Horton-Smith (68) stated that a concentration 0.05 per cent sulfaquinoxaline administered in the drinking water to experimentally infected chicks was as effective as 0.2 per cent of sulfamethazine. Bankowski (4) found that 0.05 per cent and 0.1 per cent sulfaquinoxaline in feed continuously for 42 days was effective in controlling an outbreak of coccidiosis in chickens. Kendall (75) reported that low concentrations of sulfamethazine inhibited the second generation schizonts and thereby checked hemorrhage. Two per cent sodium sulfamethazine in the drinking water or 0.4 per cent in the feed gave maximum therapeutic effect even to the extent of preventing the development of natural immunity. The resistance will develop satisfactorily if interrupted therapy is practiced.

Chapman (17) found that 0.05 per cent sulfaquinoxaline in the drinking water of rabbits, after challenge with 100,000 *Eimeria stiedae* oocysts, controlled coccidiosis of the liver. Moore (92) reported that 0.031 per cent sulfaquinoxaline in mash for turkeys was a satisfactory method of control of an outbreak of coccidiosis.

Christensen and Foster (18) found that 0.2 per cent and 0.45 per cent sulfaguanidine in the ration of lambs (3 grams average dose per day) during the incubation period of coccidiosis, during an expected clinical phase of the disease, prevented onset of clinical symptoms. Boughton and Davis (6) found that sulfaguanidine was of value in the control of coccidiosis of calves. Twelve calves were exposed to coccidia by contact with contaminated litter. Administration of 30 grams per week for five or six weeks reduced the severity of infection as compared to the controls.

Several workers (26, 93, 117) have reported that the continuous administration of sulfaquinoxaline and sulfaguinoxaline in combination with other drugs to poultry may be related to hypoplastic type anemia and certain degenerative blood vascular changes frequently encountered in chickens. Histopathological studies on these birds are suggestive that such a relation-

ship exists. The frequency of these toxic symptoms serves to encourage more discriminate use of the drug than was once practiced. Cover *et al.* (22) made a study of thirty-one field cases of hemorrhagic disease of young chickens. The pathology and hematology described was dissimilar to that produced in the laboratory as a result of vitamin K deficiency. The etiology of the field conditions could not be determined. In controlled experiments administration of sulfaquinoxaline substantially increased clotting time of plasma samples.

Nitrophenide. Gardiner *et al.* (49) reported that the inclusion of nitrophenide in the ration of chicks, experimentally infected with coccidiosis starting at 48 hours post-inoculation fed continuously through 96 hours post-inoculation was effective in preventing the ravages of the disease.

Nitrofurans. Harwood and Stung (64) reported that the continuous feeding of 0.0055 per cent nitrofurazone in the feed of chicks prevented death losses but permitted the development of immunity. Francis and Shaffner (48) fed nitrofurazone and furazolidone to young chickens. Some histological changes were observed in several glands but these changes had little effect on egg production, quality, or hatchability.

Foster (44) recommended that for the prevention of coccidiosis sulfaquinoxaline should be fed continuously at a concentration of 0.0125 per cent in the feed or in the drinking water at 0.0066 per cent with a sodium salt. For treatment in outbreaks, the concentration should be increased to 0.1 per cent in the feed for two days or 0.04 per cent in the water. If relapse occurs, a higher dosage may be repeated in three or four days. Nitrofurazone, 0.0056 per cent, should be fed continuously in the feed between the ages of two and fifteen weeks. For treatment of field outbreaks, concentration of 0.0012 per cent should be fed for a period of four to five days. For prevention, nitrophenide should be fed in a concentration of 0.0125 per cent a complete ration. Treatment should be discontinued four to five days before slaughter to allow for excretion of absorbed material.

Enheptin. 2-Amino-5-nitrothiazole was reported by Walet-

sky *et al.* (133) to be effective in the control of experimental blackhead infections of turkey poults. McGregor (89) found 0.0125 per cent, 0.025 per cent, and 0.05 per cent concentrations of the drug in turkey feed had a limited prophylactic effect against this disease under field conditions. It also showed some activity in stopping a field outbreak when fed in concentrations of 0.2 per cent for three days, 0.1 per cent for seven days, followed by 0.05 per cent continuously. Jungherr and Winn (71) obtained similar results with 0.05 and 0.1 per cent concentrations. Price and Bottorf (112) fed 0.025 per cent, 0.05 per cent, and 0.1 per cent concentrations to turkey hens. Their results were inconsistent, but there appeared to be no adverse effect of the drug on fertility or hatchability. This finding was also confirmed by Grumbles *et al.* (57).

Nicarbazin. Ott *et al.* (100) reported that an equimolecular complex of 4,4-dinitrocarbanilide and 2 hydroxy-4,6-dimethyl pyrimidine (Nicarbazin) had anticoccidial properties. Neither of the compounds was very effective individually or in a physical mixture; however, the complex had substantially greater activity than the sum of their individual actions.

Cuckler *et al.* (24) outlined the application and possible limitations of Nicarbazin for the control of coccidiosis as follows. In 1955-1956, 12 months use, 33 cases of coccidiosis were reported to the diagnostic laboratories of Delaware and Maryland while the average for the three previous years had been 657 cases, a reduction of 95 per cent. This difference was attributed to the feeding of Nicarbazin. The results obtained from feeding Nicarbazin to chickens, turkeys, and ducks showed that all tolerated the product satisfactorily. Four hundredths per cent or higher levels of the drug depressed growth of chicks reared in battery brooders to three weeks of age. Pen rearing studies under field conditions showed that Nicarbazin permitted good growth and feed efficiency when fed in concentrations of 0.005 to 0.02 per cent in commercial rations to chickens at ages of one day to ten or eleven weeks.

Ott *et al.* (99) noticed no adverse effects when Nicarbazin was fed to chicks at ages between one day and sexual maturity.

However, when it was fed to laying hens in the approved concentration range (0.0 to 0.02 per cent), several adverse effects were observed, but these disappeared rapidly after discontinuance of the medicated feed. One hundredth per cent caused production of eggs with less shell pigment than normal. The feeding of 0.07 per cent caused production to chalk white eggs of breeds that normally have brown eggs. Hatchability was depressed when 0.003 per cent was fed continuously. The feeding of 0.07 per cent reduced hatchability to zero. Polin et al. (107) reported 4,4-dinitrocarbanilide was absorbed and the concentrations which appeared in the yolk were related to depressed hatchability.

Trithiadol.   Newman (94) controlled *E. tenella* with a combination of bithianol and merthiotriazamine mixed in a complete broiler ration. In preliminary tests the mixture was found to be compatible with other feed additives and had no adverse effect on growth, pigmentation, egg production, shell quality, or color.

Miller *et al.* (90) found that tetracyclines inhibited growth of *Anaplasma marginale* in tests with splenectomized calves; however, subsequent anemia still developed. Additional tests are needed to determine the value of these drugs in the elimination of the carrier state. Brock *et al.* (11) reported calves which consumed 0.5 milligram per 1.0 milligram of Aureomycin per pound of body weight for sixty days after inoculation with blood from carrier animals failed to develop the disease, while five calves that received the ration without antibiotic became infected with the disease agent.

Conclusions

For many years efforts to correct disease problems have been directed toward treatment of the animal showing clinical symptoms. It has now been demonstrated that the value of this approach is questionable. We must devise drugs and maintain control systems that will prevent diseases in preference to curing them. The older anthelmintics are very toxic to the host and only effective in removal of the mature parasites; there-

fore, the use of these agents has not contributed greatly to the reduction of parasite populations. Newer drug actions are more specific for the parasite and relatively less toxic for the host. These two advantages should greatly improve our possibilities for reducing future losses resulting from parasitism.

Recent trends suggest that future antiparasitic agents for domestic animals may be administered continuously. Such agents will be capable of breaking the life cycle by interfering with reproduction or development of immature forms. This would decrease the parasite population and thus reduce the exposure opportunity for young susceptible animals and the likelihood of reinfection of older animals. Even with the success of such materials, good sanitation practices will be necessary since the possibility of the development of forms resistant to chemicals is ever present.

The effectiveness of demonstrated antiparasitic agents is very encouraging. We are entering an era in which the judicious use of chemical agents and strict attention to sanitation practices should eliminate some of our animal parasite problems. Future emphasis in research should be placed on eradicating parasite populations rather than merely attempting to control them.

ACKNOWLEDGMENT

I wish to thank Miss J. J. Jackley for her secretarial assistance and Dr. C. Leben for his constructive criticism and suggestions in the preparation of this manuscript.

REFERENCES

1. Alicata, J. E., and J. H. Koshi. Observations on the stability of phenothiazine in cane molasses in relation to parasite control. *J. Am. Vet. Med. Assoc. 129*:428-429 (1956).
2. Allen, R. W., and P. K. Jackson. Evaluation of Di-phenthane-70 in removing fringed tapeworms from sheep. *Vet. Med. 48*:352-354 (1953).
3. Andrews, J. A., C. M. Muniz, and F. Orihuela. Preliminary note on the administration of non-conditioned phenothiazine in small daily doses, for the control of gastrointestinal parasites of cattle in Puerto Rico. *J. Agr. Univ. Puerto Rico 27*: 125-129 (1943).

4. Bankowski, R. A. Use of sulfaquinoxaline as a preventive against mild outbreaks of coccidiosis of chickens under field conditions. *Am. J. Vet. Research* 12:349-354 (1951).
5. Blair, H. E. Vermiplex, a new anthelmintic for dogs. *N. Am. Vet.* 30:306-309 (1949).
6. Boughton, D. C., and L. R. Davis. An experiment with sulfa-quanidine in the treatment of naturally acquired bovine coccidiosis. *Am. J. Vet. Research* 4:150-154 (1943).
7. Bradley, R. E. Observations on the anthelmintic effect of piper-azine citrate in chickens. *Vet. Med.* 50:444-446 (1955).
8. Britton, J. W. Phenothiazine in cattle practice. *Vet. Med.* 39: 239-242 (1944).
9. Britton, J. W., and R. F. Miller. The practical application of anthelmintic medication of lambs. *J. Am. Vet. Med. Assoc.* 104:270-272 (1944).
10. Brock, W. E., C. C. Pearson, and A. B. Kliewer. Daily minimal dosage of phenothiazine in control of nematode infections in cattle. *Proc. Book Am. Vet. Med. Assoc.* 1952:167-171.
11. Brock, W. E., C. C. Pearson, E. E. Staley, and I. O. Kliewer. The prevention of anaplasmosis by feeding chlortetracycline. *J. Am. Vet. Med. Assoc.* 130:445-446 (1957).
12. Brown, H. W., P. H. Mann, and I. Fratta. The effectiveness of antibiotics against intestinal helminths of the cat. *Antibiotics & Chemotherapy* 3:243-248 (1953).
13. Bunde, C. A., H. E. Blair, G. R. Burch, and J. W. Lee. As-caricidal action of cadmium. *Proc. Soc. Exptl. Biol. Med.* 87:549-550 (1954).
14. Burch, G. R. A new oral anthelmintic for canine whipworms. *Vet. Med.* 49:291 (1954).
15. Burch, G. R., and H. E. Blair. A new ascaricide for swine. *J. Am. Vet. Med. Assoc.* 126:304-308 (1955).
16. Cauthen, G. E. The effect of small daily doses of phenothiazine on the development of larvae of the gastrointestinal parasites of cattle. *Am. J. Vet. Research* 14:30-32 (1953).
17. Chapman, M. P. The use of sulfaquinoxaline in the control of liver coccidiosis in domestic rabbits. *Vet. Med.* 43:375-379 (1948).
18. Christensen, J. F., and A. O. Foster. Further studies with sulfa-quanidine in the control of swine coccidiosis. *Vet. Med.* 38: 144-147 (1943).
19. Clore, E. E., and T. Wille, Jr. Observations on the use of sodium silicofluoride in feed for the removal of whipworms from swine. *J. Am. Vet. Med. Assoc.* 130:495-496 (1957).
20. Colglazier, M. L., and F. D. Enzie. Notes on Caricide as an

anthelmintic for cats and dogs. *Proc. Helminthol. Soc. Wash.* *18*:50-52 (1951).

21. Colglazier, M. L., and J. H. Turner. An experiment on the cumulative efficacy of phenothiazine-salt mixture against nematodirus and haemonchus in lambs during a second grazing season. *Am. J. Vet. Research 16*:558-562 (1955).

22. Cover, M. S., W. J. Meller, and E. Gill. Studies of hemorrhagic syndromes in chickens. *Cornell Vet. 45*:366-386 (1955).

23. Craige, A. H., Jr., and A. L. Kleckner. Teniacidal action of Di-phenthane-70. *North Am. Veterinarian 27*:26-30 (1946).

24. Cuckler, A. C., W. H. Ott, and D. E. Fogg. Factors in the evaluation of coccidiostats in poultry. *Cornell Vet. 47*:400-412 (1957).

25. Dennis, W. R., L. E. Swanson, and W. M. Stone. Experimental feeding by low-level phenothiazine in Florida cattle. *Vet. Med. 50*:379-389, 392 (1955).

26. Delaphane, J. P., and J. H. Milliff. The gross and micropathology of sulfaquinoxaline poisoning in chicks. *Am. J. Vet. Research 9*:92-96 (1948).

27. Douglas, J. R., N. F. Baker, and W. M. Longhurst. Trial with Di-phenthane-70 on stomach and intestinal nematodes in sheep. *J. Am. Vet. Med. Assoc. 128*:361-362 (1956).

28. ———. The effect of divided dosage on the anthelmintic efficacy of phenothiazine in lambs. *J. Am. Vet. Med. Assoc. 131*:369-371 (1957).

29. Downing, W., P. A. Kingsbury, and J. E. N. Sloan. Critical tests with piperazine adipate in horses. *Vet. Record 67*:641-644 (1955).

30. Drudge, J. H. Arsenamide in the treatment of canine filariasis. *Am. J. Vet. Research 13*:220-235 (1952).

31. Drudge, J. H., S. E. Leland, Jr., and Z. N. Wyant. Strain variations in the response of sheep nematodes to action of phenothiazine. I. Studies of mixed infections in experimental animals. *Am. J. Vet. Research 18*:133-141 (1957).

32. ———. Strain variations in the response of sheep nematodes to action of phenothiazine. II. Studies on pure infections of *Haemonchus contortus. Am. J. Vet. Research 18*:317-325 (1957).

33. Drudge, J. H., S. E. Leland, Jr., Z. N. Wyant, and L. B. Hutzler. Field studies with piperazine-carbon disulfide complex against parasites of the horse. *J. Am. Vet. Med. Assoc. 131*: 231-233 (1957).

34. Durbin, C. G. Emetine hydrochloride for the treatment of sheep and goats infested with protostrongyline lungworms.

Bull. Univ. Pennsylvania 54 (13). *Vet. Extension Quart. 133:* 49 (1954).

35. Edgar, S. A., D. C. Davis, and J. A. Frazier. The efficacy of some piperazine compounds in the elimination of helminths from experimentally and naturally infected poultry. *Poultry Sci. 36:*495-510 (1957).
36. Ehrenford, F. A. A new effective anthelmintic for canine trichuris. *J. Parasitol. 40:*481 (1954).
37. Ellison, M. S., and A. C. Todd. The metabolism of phenothiazine, N. F., in dairy calves. I. Chronological distribution of drug in digestive tract contents. *Am. J. Vet. Research 18:* 519-522 (1957); II. Chronological levels of drug in digestive tract contents. *Ibid. 18:*522-525 (1957); III. Chronological levels of drug in liver, kidney, spleen, and mesenteric lymph nodes. *Ibid. 18:*526-527 (1957); IV. Chronological total drug recovery. *Ibid. 18:*527-529 (1957).
38. Enzie, F. D., and M. L. Colglazier. Toluene (methylbenzene) for intestinal nematodes in dogs and cats. *Vet. Med. 48:*325-328 (1953).
39. ———. Present-day trends in anthelmintics for swine. *Proc. Book Am. Vet. Med. Assoc. 1955:*153.
40. Enzie, F. D., M. L. Colglazier, and E. H. Wilkens. Newer treatments for helminthic infections. I. *Vet. Med. 52:*267-273 (1957); II. *Ibid.,* 52:331-336, 356 (1957); III. *Ibid.* 52:387-394 (1957).
41. ———. The use of piperazines as anthelmintics for swine. *Am. J. Vet. Research 19:*19-24 (1958).
42. Enzie, F. D., A. O. Foster, L. R. Sinclair, and M. L. Colglazier. Trials with Di-phenthane-70 on the sheep tapeworm *Moniezia expansa. J. Am. Vet. Med. Assoc. 122:*29-30 (1953).
43. Foley, R. J. The treatment of canine filariasis. *Vet. Med. 45:* 485-489 (1950).
44. Foster, A. O. The administration of antiparasitic drugs in feeds. *Vet. Med. 46:*324-326 (1951).
45. ———. Free-choice phenothiazine for cattle. *Vet. Med. 48:*208-209 (1953).
46. ———. The practical aspect of low-level phenothiazine for cattle. *Vet Med. 50:*93-94 (1955).
47. Foster, A. O., and R. T. Habermann. Lead arsenate for removal of ruminant tapeworms. *J. Am. Vet. Med. Assoc. 113:* 51-54 (1948).
48. Francis, D. W., and C. S. Shaffner. An investigation of the morphological changes in young chickens and the reproduction performance of adult chickens fed furazolidone or nitrofurazone. *Poultry Sci. 35:*1371-1381 (1956).

49. Gardiner, J. L., M. M. Farr, and E. E. Wehr. The coccidiostatic action of nitrophenide on *Eimeria tenella*. *J. Parasitol.* 38: 517-524 (1952).

50. Garnier, W. A progress report on the use of Caricide as a preventive of canine filariasis. *Vet. Bull.* (*Lederle*) 13:13 (1954).

51. Giiralp, N., J. Kavanaugh, and D. Baker. Some further evaluation of emetine therapy against sheep and goat lungworms. *Cornell Vet.* 47:515-524 (1957)

52. Goldsby, A. I., and A. C. Todd. A new swine anthelmintic. *North Am. Veterinarian* 38:101-104 (1957).

53. ————. Control of lungworms and several other nematodes parasitic for swine achieved by feeding a new antibiotic. *North Am. Veterinarian* 38:140-144 (1957).

54. Gordon, H. McL. Studies on anthelmintics for sheep. Piperazine compounds. *Australian Vet. J.* 33:1-7 (1957).

55. Gossett, F. O., and M. E. Callender. The effect of "Hygromix" on intestinal helminths of swine. *Vet. Med.* 1960 (in press).

56. Green, L. E., and F. Grusser. Canine whipworm treatment with whipcide. *Mich. State Coll. Vet.* 15:42 (1954).

57. Grumbles, L. C., W. A. Boney, and R. D. Turk. Chemotherapy of enterohepatitis of turkeys. II. The effect of 2-amino-5-nitrothiazole and 2-acetylaminonitrothiazole on egg production, fertility, and hatchability in turkey hens. *Am. J. Vet. Research* 13:386-387 (1952).

58. Guthrie, J. E. Critical test with cadmium anthranilate as an ascaricide in swine. *Vet. Med.* 49:413-418 (1954).

59. ————. Further observations on the efficacy of cadmium anthranilate as an ascaricide in swine. *Vet. Med.* 49:500 (1954).

60. ————. Critical tests with piperazine as an ascaricide in swine. *Vet. Med.* 51:235 (1956).

61. Guthrie, J. E., and P. D. Harwood. Phenyl mercuric compounds for the removal of tapeworms from poultry. *J. Parasitol.* 34: Suppl. 15, December 1948.

62. Habermann, R. T., F. D. Enzie, and A. O. Foster. Tests with fluorides especially sodium fluoride as anthelmintics for swine. *Am. J. Vet. Research* 6:131-144 (1945).

63. Habermann, R. T., and D. A. Shorb. The development of parasite larvae in the feces of sheep. *North Am. Veterinarian* 23: 318-321 (1942).

64. Harwood, P. D., and D. I. Stung. Efficacy of 0.0055 percent nitrofurazone fed continuously for the control of avian coccidiosis under conditions of natural infection. *J. Parasitol.* 27:13 (1951). Abstract of paper given at 26th Annual Meeting of American Society of Parasitologists.

65. Herlich, H., and D. A. Porter. Control of intestinal parasites of cattle by free-choice administration of phenothiazine. *Vet. Med. 49*:103-106 (1954).

66. Hewitt, R. W., E. White, and Y. SubbaRow. The treatment of ascariasis in dogs with 1-diethylcarbamyl-4-methylpiperazine hydrochloride. *J. Parasitol. 34*:237-239 (1948).

67. Hoekenga, M. T. Ocular toxicity of whipcide (3-methyl-1-pentyn-3-yl acid phthalate in humans. *J. Am. Med. Assoc. 161*:1252-1253 (1956).

68. Horton-Smith, C. Veterinary parasitology, papers presented at the Meeting of the Assoc. Vet. Teachers and Research Workers, Royal Vet. College, April 1952. *Vet. Record 64*:437 (1952).

69. Jarrett, W. F. H., W. I. M. McIntyre, and G. M. Urquhart. Husk in cattle. A review of a year's work. *Vet. Record 66*: 665-675 (1954).

70. Jordon, J. E. Treatment of canine whipworms (*Trichuris vulpis*) with whipcide. *J. Am. Vet. Med. Assoc. 126*:220 (1955).

71. Jungherr, E. L., and J. D. Winn. Field experiments with enheptin-T on the control of histomoniasis (blackhead) in turkeys. *Poultry Sci. 29*:462-465 (1950).

72. Kanegis, L. A. A new treatment for ascariasis in dogs and cats. *J. Am. Vet. Med. Assoc. 113*:579-581 (1948).

73, Kelley, G. W., L. S. Olsen, and V. Garwood. A field evaluation of ascaricides in swine. *Vet. Med. 51*:97 (1956).

74. Kelley, G. W., L. S. Olsen, L. Sumption, and J. Adams. A field evaluation of hygromycin B as an ascaracide in swine. *Vet. Med. 53*:120-126 (1958).

75. Kendall, S. B. Caecal Coccidiosis. Breakdown in sulfamethazine therapy. *Vet. Record 63*:422 (1951).

76. Kerr, K. B. Butynorate, an effective and safe substance for the removal of *Raillietina cesticillus* from chickens. *Poultry Sci. 31*:328-336 (1952).

77. Kume, S. Chemotherapy of canine filariasis. *Am. J. Vet. Research 18*:912-923 (1957).

78. Kume, S., and I. Oishi. Observations on the chemotherapy of canine heartworm infection with arsenicals. *J. Am. Vet. Med. Assoc. 131*:476-479 (1957).

79. Lee, R. P. The anthelmintic efficiency of piperazine adipate against *Neoascaris vitulorum* (Goeze 1782). A preliminary report. *Vet. Record 67*:146-149 (1955).

80. Leiper, J. W. G. The piperazine compound V.19 for the removal of ascaris and oesophagostomum from the pig. *Vet. Record 66*:596 (1954).

81. Leland, S. E., Jr., J. H. Drudge, Z. N. Wyant, and G. W. Elam. Strain variations in the response of sheep nematodes to action of phenothiazine. III. Field observations. *Am. J. Vet. Research 18*:851-860 (1957).

82. Lindquist, W. D. The use of low-level piperazine on pigs experimentally infected with Ascaris lumbricoides. *Am. J. Vet. Research 18*:119-120 (1957).

83. Link, R. P., and J. C. Smith. Treatment of canine tapeworms with Atabrine. *J. Am. Vet. Med. Assoc. 125*:461-462 (1954).

84. Magrane, H. J., Jr. Treatment of canine trichuriasis with whipcide. *North Am. Veterinarian 35*:761 (1954).

85. Mayhew, R. L. Studies on bovine gastrointestinal parasites. XVI. Some results of feeding small amounts of phenothiazine on pure infections of the hookworm, *Bunostomum phlebotomum. J. Parasitol. 36*:536-540 (1950).

86. McCowen, M. C., M. E. Callender, and M. C. Brandt. Antiparasitic activity of the antibiotic hygromycin. *Antibiotics Annual* 833-886, 1956-1957.

87. McCowen, M. C., F. O. Gossett, M. E. Callender, and M. C. Brandt. Anthelmintic effect of hygromycin B in swine. *Vet. Med. 54*:103-105 (1959).

88. McCowen, M. C., F. O. Gossett, and J. F. Downing. The effect of Streptomyces hygroscopicus fermentation products on intestinal helminths of swine. *Vet. Med.* 1960 (in press).

89. McGregor, J. K. Studies on the use of 2-amino-5-nitrothiazole in the control of enterohepatitis (blackhead) in turkeys. *Am. J. Vet. Research 13*:108-109 (1952).

90. Miller, J. G., H. E. Levy, B. J. Torbet, and W. T. Oglesby. A method of screening drugs to be used in the treatment of anaplasmosis results of testing with aureomycin and terramycin. *Proc. Book Am. Vet. Med. Assoc. 1952*:160-167.

91. Monnig, H. O. The chemotherapy oesophagostomiasis of sheep. II. *Onderstepoort J. Vet. Sci. Animal Ind. 5*:419-438 (1935).

92. Moore, E. N. Sulfaquinoxaline as a treatment for coccidiosis in turkeys. *Cornell Vet. 39*:223-228 (1949).

93. Newberne, P. M., and W. B. Buck. The influence of various levels of sulfaquinoxaline on growth and development of chicks. *Poultry Sci. 35*:1259-1264 (1956).

94. Newman, H. J., Sterwin Chemicals, Inc., New York 18, New York. Personal communication.

95. Nordquist, A. V., and C. H. Pals. *Yearbook of Agr. U. S. Dept. Agr. 1956*:11-14.

96. Olsen, O. W. Hexachloroethane-bentonite suspension for the removal of common liver flukes, *Fasciola lepatica* from sheep. *Am. J. Vet. Research 7*:358-364 (1946).

97. ———. An evaluation of medicaments with special reference to Teniatol for removing fringed tapeworms (*Thysanosoma actenoides*) from the livers of sheep. *Am. J. Vet. Research* 14:616-620 (1953).

98. Olsen, O. W., and L. L. Wade. Nematocidal efficacy of Hexachloroethane-bentonite suspension in sheep and goats. *North Am. Veterinarian* 31:740-742 (1950).

99. Ott, W. H., A. M. Dickenson, and A. C. Peterson. Studies on the effect of nicarbazin on reproduction in chickens. *Poultry Sci.* 35:1163 (1956).

100. Ott, H. W., S. Huna, C. C. Porter, A. C. Cuckler, and D. E. Fogg. Biological studies on nicarbazin, a new anticoccidial agent. *Poultry Sci.* 35:1355-1367 (1956).

101. Otto, G. F. Studies on the chemotherapy of filariasis. *Am. J. Hyg.* 50:92-141 (1949).

102. ———. Studies on the excretion and concentration of antimony in blood and other tissues following the injections of trivalent and pentavalent antimonials into experimental animals. *Am. J. Hyg.* 51:370-385 (1950).

103. ———. The treatment of canine filariasis. *Auburn Vet.* 8 (2): 2 (1952).

104. Otto, G. F., and T. H. Maren. Treatment of canine filariasis with trivalent arsenicals (p-arsenosobenzamides). *J. Parasitol.* 31:17, December Suppl. (1945).

105. ———. Possible use of an arsenical compound in the treatment of heartworm in dogs. *Vet. Med.* 42:128 (1947).

106. ———. Comparative review of the possible therapeutic agents available for canine and human filariasis. *Am. J. Hyg.* 51: 385-395 (1950).

107. Polin, D. P., J. L. Gilfillan, W. H. Ott, and C. C. Porter. 4,4'-Dinitrocarbanilide in egg yolks from hens fed nicarbazin. *Poultry Sci.* 35:1367-1371 (1956).

108. Poynter, D. Piperazine adipate as an equine anthelmintic. *Vet. Record* 67:159-163 (1955).

109. ———. The efficiency of piperazine adipate administered in bran mash to horses. *Vet. Record* 67:625 (1955).

110. ———. A comparative assessment of the anthelmintic activity in horses of four piperazine compounds. *Vet. Record* 68:291-297 (1956).

111. ———. Piperazine 1-carbodithioic acid as an anthelmintic against *Parascaris equorum* in horses. *Vet. Record* 68:429-431 (1956).

112. Price, R. J., and C. A. Bottorf. Effect of 2-acetamido-5-nitrothiazole and 2-amino-5-nitrothiazole on egg production, fer-

tility, hatchability, and weight gains in turkeys. *Poultry Sci.* 33:952-957 (1954).

113. Price, D. A., and W. T. Hardy. Activity of certain drugs against the fringed tapeworm. *J. Am. Vet. Med. Assoc. 122:* 216-220 (1953).

114. Reidel, B. B., and E. J. Larson. The critical evaluation of a new swine anthelmintic containing piperazine and carbon disulfied-Parvex. *J. Am. Vet. Med. Assoc. 129:*156 (1956).

115. Ryff, J. F., J. Brown, H. L. Stoddard, and R. F. Honess. Removal of the fringed tapeworm from sheep. *J. Am. Vet. Med. Assoc. 117:*471-473 (1950).

116. Ryff, J. F., R. F. Honess, and H. L. Stoddard. Removal of fringed tapeworm from sheep. *J. Am. Vet. Med. Assoc. 115:* 179-180 (1949).

117. Sadek, S. E., L. E. Hansen, and J. O. Alberts. Suspected drug-induced anemias in the chicken. *J. Am. Vet. Med. Assoc. 127:*201-203 (1955).

118. Shelton, G. C., A. Moles, and A. J. Dyer. Parasitism in sheep on irrigated pastures. *J. Am. Vet. Med. Assoc. 131:*315-317 (1957).

119. Shumard, R. F. The toxicity to chickens and the anthelmintic effect of two forms of a piperazine-carbon disulfide complex on *Ascaridia galli* and *Heterakis gallinae. Poultry Sci. 36:* 613-618 (1957).

120. Shumard, R. F., and D. F. Eveleth. A preliminary report on the anthelmintic action of piperazine citrate on *Ascaridia galli* and *Heterakis gallinae* in hens. *Vet. Med. 50:*203-205 (1955).

121. Sinclair, L. R., and F. D. Enzie. Toluene against ascarids and bots in horses. *Am. J. Vet. Research 14:*49-50 (1953).

122. Sloan, J. E. N., P. A. Kingsbury, and D. W. Jolly. Preliminary trials with piperazine adipate as a veterinary anthelmintic. *J. Pharm. and Pharmacol. 6:*718-724 (1954).

123. Smith, H. M. Toluene therapy for ascariasis and bot infestations in horses. *J. Am. Vet. Med. Assoc. 127:*245-246 (1955).

124. Smith, H. R. "Hygromix" as a control of internal parasites in swine. Swine day report of the Ohio Agricultural Experiment Station, Sept. 6, 1957, and Animal Science Mimeo.

125. Soltys, A. Use of enzymes in heartworm therapy. *Vet. Med. 51:*187 (1956).

126. Todd, A. C. Effect of antibiotic agents upon experimental *Ascaridia galli* infections in chickens. *Poultry Sci. 30:*763-766 (1951).

127. Todd, A. C., and R. G. Brown, Jr. Critical tests with toluene

for ascarids and bots in horses. *Am. J. Vet. Research 13*: 198-200 (1952).

128. Todd, A. C., M. F. Hansen, G. W. Kelley, and Z. N. Wyant. Continuous phenothiazine therapy for horses. I. The effect on the worm parasite. *Vet. Med. 44*:411-414 (1949).

129. Todd, A. C., G. W. Kelley, and M. F. Hansen. Critical tests with sodium fluoride as an anthelmintic for ascariasis in horses. *Am. J. Vet. Research 11*:26-28 (1950).

130. Todd, A. C., and W. M. Stone. Effect of penicillin in the diet upon experimental *Ascaridia galli* infections in chickens. *Poultry Sci. 31*:202-203 (1952).

131. Turk, R. D. and F. Hale. Observations on ascaricides of swine. *J. Am. Vet. Med. Assoc. 128*:405-407 (1956).

132. Turner, J. H., and M. L. Colglazier. Control of pasture-acquired infections of *nematodirus spothiger* and *Haemonchus contortus* in lambs with phenothiazine salt mixture. *Am. J. Vet. Research 15*:564-573 (1954).

133. Waletsky, E., M. C. Brandt, A. Bliznick, and C. O. Hughes. Some chemotherapeutic agents in experimental enterohepatitis (blackhead) of turkeys. *J. Parasitol. 35*:16 (1949).

134. Walley, J. K. A new drug for the treatment of lungworms in domestic animals. *Vet. Record 69*:815-824, 850-853 (1957).

135. ———. A new drug, cyanacethydrazide, for the oral and subcutaneous treatment of lungworm diseases in animals. *J. Am. Vet. Med. Assoc. 131*:539-544 (1957).

136. Whitney, L. F. Concerning the safety of *n*-butyl chloride as a whipworm anthelmintic. *Vet. Med. 52*:606 (1957).

137. Whitney, L. F. and G. D. Whitney. Contrasting tetrachloroethylene and *n*-butyl chloride as canine anthelmintics. *Vet. Med. 48*:495-499 (1953).

138. ———. Removal of whipworms by *n*-butyl chloride. *Vet. Med. 49*:78-88 (1954).

139. Worley, D. C., M. F. Hansen, and B. R. B. Persaud. Action of piperazine compounds on lumen and tissue phase larvae of *Ascaridia galli* (Schrank), a roundworm of chickens. *Poultry Sci. 36*:865-870 (1957).

140. Ziegler, C. G. Treatment of canine filariasis with Caricide diethylcarbamazine. *J. Am. Vet. Med. Assoc. 116*:209-210 (1950).

III BIOLOGICAL CONTROL OF PESTS

Antagonism As a Plant Disease Control Principle

William C. Snyder

Department of Plant Pathology,
University of California, Berkeley

There are two approaches to the control of plant diseases. One, chemical control, depends mainly upon the application of a poison to check or kill the pathogen; the other, biological control, relies largely upon an interruption of host-parasite relationships through biological means. Biological control may be accomplished by imparting resistance to the host, usually through plant breeding or by modifying the culture of the crop so as to avoid or reduce infection. Modification of crop culture by utilizing the action of other organisms against the pathogen invokes antagonism, and is the kind of biological control with which we are concerned here.

What Is Antagonism?

Antagonism, simply stated, is the activity of one organism against another. Or, as Wood and Tveit (12) have said, it is "the activity of an organism which in some way adversely affects another growing in association with it." In a broad sense, this activity of the antagonist may include physical destruction and parasitism, antibiotic excretions and the more subtle forms of attrition, or competition for nutrients and space. Antagonism is the sum total of the unfavorable influences which one organism exerts against another. We seem obliged to take this broader view of antagonism since, as Skinner (10) has aptly pointed out, it is not always feasible to know the exact mode of action of an antagonist at a particular time, especially when its habitat is the soil.

Clearly then, antagonism has been with us always. It is as old as life itself. As soon as there were two organisms on earth,

together, there was antagonism. Since in their struggle for survival all organisms interact directly or indirectly with other organisms with which they come in contact, the phenomenon of antagonism becomes a first principle of biology along with the alternate phenomenon, cooperation. Antagonism is the balance wheel of nature. Where there is life, there is antagonism.

In this discussion, however, the use of the term antagonism will be restricted to microorganisms in the soil in order to avoid becoming involved with the whole spectrum of man's special antagonisms which he has developed in the process of becoming civilized, as well as the antagonisms of all other forms of life in the air, the sea, and on land. Furthermore, it is not within the scope of this discussion to consider all ways of using antagonism in the various areas even of plant pathology.

It is possible and, in some cases, feasible to hold above-ground diseases in check by biological means through antagonism. However, by far the greatest interest in this means of control, in recent years, has been with root disease fungi. There are probably two principal reasons for this. First, many root diseases have not lent themselves to other means of control, for neither chemical control nor resistant varieties have been available. Biological control through antagonism has been turned to as an interim expedient until other means of control may be developed, or as a last resort when no other approach has shown promise. Second, if antagonism is to be employed in plant disease control, the soil environment with its immense and varied biological activity lends itself rather logically to this approach. The forces of antagonism already are continuously at work in the soil beneficially restraining in some degree the soil-borne pathogens. It seems only reasonable that man, with increasing knowledge of the biology of soil, should be able to influence at least temporarily the course of antagonism to his benefit.

Manifestations of Antagonism

In light of today's knowledge we may say that man unknowingly used biological control early in the history of agriculture, when he practiced crop rotation in order to cope with crop

production problems. Much of the benefit accruing from crop rotation systems comes about through a disproportionate, decreased activity of the root pathogens of a given crop. In the last analysis this unfavorable effect upon a pathogen, accomplished through the culture of a non-host crop, is believed to result from the antagonistic action of various elements of the soil flora (and fauna). To be sure, the approach of the early agriculturist to avoid crop production problems was empirical at most, but crop rotation as a means of avoiding plant diseases has emerged as a principle in modern plant pathology. No method of disease control, even today, is more widely or successfully used in combating plant disease. This manifestation of antagonism has long perplexed the plant pathologist. Only during the past twenty-five years, however, has he attempted seriously to meet the challenge of learning how to harness antagonism to his advantage in obtaining better control of below-ground diseases.

Real impetus to scientific thought and research on antagonism as a mechanism of biological control came in the 1920's from the work of Millard (5) and Sanford (8). They demonstrated the control of Streptomyces scab of potato by the addition of organic supplements to the soil. These researches stimulated a number of investigators, hopefully, to attempt control of a variety of root-invading fungi, either by the addition of fresh organic matter to soil, or by the introduction to the soil of large numbers of an organism, particularly after the organism had been shown on agar plates to be antagonistic to the pathogen in question. Much of this work ended in disappointment, but out of it have come observations and experiences which have been of considerable value to those who continue to push the case for antagonism.

Garrett (3), Wood and Tveit (12), and others have prepared excellent reviews in this area. It will serve best here to mention only a few examples where antagonism has been demonstrated as an effective means of disease control in soil and where the method either is in current use or shows promise for the future.

There are three general methods of employing antagonism in

the control of root disease fungi. One is the controlled colonization of sterilized soil with appropriate antagonists. The stage
was set for this method by the early work of Millard and Taylor
(6) and Sanford and Broadfoot (9), but the successful application of the method to agriculture was made by Ferguson (2).
He showed that the plant pathogen *Rhizoctonia solani*, introduced accidentally or by seed into flats of sterilized soil seeded
to peppers for transplantation to the field, could be checked
effectively by the introduction to the flat of one or more antagonistic organisms immediately after sterilization. Ferguson
showed that this method has considerable potential in the control of damping-off of seedlings where plants are started in containers of sterilized soil.

A second method is the infestation of planting stock, or seed,
with the antagonist at the time of planting and in the absence
of any soil treatment. McClure (4) and later Bega (1) were
able, experimentally, to reduce greatly the amount of infection
by *Fusarium oxysporum* f. *batatas* in sweet potato by dipping
healthy slips in a spore suspension of *Fusarium solani* f. *batatas*
before planting. The treatment of seeds with antagonistic organisms as a plant disease control measure is suggested by the work
of Tveit and Wood (11), and others. They obtained control of
Fusarium blight in oat seedlings by infesting the seed with
species of Chaetomium before seeding in the field.

A third method of applying antagonism to root disease control
is that of incorporating organic matter into the land either by
turning under green cover crops or through crop rotations. This
method is perhaps the most difficult to accomplish, but it is the
most widely used and has the longest record of benefit.

The ultimate measure of effective use of antagonism in root
disease control is its commercial acceptance after demonstrated
experimental success. Residue management qualifies the best.
It is interesting to note that Streptomyces scab of potato, one
of the first diseases to be investigated in this connection, is a
good example of a soil-borne disease now satisfactorily controlled
by this method in at least one major potato-growing area. This
is accomplished by turning under a green manure crop of soy-

beans after annual harvesting of the potato crop. Oswald (7) has shown in more than ten successive years of experimentally controlled cropping systems in Kern County, California, that soybeans consistently held down scab infection to a trace, with a scab index of 1. Green barley, on the other hand, increased scab to the point where the crop was largely unmarketable, and showed a scab rating of 19. When green peas were used as the cover crop following potatoes, a scab index of 9 was obtained in the succeeding potato crop, which is just about the same amount of disease that results when potatoes follow potatoes without any intervening cover crop.

Another example of successful commercial use of a green cover crop is in the control of Phymatotrichum root rot of cotton. Here a pea cover crop is used. Although peas were neutral in their effect upon potato scab, such a cover crop turned under before planting cotton makes it possible to harvest a crop. This cover-cropping practice is a proven and accepted means of combating root rot of cotton in Arizona.

In recent work on Phytophthora root rot of avocado, Zentmyer (13) showed that of all the organic materials tried only alfalfa meal was beneficial in reducing or preventing infection by *P. cinnamomi*. Not only was this favorable response obtained when the alfalfa meal was incorporated in field soil before planting but also, some measure of success in reducing progress of the disease in established trees followed surface applications to the soil about the infected trees.

Many other examples of benefit in disease reduction through the use of cover crops or crop rotations may be drawn from the literature. Our interest at this point, however, is to learn why such benefit is obtained. Once we understand why certain organic materials are beneficial in controlling root diseases and why others are not, we shall be in a position to employ biological control more intelligently than is now possible and perhaps to predict which organics will give the greatest benefit against a particular disease. Our own researches on the Fusarium foot rot of bean are of interest in this connection, even though they do not yet supply all the answers.

Nature of Antagonism

An attempt has been made to understand the manner in which the foot rot of bean, caused by *Fusarium solani* f. *phaseoli*, is reduced when barley or wheat straw is added to Fusarium-infested field soil.

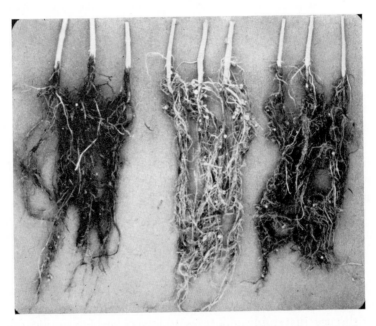

Fɪɢ. 1.   Influence of organic matter added to infested field soil in greenhouse tests on the development of Fusarium root rot of bean. The disease has been increased (left) by the addition of a green barley cover crop, and decreased (center) by the addition of mature barley straw. No amendment was added to the control (right). (Photgraph courtesy of Milton N. Shroth.)

This work stems from the observation in Monterey County, California, that the severe reduction in yield and quality of small, white, dry beans which follows from continuous cropping to beans, is temporarily corrected by rotation with barley. Growers have increased the yield of dry beans several hundred pounds per acre on heavily infested land by growing a single

rotation crop of barley for grain. Stubble of the mature grain crop is turned under the soil just prior to preparation of the land for beans.

In greenhouse experiments on naturally infested field soil, the addition of 1 per cent mature barley straw markedly reduces foot rot on beans subsequently planted in it. Alfalfa straw, applied at the same rate, however, not only fails to exert control but also may actually increase the severity of the disease. Strangely enough, green barley tends to act more like the alfalfa than the mature barley straw. Of the many kinds of natural organic matter that have been tried, mature straws of the cereals (barley, wheat, and oats) have given the most benefit. These effects are shown in Fig. 1.

However, when the cereal straws in mature form are added to field soil in any large amount there is a tendency for beans growing in it to become somewhat yellow and stunted. That this is due to a nitrogen deficiency induced by the straw is indicated by the fact that the addition of a nitrogen supplement to the soil, with straw, corrects the condition. But in correcting the deficiency symptoms, the beneficial effect of the straw in preventing foot rot is eliminated. If the straw is thoroughly leached with water before adding it to the soil, bean growth appears normal, and the protection against foot rot is retained. Among the materials leached from the straw are soluble carbohydrates. Pure cellulose has been found to give about the same protection as leached barley straw.

A way has now been found to use nitrogen in the soil to maintain proper color and growth of the beans and at the same time to take advantage of a straw additive for foot rot control. The procedure for this consists in placing the nitrogen deep in the soil, in a relatively insoluble form yet where the bean roots can reach and draw upon it. This leaves the upper layer of soil with its straw supplement relatively free of nitrogen. Under these conditions the plant grows vigorously and the incidence of foot rot remains low.

There is not yet enough data available from which to draw definite conclusions about the nature of antagonism, but it is

interesting to consider the implications of these crop refuse experiments on the control of Fusarium foot rot of bean. It would appear now that *Fusarium solani* f. *phaseoli* requires an outside source of nitrogen in order to attack a bean plant with vigor. It is not enough for the plant itself to have an ample supply of nitrogen. A plant fed nitrogen through its lower root system still is protected against foot rot by the addition of straw to the upper soil layer. Hence it is possible to reduce foot rot in the field to a minimum by keeping the top layer of soil low in soluble nitrogen while feeding nitrogen to the plant either through deep soil applications or through the foliage.

Bean foot rot in some ways is suggestive of the take-all disease of wheat caused by *Ophiobolus graminis*. Garrett (3) reports that organic manures low in available nitrogen reduce longevity of the fungus when added to infested soils, whereas those high in available nitrogen produce the contrary effect. Furthermore, nitrogen made available to the wheat plant enables it to withstand better the attacks of the fungus because of root stimulation. Thus, it would seem that both take-all of wheat and foot rot of bean could be reduced in the field by keeping down the supply of available nitrogen in the shallow zone of fungus infection, without interference with the nitrogen fertilization of the plant itself.

In terms of antagonism it appears clear that competition for nutrients, in this case, nitrogen, is operative through elements of the soil microbial population. Nitrogen is tied up in the process of their decomposing cereal straws. Thus the Fusarium is deprived, in the presence of straw, of an adequate supply of nitrogen needed in an attack on the living bean plant. This does not mean that the fungus is completely unable to infect in the absence of nitrogen, but rather that nitrogen is needed for a damaging invasion. Alfalfa straw carries with it sufficient nitrogen to supply both the needs of Fusarium for pathogenesis and the needs of the microorganisms of the soil which decompose the straw. This accounts for the accentuation of foot rot occasioned by the addition of alfalfa straw to infested soil. Conversely, when alfalfa straw is thoroughly leached with water

to remove soluble materials before adding it to infested soil, foot rot is reduced rather than accentuated.

It would be oversimplification of the problem to suggest that the total effect of a straw additive in reducing foot rot is only one kind of antagonism—that of competition for nutrients. Many organisms have been recovered from decomposing straw in these experiments and shown to produce substances detrimental to growth of the pathogen. It is possible that parasitism of the Fusarium also takes place with the increased competitive activity of the soil flora and fauna.

One is left to conclude that the total antagonism potential of soil upon which the plant pathologist may draw is enormous. The soil abounds with powerful antagonists which compete with, parasitize, or poison plant pathogens. These antagonists are selective for the pathogens they antagonize; they are selective for the kinds of organic materials upon which they thrive; and they are antagonized in turn by other elements of the flora of the soil even as they antagonize. The opportunities for playing one soil organism against another to man's advantage are there, and only await man's cleverness in dealing with antagonists.

REFERENCES

1. Bega, Robert, 1954. Biological control of Fusarium wilt of sweet potato. (Abstr.) *Phytopathology* 44:482 (1954).
2. Ferguson, John. Beneficial soil microörganisms. In "The U. C. System for Producing Healthy Container-Grown Plants," Kenneth F. Baker, Editor. *Calif. Agr. Expt. Sta. Manual 23*: 237-254 (1957).
3. Garrett, S. D. *Biology of the Root-Infecting Fungi.* Cambridge University Press, Cambridge, England, 1956.
4. McClure, T. T. Fusarium foot rot of sweet-potato sprouts. *Phytopathology* 41:72-77 (1951).
5. Millard, W. A. Common scab of potatoes. *Ann. Appl. Biol. 10*: 70-88 (1923).
6. Millard, W. A., and C. B. Taylor. Antagonism of micro-organisms as the controlling factor in the inhibition of scab by green-manuring. *Ann. Appl. Biol. 14*:202-216 (1927).

7. Oswald, John W., and O. A. Lorenz. Soybeans as a green manure crop for the prevention of potato scab. (Abstr.) *Phytopathology* 46:22 (1956).

8. Sanford, G. B. Some factors affecting the pathogenicity of *Actinomyces scabies. Phytopathology* 16:525-547 (1926).

9. Sanford, G. B., and W. C. Broadfoot. Studies of the effects of other soil-inhabiting micro-organisms on the virulence of *Ophiobolus graminis* Sacc. *Sci. Agr.* 11:512-528 (1931).

10. Skinner, F. A. Inhibition of *Fusarium culmorum* by *Streptomyces albidoflavus. Nature* 172:1191 (1953).

11. Tveit, M., and R. K. S. Wood. The control of *Fusarium* blight in oat seedlings with antagonistic species of *Chaetomium. Ann. Appl. Biol.* 43:538-552 (1955).

12. Wood, R. K. S., and M. Tveit. Control of plant diseases by use of antagonistic organisms. *Botan. Rev.* 21:441-492 (1955).

13. Zentmyer, George A., and Albert O. Paulus. Phytophthora avocado root rot. *Calif. Agr. Expt. Sta. Circ. 465,* 1957

Pathogens for the Control of Pests

JOHN D. BRIGGS*

*Illinois Natural History Survey,
Urbana, Illinois*

The term "microbial control" as first used by Steinhaus (21) best expresses the idea of utilizing microorganisms for the control of pests. Microbial control of insects is demonstrated in nature by the natural dissemination of pathogens causing frequent outbreaks of infectious diseases leading to epizootics. Diseases thus play an important role in regulating natural insect populations.

The distribution of pathogens by man to control insect pests is becoming a common practice. This brief discussion is intended to give the reader some awareness of recent developments and the present status of pathogens for the control of insects. A history of microbial control is provided by Steinhaus (24). From the extensive literature available on each group of insect pathogens only publications that serve as examples are cited.

Nematodes

Insect pathologists in the United States Department of Agriculture laboratories at Beltsville, Maryland, recently isolated a microscopic nematode parasite from larvae of the codling moth (12). The effectiveness of the nematode in killing its host is dependent to a large degree on a species of bacteria carried within the body of the nematode. In penetrating the body wall of its host, the nematode fatally infects the insect with the

* Present address: Bioferm Corporation, Wasco, California.
Special thanks are due Dr. Jaroslav Weiser, Czechoslovakia; Dr. Jost Franz, Germany; and Dr. P. Grison, France, for their generosity in furnishing information on recent developments in Europe.

bacteria. Screening tests show that this nematode pathogen attacks a wide variety of insects. Investigations are in progress to develop a method for culturing the nematode outside a living host. Discovery of an economical substitute medium will bring within the scope of all entomologists an aggressive pathogen for use in the microbial control of certain insects. Nematode parasites are particularly interesting as control agents because their motility allows them greater opportunity than some other pathogens to contact a host.

Culture of nematode parasites outside the hosts is a prerequisite to their economical use in control programs. Nearly thirty years ago in the United States, a nematode pathogenic for the Japanese beetle was successfully cultured on a substitute medium. However, production was not enough to insure the nematode a permanent place in the commercial control of Japanese beetle grubs, especially in view of other microbial control measures which were found to be more efficient.

Use of a nematode parasite in reducing populations of the sawfly *Acantholyda nemoralis* Pol. was reported by Weiser and Kohler (37). This pathogen of the sawfly belongs to the same genus (*Neoaplectana*) as that attacking the Japanese beetle.

A review of the entomophagous nematodes by Welch (35) provides sound background information necessary to perpetuate the renewed activity in this branch of microbial control.

Protozoa

The order Microsporidia in the class Sporozoa includes the most important protozoan parasites of insects. Representatives of this order are found within virtually every order of insects in addition to a wide variety of other invertebrates.

A microsporidian disease of an important lepidopterous insect in the United States is that of the European corn borer (*Pyrausta nubilalis* Hbn.) caused by *Perezia pyraustae* Pail. This parasite may be found in nearly every population of the European corn borer. Recent studies (18, 41) have shown this disease significantly reduces the egg-laying potential of the host. In addition, infected larvae are more limited in their

ability to withstand temperature extremes than are uninfected larvae.

The chronic nature of this and other protozoan diseases of insects would appear to limit their use when compared to acute infections caused by other pathogens. However, a study by Weiser and Rosicky (38) showed that reduced amounts of chemical insecticides are needed to kill sugar beet weevils (*Otiorrhynchus ligustici* L.) which are infected by a microsporidian pathogen (*Nosema otiorrhynchi* Weiser). This report from Czechoslovakia opens new possibilities in control practices.

The artificial distribution of microsporidian pathogens of the brown tail moth (*Euproctis chrysorrhoea* Don.) and the fall webworm (*Hyphantria cunea* Drury) is being studied by Weiser (36). Stocks of the pathogens for dissemination were accumulated either by collection of infected individuals in nature or rearing diseased hosts in the laboratory.

In the light of present knowledge, commercial availability of microsporidian pathogens for the control of insects must, as in the case of other obligate parasites, await the development of insect tissue culture.

Viruses

In the last decade, work with virus diseases of insects destructive to forests in North America (6) and forage crops in the western United States (31, 32) provide outstanding examples of success. The virus diseases of insects are exceedingly virulent. However, against a few noxious insects, the use of a virus disease is not entirely practical. This is the case because of the time necessary (perhaps a matter of days) for the disease to kill or cause an interruption of the insect's activities. The time factor may not be critical on a crop grown over a number of years. In forests, for example, the loss of some foliage can be tolerated during the incubation period of the disease. On the other hand, the amount of damage done to an annual crop during this period could render it unmarketable. The corn earworm (*Heliothis zea* Bod.) in ears of corn or tomato fruit are

examples of situations in which a long incubation period for a disease is not acceptable. On alfalfa, a perennial yielding several crops per year in some areas, efficient microbial control of the alfalfa caterpillar (*Colias philodice eurytheme* Boisd.) only follows proper timing of the introduction of the disease into the insect population.

On a perennial crop, dead and dying insects will contaminate food of subsequent pest generations thus perpetuating the disease. This is generally not the case on an annual crop product where the dead insect may actually pay a disservice by its presence, as on a processed food in which animal parts cannot be tolerated (23).

In the virus pathogens of insects we have an insecticidal material which might be characterized as possessing a low "lethal dose" but a relatively high "lethal time." Consequently, much of the applied research underway reflects the opinion that, where time is not critical, the insect viruses are virtually unrivaled as control agents.

A comprehensive annotated list of insects reported to have virus diseases was published by Hughes (17). In Egypt, Abul-Nasr (1) reported a virus disease of the cotton leafworm (*Prodenia litura* F.) which may have a great potential against this pest in cotton. Tschugunin (33) got good results with aerial sprays of virus against larvae of the gypsy moth, *Porthetria dispar* (L.), in the Crimea. A water suspension of crushed dead larvae was applied over large forest areas. The Hungarian government, according to Weiser (36), has patented the use of virus against the fall webworm. Quantities of the pathogen are produced in live host larvae by the Phylaxia Serum Institute in Budapest. Dr. Machay, who is engaged in the Hungarian virus study, has several papers in press on this microbial control program. In the western United States, the studies of Clark and Reiner (10) and Hall (14) have indicated the use of viruses to control the Great Basin tent caterpillar, *Malacosoma fragile* (Stretch), and the cabbage looper, *Trichoplusia ni* (Hbn.), respectively.

A forerunner of any commercial production of insect viruses

is research on culture of host insect tissue. Success in culture of host tissue suitable for virus growth would free the producer from the obligation of rearing the entire host insect for virus production in a particular tissue. At the present time in the United States there are intensive studies in progress on insect tissue culture in the Laboratory of Insect Pathology at the University of California. In the Insect Pathology laboratory at Sault St. Marie, Canada, fundamental work is also in progress on the development of insect viruses in their hosts, the physiology of insect viruses, and the biochemistry of pathogen-host relationships during the process of virus infection. It is only through studies such as these that a genuine understanding of insect viruses and effective use of their full potential in microbial control will be forthcoming.

Fungi

Many of the early attempts at microbial control of insects were with entomogenous fungi. A number of these early projects failed. Such early failures played a large part in the hesitancy exhibited thereafter by entomologists in this research area. Consequently it is encouraging to note the amount of field testing reported recently with entomogenous fungi. Despite the important environmental factors (moisture, temperature) which may limit the effectiveness of entomogenous fungi, their efficiency qualifies these fungi to be seriously considered in the microbial control of insects. However, so that we do not fall into the same pitfalls of earlier workers, particular care must be taken in selecting situations where as many factors as possible are understood which will insure the successful operation of the fungi.

An excellent example of success through careful study and selection of an insect and environment is the control of first-generation European corn borer larvae through the use of the fungus *Beauvaria* sp. (40). First generation corn borers spend a short period of their early development in the center leaf whorl of the immature corn plant. The free moisture, elevated temperature, and number of larvae concentrated in the plant

whorl provided the optimum conditions for operation of the entomogenous fungus. For the case in point, the spores of *Beauvaria* sp. were artificially distributed in a powder form. Thus by an understanding of the insect's habits and the factors necessary for fungus development, the entomologist was able to exploit a situation where a region of optimum conditions was common to both insect and pathogen.

In California a striking reduction in populations of the spotted alfalfa aphid, *Therioaphis maculata* (Buckton), has resulted from parasitization by fungi of the genus *Entomophthora* (16). It was found necessary on occasion to manipulate the environmental conditions in alfalfa fields by irrigation in order to raise the humidity and increase the spread of the fungus (15). With the insects, the pathogens, and the correct conditions, the desired results were forthcoming.

Fungus pathogens of insects are not always used by themselves in control programs. In Czechoslovakia (36), *Beauvaria bassiana* (Bals.) was used in combination with an unidentified insecticide on the sugar beet moth, *Gnorimoschema ocellatellum* Boyd. Telenga (30), in the Soviet Union, reported good results with a combination control measure against the beet root weevil, *Bothynoderes punctiventris* (L.). Three materials were used, two fungi, *B. bassiana* and *Metarrhizium anisopliae* (Metsch.), and the chemical insecticide lindane.

The need for basic information on all insect pathogens is great; with the entomogenous fungi, the problem is particularly pressing. To be sure, much will be learned by using them; however, the real advances will come as a result of research on the physiology, nutrition, and spore germination of these fungi. In addition, an understanding is needed of those factors that influence infection, reproduction, and dispersal of these pathogens in the field. Many of these factors are subjects of study by Canadian insect pathologists. Of vital importance are studies on differences in pathogenicity within and between species of entomogenous fungi. Research of this nature is in progress at the United States Department of Agriculture laboratories at Beltsville.

The application of various fungi to control other inverte-brate pests should not be overlooked. A comprehensive and fascinating work by Duddington (11) treats the microbial con-trol of plant parasitic nematodes with pathogenic fungi.

Bacteria

Of the bacteria pathogenic for insects, the sporeforming species belonging to the genus *Bacillus* possess a combination of desirable attributes. These pathogens are easily cultured on artificial media, and form a resistant stage which allows great versatility in formulations in addition to acting as a material with a residual property. When ingested by a susceptible host, these bacilli are virtually unrivaled in the speed with which insects are affected. Many times symptoms are evident within a matter of hours.

A long list of insects are affected by members of the genus *Bacillus*. One insect used as a classical example of microbial control by bacteria is the Japanese beetle, *Popillia japonica* New. The larvae of the beetle succumb to infection by *Bacillus popilliae* Dutky, commonly known as "milky disease."

Another member of the genus, *B. thuringiensis* Berliner, has and is continuing to create a great deal of interest as an insect pathogen. This species has been reported to be pathogenic to several scores of insects. Recently a mimeographed list of insects susceptible to *B. thuringiensis* and closely related species was issued by Steinhaus (25).

Because of its versatility, *B. thuringiensis* is being field tested in a number of countries almost exclusively against noxious lepidopterous larvae. Published reports from France (5) and Germany (19) indicate success in experimental trials on larvae of the cabbage butterfly, *Pieris brassicae* L. Vasiljevic (34) re-ports similarly on tests to control the fall webworm in Yugo-slavia. In the Soviet Union, *B. dendrolimus* has been used successfully against a tent caterpillar *Dendrolimus sibiricus* on conifers (28).

Workers have been experimenting with *B. thuringiensis* against lepidopterous pests on cabbage in Hawaii (29), forage

crop insects in California (22), the European corn borer in Iowa and Illinois (7, 39), and for the control of hornworms, *Protoparce* spp., on tobacco in North Carolina (20).

With the amount of research on sporeforming bacteria, it is refreshing to note that work on the nonsporeforming bacterial pathogens of insects is not neglected. In the Entomology Laboratory at Belleville, Ontario, Canada, studies on a nonsporeforming bacterium pathogenic for grasshoppers is particularly important (9). Stephens (27) contributed to a better understanding of the possible use of nonsporulating bacteria by a study on their survival after air drying.

The faculties which may be possessed by insects to acquire immunity to microbial pathogens deserve close study. There has been no authenticated instance of an insect acquiring immunity to a pathogen in nature. It has been demonstrated that some insects do have the ability to acquire tolerances to injected pathogens (8). These studies indicate that the acquired activity may be demonstrated *in vitro*.

Several closely related species of the genus *Bacillus* possess the ability to form a "crystal" or paraspore which develops in addition to the spore within each sporulating cell. The crystals are thought to be intimately associated with the pathogenicity of those species in the so-called crystal bearing complex. Studies are in various stages of completion on the nature (chemical, structural, morphological) of the crystals which appear to be concentrations of bacterial toxin (2–4, 13). The possibility of toxic materials produced by insect pathogens being of practical importance as insecticides should not be lightly dismissed. The promise such materials hold only time and research will tell.

The adaptability and ease of production of some sporeforming bacteria has aroused interest in the ranks of industry. The result is that several companies have produced experimental quantities of powders consisting principally of *B. thuringiensis* spores. Laboratory and field testing of this new insecticide was extensive during 1958 at a number of state agricultural experiment stations in the United States. In December 1958 the Food and Drug Administration granted the first temporary exemp-

tion from a tolerance for a microbial insecticide on a wide group of food and forage crops. This significant stride in microbial control was achieved by Bioferm Corporation, Wasco, California, with the *Bacillus thuringiensis* spore preparation called Thuricide.

The commercial availability of a material for the biological control of an insect is not new. For a number of years, a compound containing spores of *Bacillus popillae* has been available on the retail market for the microbial control of the Japanese beetle. However, a significant factor is that *B. thuringiensis* is cultured on artificial media whereas the Japanese beetle pathogen must be cultured in the host insect. The use of artificial media, combined with efficient industrial methods could conceivably guarantee an unlimited supply of an insect pathogen at a reasonable price for use in control programs.

The use of insect pathogens to control insects on agricultural crops has brought to light many points which deserve careful consideration. Steinhaus (26) gives an excellent and exhaustive coverage to the problems, issues, and questions which have arisen on the safety and standardization of microbial control agents.

Conclusion

Availability of materials with which to work is the limiting factor in many insect control programs. The recent interest of some branches of the pharmaceutical and fermentation industry in producing pathogens for pest control is the first step in relieving this difficulty. The commercially produced materials bring with them all the problems, and more, faced by the chemical industry in introducing a chemical insecticide. Not the least of these is assay of the product with subsequent standardization, difficult enough for chemicals but confounded in this situation by a living organism with inherent variability.

With a possible source of quantities of living agents in the near future, the agricultural or medical entomologist may have the opportunity to use them to supplement and in some cases replace chemical insecticides. Contrary to some opinions, mi-

crobial control measures pose no serious threat to the chemical industry but afford yet another means for the economic entomologist to do a difficult job more efficiently and safely. Their nontoxicity to warm-blooded animals, other vertebrates, and plants, as well as their specificity for use with parasitic and predaceous insects will be great assets in widespread selective insect control programs.

Most of the applied studies in the use of pathogens have been with phytophagous pests of agricultural importance. Insects of medical and public health importance form a large group which have been generally neglected with respect to their microbial control. In this area unprecedented research opportunities await the investigator, and great contributions to mankind seem assured.

REFERENCES

1. Abul-Nasr, S. E. Polyhedrosis-virus disease on cotton leaf-worm, *Prodenia litura* F. *Bull. Soc. Entomol. Egypte* 40:321-332 (1956).

2. Angus, T. A. General characteristics of certain insect pathogens related to *Bacillus cereus*. *Can. J. Microbiol.* 2:111-121 (1956).

3. ———. Association of toxicity with protein-crystalline inclusions of *Bacillus sotto* Ishiwata. *Can. J. Microbiol.* 2:122-131 (1956).

4. ———. Extraction, purification, and properties of *Bacillus sotto* toxin. *Can. J. Microbiol.* 2:416-426 (1956).

5. Beguin, S., and D. Martouret. Essais de traitement microbiologique par poudrage. *IVᵉ Congrès International de lutte contre les ennemis des Plantes.* Hamburg, September 1957.

6. Bird, F. T. The use of a virus disease in the biological control of the European pine sawfly, *Neodiprion sertifer* (Geoffr.). *Can. Entomologist* 85:437-446 (1953).

7. Briggs, J. D. Unpublished data, 1956.

8. ———. Humoral immunity in lepidopterous larvae. *J. Exptl. Zool.* 138:155-188 (1958).

9. Bucher, G. E., and J. M. Stephens. A disease of grasshoppers caused by the bacterium *Pseudomonas aeruginosa* (Schroeter) Migula. *Can. J. Microbiol.* 3:611-625 (1957).

10. Clark, E. C., and C. E. Reiner. The possible use of a polyhedrosis virus in the control of Great Basin tent caterpillar. *J. Econ. Entomol.* 49:653-659 (1956).

11. Duddington, C. L. *The Friendly Fungi.* Faber and Faber, London, 1957.

12. Dutky, S. R., and W. S. Hough. Note on a parasitic nematode from codling moth larvae, *Carpocapsa pomonella. Proc. Entomol. Soc. Wash.* 57:244 (1955).

13. Fitz-James, P. C., C. Toumanoff, and I. E. Young. Localization of a toxicity for silkworm larvae in the parasporal inclusion of *Bacillus cereus* var. *alesti. Can. J. Microbiol.* 4:385-392 (1958).

14. Hall, I. M. Use of a polyhedrosis virus to control the cabbage looper on lettuce in California. *J. Econ. Entomol.* 50:551-553 (1957).

15. Hall, I. M., and P. H. Dunn. Fungi on spotted alfalfa aphid. *Calif. Agr.* 11(2):5 (1957).

16. ———. Entomophthorous fungi parasitic on the spotted alfalfa aphid. *Hilgardia* 27:159-181 (1957).

17. Hughes, K. M. An annotated list and bibliography of insects reported to have virus diseases. *Hilgardia* 26:597-629 (1957).

18. Kramer, J. P. Some relationships between *Perezia pyraustae* Paillot (Sporozoa, Nosematidae) and *Pyrausta nubilalis* Hübner (Lepidoptera, Pyralidae). *J. Insect. Pathol.* 1:25-33 (1959).

19. Krieg, A. Über die Moglichkeit einer Bekampfung des Kohlweisslings (*Pieris brassicae*) durch kunstliche Berbreitung einer Bakteriose. *Z. Pflanzenkrankh. u. Pflanzenschutz* 64: 321-327 (1957).

20. Rabb, R. L., E. A. Steinhaus, and F. E. Guthrie. Preliminary tests using *Bacillus thuringiensis* Berliner against hornworms. *J. Econ. Entomol.* 50:259-262 (1957).

21. Steinhaus, E. A. *Principles of Insect Pathology.* McGraw-Hill Book Co., New York, 1949.

22. ———. Possible use of *Bacillus thuringiensis* Berliner as an aid in the biological control of the alfalfa caterpillar. *Hilgardia* 20:359-381 (1951).

23. ———. Potentialities for microbial control of insects. *Agr. Food Chem.* 4:676-680 (1956).

24. ———. Microbial control—the emergence of an idea. *Hilgardia* 26:107-160 (1956).

25. ———. List of insects and their susceptibility to *Bacillus thuringiensis* Berliner and closely related bacteria. No. 4, Mimeo. ser. Laboratory Insect Pathology, University of California, Berkeley, Calif., 1957.

26. ———. Concerning the harmlessness of insect pathogens and the standardization of microbial control products. *J. Econ. Entomol.* 50:715-720 (1957).

27. Stephens, J. M. Survival of *Pseudomonas aeruginosa* (Schroeter) Migula suspended in various solutions and dried in air. *Can. J. Microbiol.* 3:995-1000 (1957).

28. Talalaev, E. V. On the artificial induction of epizootia of septicaemia in caterpillars of *Dendrolimus sibiricus*. *Entomologitscheskoe obozrenije* 36:845-859 (1957) (in Russian).

29. Tanada, Y. Microbial control of some lepidopterous pests of crucifers. *J. Econ. Entomol.* 49:320-329 (1956).

30. Telenga, N. A. Today's state and perspectives of the use of biological means for control of the beet root weevil and the codling moth. Conference for problems of the biological control of noxious insects. Leningrad, March 1957 (in Russian), 1957.

31. Thompson, C. G. Field tests during 1950 using a polyhedrosis virus to control the alfalfa caterpillar. *J. Econ. Entomol.* 44:225-226 (1951).

32. Thompson, C. G., and E. A. Steinhaus. Further tests using a polyhedrosis virus to control the alfalfa caterpillar. *Hilgardia* 19:411-445 (1950).

33. Tschugunin, J. V. Biological control of the codling moth. Conference for problems of the biological control of noxious insects. Leningrad, March 1957 (in Russian), 1957.

34. Vasiljevic, L. J. Les recherches sur la pathologie de l'Écaille filuse (*Hyphantria cunea* Dr.) en Yugoslavie. Ein Symposium uber insectenpathologie in Darmstadt, 1956. *Entomophaga* 1:98-100 (1956).

35. Welch, H. E. A review of recent work on nematodes associated with insects with regard to their utilization as biological control agents. *Proc. Tenth Intern. Congr. Entomol.* 4:863-868 (1958).

36. Weiser, J. Personal communication, 1957.

37. Weiser, J., and W. Kohler. Hlistice (Nematoda) jako cizopasnici larev ploskohrbetky, *Acantholyda nemoralis* Thoms. w Polsce., *Csl. parasitologie* 2:185-190 (1955).

38. Weiser, J., and B. Rosicky. Nosematosis of *Otiorrhynchus ligustici*, I and II. *Vestr. K Ces Koslov. zool. spol.* 15:209-234 (1951).

39. York, G. T. Personal communication, 1956.

40. ———. Field tests with the fungus *Beauvaria* sp. for control of the European corn borer. *Iowa State J. Sci.* 33:123-129 (1958).

41. Zimmack, H. L., and T. A. Brindley. The effect of the protozoan parasite *Perezia pyraustae* Paillot on the European corn borer. *J. Econ. Entomol.* 50:637-640 (1957).

Nutrition of the Host and Reaction to Pests

J. G. Rodriguez

University of Kentucky, Lexington

The green plant is a complex biochemical system that reacts to temperature, light, moisture, and nutrients. The well-being of a phytophagous pest depends in part upon the chemical makeup of its host. It is the purpose of this paper to discuss how nutritional changes in the host are generally brought about and how these nutrients may influence reactions of phytophagous insects or mites. Although this is a rather broad field, reviews of insect nutrition in general are available (19, 27, 80, 118, 119), as is a review dealing with the nutritional requirements of phytophagous insects (47). All reviewers agree that too little definite information is available as yet on the general subject of insect nutrition.

Effecting Nutritional Changes in the Host

Nutritional changes can be brought about in the host by feeding through the foliage (56, 85, 114). Insecticidal applications to the aerial parts of a plant can change its physiological makeup. For example, potato yields have been increased by insecticidal sprays to a much greater extent than was warranted by mere insect control, and this effect is believed to be due to nutritional value of the insecticide (126). The growth of potatoes, among other plants, has been stimulated by low concentrations of DDT, whereas higher levels produced stunting, injury, and chlorosis (25). Phosphatic insecticide sprays have increased the nitrate and sugar content of legumes (128). Fleschner (45) and other workers in California (59) have obtained evidence regarding the stimulative effect of DDT on mite populations in citrus and pear trees. They concluded that the effect is partially due to induced physiological changes in

the host plant. Morgan and co-workers (88, 89) found apple tree vigor increased with sprays of several fungicides. Maneb stimulated tree growth and resulted in larger leaves, generally denser and darker and able to withstand clover mite (*Bryobia praetiosa* Koch) infestations with little evidence of foliage damage. The same reaction to foliage occurred with ferbam and karathane sprays. Peak infestation of European red mite (*Panonychus ulmi* Koch) on ferbam-sprayed trees was two weeks later than that of the check plot.

The more conventional method of feeding plants, however, is through the roots, that is, the time-honored method of applying fertilizers to the soil or growth medium. Early insect nutrition experiments in artificial culture utilized cuttings in sand watered with various salt solutions (120). This evolved into the more precise method of artificial culture of plants in which mineral supply is measured (1, 2, 4, 5, 31, 35, 48, 52, 54, 65, 94, 95, 97, 103, 111, 127). Work is also continuing with addition of mineral fertilizers to the soil (3, 10, 11, 32, 35, 36, 40, 41, 48, 51, 58, 75, 83, 84, 96, 99, 111–113). It has been shown that mineral supply and mineral absorption may not be positively correlated because of antagonism that exists between ions or groups of ions (85, 94). Analysis of the host is valuable in this type of experimention (51, 94, 95, 106). The exact mineral requirements of any phytophagous pest are yet to be determined.

Soil treatments include insecticides as well as fertilizers. Applications of such insecticides have diversified effects on soil microorganisms such as nitrifying bacteria (12, 13, 68, 102, 105, 125). Klostermeyer and Rasmussen (76) thought that mite population increases brought on by soil insecticides were probably due to changes in plant nutrition or composition. The fact that soil insecticides actually do affect plant composition has been shown in our laboratory (98). Chlorinated hydrocarbons added to the soil affected plant composition and *Tetranychus telarius* population in diverse ways on Black Valentine beans, soybeans, and cotton. BHC and lindane produced the most striking changes, followed by chlordane, aldrin, dieldrin, and

DDT. Plant growth was stimulated at low levels of application and suppressed at high levels. Generally, increased populations were associated with stimulation of growth and depressed nitrogen content. Decreased populations were associated with increased nitrogen and phosphorus, or growth suppression, or in some cases, both. *T. telarius* appeared to be more sensitive than *T. tumidus* to soil insecticides on cotton. When soil insecticides were applied to apple trees (Rodriguez, unpublished data) the NPK composition of the foliage was significantly affected only by parathion at extremely high levels, although DDT at moderately high dosages increased *T. telarius* populations. Investigations concerning the effects of soil insecticides on the sugar content of plants have been initiated in our laboratory, and it has been found that DDT in the soil increased the sugar content of Black Valentine beans and soybeans.

A precursor to the present day systemic insecticides was selenium; this element was shown to replace sulfur in the plant (60). The use of selenium as a pesticide (42, 61, 90, 91) has been largely discontinued because of its peculiar toxicity to mammals. Work by Hacskaylo (49) has demonstrated that one systemic pesticide (thimet) changes the composition of the young cotton plant by increasing carbohydrates and phosphorus and decreasing nitrogen; another (schradan) increases soluble nitrogen, chlorophyll, and carotenoid pigments and reduces total sugars. Casida and co-workers (20, 21) found that schradan also interacts with phosphorus in absorption by the roots of plants. As phosphorus was increased in the nutrient solutions in which pea plants were grown, per cent phosphorus increased in the plants and per cent schradan decreased. The insecticidal activity of the plant was thus decreased by higher levels of phosphorus. Hacskaylo and Ergle (50) found the same interaction of schradan with phosphorus as well as with nitrogen, in the cotton plant, but little or no interaction with potassium.

Of course, the composition of the plant changes from day to day and even within the day, through the action of light, temperature, nutrients, and water. A deficiency of water causes

diverse effects on the host; in some species, the nitrate uptake of plants exceeds the capacity of the drought-stricken foliage to reduce it (46, 85, 86). A moderate loss of water in the leaf causes the change from sugar to starch; a more pronounced loss causes the reverse reaction (85). It is a common occurrence for mites to develop in high numbers in orchards and field crops under drought conditions; this may be partially due to favorable nutrition. It has been demonstrated that increased oviposition occurs in a dry atmosphere (17, 124). Water deficiency has been associated with cannibalism and irritability in grasshoppers (110), also with reduced size in immature forms of the variegated cutworm (107). This is not unexpected, since phytophagous insects normally feed on a diet high in water content.

General Host Differences

Of some significance to this discussion were the findings that some insects including grasshoppers, the cotton bollworm, the variegated cutworm, the European corn borer, and wireworms (15, 16, 37, 55, 64, 107, 110) developed more favorably on certain species of host plants. The differential development is not to be confused with host plant perception (39) or with resistance (92). The preferred host of an insect in a given situation may not coincide with the optimum nutritional condition (110). However, Thorsteinson (115, 116) suggests that there is considerable correlation between the chemotactic stimuli that govern feeding and the nutritional requirements of insects. He has been able to elicit feeding responses from both polyphagous and oligophagous forms, by using nutrients such as thiamin, ascorbic acid, sugars, betaine, and monosodium glutamate. He also points out that in oligophagous species the additional effect of (token) phagostimulants is generally involved. Beck's work with the nutrition of the European corn borer using purified diets has also shown that nutrients can act as feeding stimulants. The most pronounced effects were from sugars, and he expresses this behavior of larvae to sugars as "saccharotropism." Larval saccharotropism is evident in

early instars though the requirement for sugar was negligible at that stage. The borer tends to concentrate its feeding on the tissues containing the highest levels of total sugar, after its initial reactions to light and contact pressure have been satisfied. In later instars the requirement for sugar is high, and Beck suggests that saccharotropism manifested in the early instars may lead the borer to parts of the plant which will satisfy this later requirement (6–9).

Dahms and co-workers (30, 34) discerned that differences in resistance to attack, chinch bug development, and plant injury were due to variety and age of sorghum plants. Oviposition and longevity of the bugs increased as the plant became older. Other workers have conducted extensive studies of the chemical composition of sorghum in an effort to ascertain whether differences in nutrients were associated with the extent of chinch bug injury. Results, although contributing valuable information on plant composition, did not reveal any consistent or significant differences that could be correlated with injury (121–123).

Differences in Parts of Plants

Different parts of the same plant present differences in nutritional effects to the pest. With the European corn borer, corn leaves relatively high in protein and low in sugar produced high survival but low weights of larvae, while internodes higher in sugar, low in protein, produced high weights and low survival. Kernels produced high weights and survival (16). In the opinion of Luckmann (81), the growth and development of the tassel and the shedding of pollen are perhaps the most important functions of the corn plant relative to survival of the borer. He showed that when young corn plants nutritionally inadequate for the borer were dusted with pollen from more mature plants, the borers were able to survive. Chant (23) found that phytoseiid mites, which are predators of orchard mites, did not survive very long on plant juices but were able to survive on apple pollen, and undoubtedly do so in the spring until animal proteins become available. Analysis of pollen (117)

indicated that the crude protein percentage is approximately that of other good vegetable proteins. These findings are in line with those of Dahms and Painter (33) that aphids confined on flowering branches of alfalfa reproduced much faster than those confined to vegetative branches of the same plant.

Kennedy and co-workers reported that aphids preferred flowering parts of the sugar beet, also that aphids were distributed on sugar beet and spindle bushes in relation to leaf age (63, 70, 71). Growing and senescing leaves were more susceptible to *Myzus persicae* (Sulz) colonization while *Aphis fabae* Scop. found leaves more suitable when young or just after maturity (73). Leaf analysis is difficult in this problem because leaves in a given state are used as units. He collected phloem sap and aphid honeydew and used paper partition chromatography to determine that the amino content of the honeydew closely paralleled that of sap, also that the amino acid content of sap was higher during growth and senescence than at other developmental stages of the plant (72, 87).

Other workers have related leaf age to reactions of mites. Young citrus leaves are more favorable than mature leaves for the development of the citrus red mite (*M. citri*) (53, 66, 67). The clover mite (*Bryobia praetiosa* Koch) lived longer and laid almost ten times as many eggs when it was reared on "new" apple foliage containing 2.14 per cent nitrogen compared to "old" leaves containing 1.40 per cent (106).

Effect of Inorganic Nutrients

A large portion of the work relating to nutrition of the host and reaction to pests has utilized artificial culture as a means of regulating nutrients. Unfortunately, much of this work has not been accompanied by analyses of plant parts. Such analyses are valuable, since interionic relationships can vary under different conditions. Under such conditions, mineral supply and absorption may not be positively correlated (94). It follows that the organic constituents are affected also; data are not at present available on this important phase. It is recognized that the approach through nutrient culture is a compromise be-

tween, on one hand, purified or synthetic diet experiments and, on the other, experiments dealing with the application of inorganic fertilizers to the soil. It is possible to pinpoint specific nutritional requirements by using a chemically defined diet. With a phytophagous pest, this procedure must be accompanied by a thorough interpretation of the physiology of the host and the host-pest relationship if any practical application is to be made of the findings.

ON MITES

Early reports indicated that nutritional sprays of copper and zinc were associated with increased populations of the citrus red mite, and in the case of copper, increases of the rust mite (*Eriophyes oleivorus* (Ashm.)) (56, 112). Boron-deficient olive trees were observed to have a scarcity of the olive leaf Eriophyid (*Oxypleurites maxwelli* K.), which was common in healthy trees not boron-deficient (74).

Fertilizer treatments on beans and peach trees in sand culture resulted in heavy populations of *Tetranychus telarius* (L). as compared to the unfertilized treatments (48). In a study of fertilization practices, as measured by soil-soluble salts, in tomato hothouses, a positive relationship existed between populations of *T. telarius* and high concentrations of soil-soluble salts (96). In more critical studies we found that when the concentration of all the major elements was doubled on tomato plants grown in nutrient culture, the mite population was likewise doubled. Foliage analyses disclosed that nitrogen absorption was associated with phosphorus and boron absorption. Under such a condition nitrogen and boron were negatively correlated with mite development. Phosphorus was likewise negatively correlated with mite development when foliage analyzed 0.3 per cent or more phosphorus; ranges below that amount produced a positive correlation. Potassium absorption, although antagonistic to magnesium and calcium absorption, was generally positively related to mite development. Potassium may be indirectly an important factor from the standpoint of its influence on nitrogen metabolism.

In studies with the comparative NPK nutrition of the European red mite, *Panonychus ulmi* Koch, and the two-spotted spider mite, *Tetranychus telarius* (L.) on apple trees, Rodriguez (95) found that increasing nitrogen from low to medium levels effected a statistically significant increase in both species, and very high nitrogen elicited a further increase from *T. telarius*. In apple foliage, nitrogen and phosphorus evidenced antagonism. This condition and the fact that the absorbed nitrogen in tomato was twice that in apple probably account for the fact that the relation of nitrogen to population was positive in apple and negative in tomato. In apple, as in tomato, the correlation between per cent phosphorus and populations was positive at the lower levels of absorption and negative when percentages somewhat higher than 0.20 were reached. *T. telarius* responded with more sensitivity than *P. ulmi* to changes in nitrogen supply and absorption. This sensitivity to nitrogen range may explain the common field observation that the two-spotted mites are capable of bronzing apple foliage after red mite populations have declined. Mite feeding lowers the chlorophyll content of the leaf, sometimes as much as 35 per cent (24, 79).

The leaf nitrogen in apple trees in the orchard is highest early in the season at about the same time that the European red mite reaches its peak population (51). *T. telarius* peaks generally come a little later when the nitrogen content is on the decline. A report from Russia indicated that the introduction of high rates of mineral fertilizer can increase the osmotic pressure of plant sap two to three times that of normal, and also increase populations of *T. urticae* Koch to high numbers (14). Water not being a limiting factor, it follows that turgor pressure may also be increased. This introduces the interesting possibility that mites not only obtain more favorable nutrients with increased fertilization but may also have the feeding process facilitated. It is recognized that mites may not depend on turgor pressure as do aphids (72), but they have been observed feeding from leaf veins on occasion and, of course, they leave foliage that has begun to wilt.

Recent work has shown that nutrition affects the susceptibility of mites to acaricides. When *T. telarius* resistant to organic phosphates were tested, nitrogen, phosphorus, and potassium all gave responses. The effect of nitrogen appeared to vary with the season; higher per cent kill was obtained on high nitrogen in the summer and on low nitrogen in the winter (54).

ON APHIDS

The general statement can be made that aphids respond positively to increased elements, particularly nitrogen. This is true of the bean aphid (*Aphis fabae* Scop.) (36), the cabbage aphid (*Brevicoryne brassicae* L.) (43), the cotton aphid (*Aphis gossypii* Saund.) (65, 83, 84), and the pea aphid (*Macrosiphum pisi* Harr.). Regarding the latter, some qualification is necessary. Barker and Tauber (4, 5) found fecundity decreased on deficient element supply, especially nitrogen and phosphorus, though the relationship with nitrogen could be changed under modified environmental conditions. Taylor and co-workers (111) were not able to find significant differences in reproductive capacity of either pea aphids or potato aphids under their environmental conditions of varied nitrogen, phosphorus, or potassium supply. Conflicting reports exist concerning the influence of nitrogen on greenbugs (*Toxoptera graminum* (Rond.)). The work reported by Haseman (52) disclosed that nitrogen or iron deficiencies in nutrient culture affected greenbug development on wheat adversely whereas deficiencies of sulfur, potassium, magnesium, or phosphorus had no apparent ill effects. In field tests on wheat Daniels (35) found greenbugs to be the highest, per linear row-foot, on the heaviest nitrogen treatment but least per gram of foliage. In the greenhouse, fewer greenbugs per gram of foliage and less plant damage occurred where nitrogen was included in the nutrient combinations, except for the nitrogen-calcium combination. Other workers concluded that populations and injury to rye, ryegrass, or oat plants are both decreased with nitrogen and calcium applied to soil or nutrient solutions, and the effects of the two

elements appear to be interrelated (3, 11). It is known that an insufficient supply of calcium interferes with translocation of carbohydrates and amino acids (85). Virtually no analyses of plant parts have been performed in connection with the aphid studies.

ON CHINCH BUGS

As on greenbugs, the effect of nitrogen on the chinch bug appears to differ with the host plant. Haseman (52) reported that nitrogen deficiency in the solutions on which corn was grown was beneficial to the bugs. Dahms and Fenton (32) found that nitrate fertilizer decreased resistance of sorghums to chinch bugs and phosphate increased it; later (31) in nutrient culture experiments, the bugs laid more eggs on sorghum plants growing in solutions high in nitrogen or low in phosphorus than on the same varieties growing in solutions low in nitrogen or high in phosphorus. In one variety, however, there was an indication that the maturity of the plant eventually reversed the reaction.

ON LEPIDOPTEROUS LARVAE

The addition of nitrogenous fertilizers on the mulberry tree produced leaves of high nitrogen and protein content, and silkworms raised thereon produced more silk (10). Legay (78), reviewing recent studies on the nutrition of the silkworm, states that supplementation by nitrogenous compounds on the mulberry leaf has a beneficial effect on rate of growth and silk production.

The Southern armyworm is able to utilize the nitrogen of protein, amino acids, and amides but not nitrates (29). Larval development is faster and mortality is less on plants supplied with large amounts of nitrate (127).

The addition of nitrogen to corn growing under markedly nitrogen-deficient conditions evidently changes the physical characteristics of the corn, indirectly resulting in less corn earworm damage. Very high nitrogen resulted in more damage than nitrogen in balance with the needs of the plant (41, 75).

The early investigators in corn borer (57, 58) speculated on the nutritional requirements of the borer and had data showing significantly more borers developing on fertilized fields than on unfertilized. The factors involved in this reaction are now known to be confounded with host selectivity and resistance; recent developments in corn borer nutrition pertinent to this paper have been covered earlier.

A case in which nitrogen indirectly influenced less peach tree borer establishment in the tree has been described (104). Nitrogen fertilization increased tree vigor, which in turn was positively correlated with borer infestation. This was attributed to more favorable conditions for oviposition and larval establishment on trees high in vigor.

The classic example of biological control of a noxious plant is that of the prickly pear in Australia (40). The prickly pear grown in poor soil was abnormally yellow and chlorotic and contained only about half as much nitrogen as pear growing in richer soil. *Cactoblastis cactorum* (Berg.) did not survive nearly so well on the yellowed pear as on the normal pear.

The larvae of the large white butterfly, *Pieris brassicae*, fed on cruciferous leaves grown in nitrogen- or iron-deficient solutions, showed reductions of larval weight and relative growth rate, increased larval mortality, and delayed pupation. Reduction of larval weight and delayed pupation also resulted on phosphorus-deficient and potassium-deficient solutions (2).

Copper and zinc deficiency increased the mortality rate of the cotton leafworm *Alabama argillacea* (Hbn.) (28).

Minor elements undoubtedly play a role in the problem, but there is a lack of information on this point.

ON OTHER INSECTS

An example of the reaction of a polyphagous pest to inorganic nutrient differences involved the grasshopper, *Melanoplus mexicanus mexicanus* (Sauss) (103). Wheat was grown on three levels of nitrogen and fed to the grasshopper. Per cent absorbed nitrogen was positively correlated with percentage adult survival, rapidity of development, and egg pro-

duction. There was no effect on hatchability, weight of adults, or sex ratio.

Mustard beetles fed leaves of watercress grown in solutions deficient in nitrogen, phosphorus, potassium, or iron produced significantly less eggs than the same beetles fed on full-nutrient leaves. Reduction occurred within two or three days after the change from full nutrients (1).

Among homopterous insects, the potato leafhopper reacted to copper sprays on beans and potatoes in such a way that toxicity was not noted initially but three to five days later. It was postulated that this was due to metabolic changes in the host plant (38).

Magnesium sprays to correct deficiency on grapefruit trees bring about heavy infestations of the purple scale (*Lepidosaphes beckii* Newm.) (114). Work in neglected apple orchards in Illinois has shown that trees invigorated by nitrogenous fertilizers were attacked by 50 per cent more scales, principally San Jose (*Aspidiotus perniciosus* Comst.) (22). Reaction to vigorous trees apparently is related to the shade-loving propensities of the scales.

Effect of Other Nutrients

Isolated reports of correlations of vitamins in the host plant with pest populations have been made. Increasing the nitrogen supply of tomato plants in nutrient culture increased the riboflavin and niacin content of the foliage. Niacin was negatively correlated with two-spotted spider mite population; riboflavin showed a negative trend. When phosphorus supply was increased, niacin at a lower range of elaboration was positively correlated with populations (97). A highly significant positive correlation between the carotene content of mature harvested corn grain of inbred lines and the aphid infestation that develops on the growing plant was found during one season in Pennsylvania (26).

Maltais (82) has increased the nutritional value of plant sap by placing pea plant cuttings in solutions of amino acids, peptone, and B vitamins. The aphids reared thereon developed

normally on the treated cuttings and showed increased body weight over the water controls. This work elucidates the results of the experiments wherein aphids were favorably influenced by increased nitrogen supply in nutrient culture.

Specialized Reactions

DIAPAUSE

Diapause in the pink bollworm (*Platyedra gossypiella,* Saund.) has been shown to be independent of seasonal or climatic conditions and caused by food of low moisture content. The moisture content of the boll depends on age of the cotton plant and the amount of water available. Percentage diapause is negatively correlated with the amount of water in the food. Diapause can be terminated by simply wetting the larvae (44, 108, 109).

Diapause in mites is the product of three environmental agencies, temperature, photoperiod, and nutrition. Lees (77) thinks that nutrition is the limiting factor; varying percentages of European red mite "winter females" appeared on senescing apple leaves though temperatures and photoperiod tended to prevent diapause. When the leaves are young or mature and undamaged, nutrition is not a factor and diapause depends solely on photoperiod and temperature. The two-spotted spider mite reacts in the same manner as does the legume mite (*Petrobia apicalis* Banks) common in the southern United States (18).

FORM DETERMINATION

The phenomenon of wing formation in parthenogenetic viviparous aphid females has received considerable attention. The natural tendency of the insect appears to be the wingless state, for the offspring of winged forms show a strong tendency to be wingless (101). The researches of Kennedy and Booth (69) require the production of apterous and alate virginoparous *Aphis fabae* on continuous demand. They have developed a technique of mass rearing which involves manipulating the

proportion of aphids to the available food, which is broad bean plants. When the food supply is plentiful, only apterous forms are produced. The number of alate forms which appear increases as the beans become older and the infestation denser.

Crowding has been reportedly a major factor in wing production (93). The separation of crowding and nutrition effects is difficult. An attempt to treat these factors independently was made by Shifflette (100), who subjected crowded and uncrowded cotton aphid colonies (*Aphis gossypii* Glov.) to the same dietary changes. He found that unless crowding was also present, his dietary changes did not result in winged forms. He also determined that a wing incitant, if produced at all by crowded colonies, was not translocated to another section of the leaf. Evans (43) found a negative correlation between per cent nitrogen in the host plant and wing formation in the cabbage aphid (*Brevicoryne brassicae* L.).

Conclusions

The following conservative conclusions can be made:

1. Aside from the addition of fertilizers and nutritional sprays, the nutrition of the host can be influenced by the application of insecticidal and fungicidal sprays and soil insecticides.

2. It is recognized that because of the complex interrelationships between elements in the plant, the exact mineral requirements of a particular pest are difficult if not impossible to determine when utilizing the host-pest nutritional relationship approach to the problem.

3. Valuable information is obtained, nevertheless, by such studies, and optimum ranges of nitrogen and phosphorus have been defined for one phytophagous mite, *T. telarius* (L.) and suggested for another, *P. ulmi* Koch.

4. There appears to be good basis for maintaining a conservative fertilization program which is not overbalanced in any one element. Several phytophagous pests benefit either directly or indirectly from an overbalance of nitrogen, for example, mites, aphids, chinch bugs, various lepidopterous larvae, various scales, and the lesser peach tree borer.

REFERENCES

1. Allen, M. D., and I. W. Selman. *Bull. Entomol. Research 46,* 393 (1955).
2. ———. *Bull. Entomol. Research 48,* 229 (1957).
3. Arant, F. S., and C. M. Jones. *J. Econ. Entomol. 44,* 121 (1951).
4. Barker, J. S., and O. E. Tauber. *J. Econ. Entomol. 44,* 1010 (1951).
5. ———. *J. Econ. Entomol. 47,* 113 (1954).
6. Beck, Stanley D. *Ann. Entomol. Soc. Am. 49,* 399 (1956).
7. ———. *Ann. Entomol. Soc. Am. 49,* 552 (1956).
8. ———. *Ann. Entomol. Soc. Am. 49,* 582 (1956).
9. Beck, S. D., J. H. Lilly, and J. F. Stauffer. *Ann. Entomol. Soc. Am. 42,* 483 (1949).
10. Bergmann, Werner. *Textile Research 10,* 462 (1940).
11. Blickenstaff, C. C., D. D. Morey, and Glenn W. Burton. *Agron. J. 46,* 338 (1954).
12. Bolen, W. B., H. E. Morrison, and H. H. Crowell. *J. Econ. Entomol. 47,* 302 (1954).
13. ———. *J. Econ. Entomol. 47,* 307 (1954).
14. Bondarenko, N. V. *The Spider Mite as a Pest of Hothouse Cultures in the Conditions of the Leningrad Area* (in Russian), (Abstr. Doctoral Dissertation, Ministry of Higher Education of U.S.S.R., Leningrad Agr. Inst., 1949).
15. Bottger, G. T. *J. Agr. Research 60,* 249 (1940).
16. ———. *J. Econ. Entomol. 44,* 40 (1951).
17. Boudreaux, H. Bruce. *J. Ins. Physiol. 2,* 65 (1958).
18. Brooking, B. C., Jr. *A Study of the Evocation and Termination of Diapause in Petrobia apicalis* (Banks) (*Acarina, Tetranychidae*) M.S. Thesis, L.S.U., 1957.
19. Brues, C. T. *Insect Dietary.* Harvard University Press, Cambridge, Mass., 1946.
20. Casida, J. E., and M. A. Stahmann. *Agr. Food Chem. 1,* 883 (1953).
21. Casida, J. E., R. K. Chapman, and T. C. Allen. *J. Econ. Entomol. 45,* 568 (1952).
22. Chandler, S. C., and Ron Meyer. Personal communication, 1957.
23. Chant, D. A. *Proc. Tenth Intern. Congr. Entomol.* (1956) *4,* 649 (1958).
24. Chapman, P. J., S. E. Lienk, and O. F. Curtis, Jr. *J. Econ. Entomol. 45,* 815 (1952).

25. Chapman, R. K., and T. C. Allen. *J. Econ. Entomol. 41*, 616 (1948).
26. Coon, B. F., R. C. Miller, and L. W. Aurand. *Correlation between Carotene Content of Corn and Infestation by the Corn Leaf Aphid.* Pennsylvania State College School of Agriculture (Mimeo.).
27. Craig, R., and W. M. Hoskins. *Ann. Rev. Biochem. 9*, 617 (1940).
28. Creighton, J. T. *J. Econ. Entomol. 31*, 735 (1938).
29. Crowell, H. H. *Ann. Entomol. Soc. Am. 34*, 503 (1941).
30. Dahms, R. G. *J. Agr. Research 76*, 271 (1948).
31. ———. *J. Econ. Entomol. 40*, 841 (1947).
32. Dahms, R. G., and F. A. Fenton. *J. Econ. Entomol. 33*, 688 (1940).
33. Dahms, R. G., and R. H. Painter. *J. Econ. Entomol. 33*, 482 (1940).
34. Dahms, R. G., R. O. Snelling, and F. A. Fenton. *J. Econ. Entomol. 29*, 1147 (1936).
35. Daniels, Norris E. *J. Econ. Entomol. 50*, 793 (1957).
36. Davidson, J. *Ann. Appl. Biol. 12*, 472, (1925).
37. Davis, G. R. F. *Ann. Entomol. Soc. 50*, 578 (1957).
38. DeLong, D. M. *Science 80*, 2075 (1934).
39. Dethier, V. G. *Trans. Ninth Intern. Congr. Entomol. 2*, 81 (1953).
40. Dodd, Allan P. *Bull. Entomol. Research 27*, 503 (1936).
41. Douglas, W. A., and R. C. Eckhardt. *Proc. Assoc. Southern Agr. Workers*, p. 115 (1953).
42. English, L. L. *J. Econ. Entomol. 44*, 208 (1951).
43. Evans, A. C. *Ann. Appl. Biol. 25*, 558 (1938).
44. Fife, L. C. *U. S. D. A. Tech. Bull. No. 977*, 1949.
45. Fleschner, C. A. *Proc. Tenth Intern. Congr. Entomol.* (1956) 2, 669 (1958).
46. Flynn, L. M., C. W. Gehrke, M. E. Muhrer, G. E. Smith, and M. S. Zuber. *Missouri Agr. Expt. Sta. Research Bull. No. 620*, 1957.
47. Friend, W. G. *Ann. Rev. Entomol. 3*, 57 (1958).
48. Garman, Philip, and B. H. Kennedy. *J. Econ. Entomol. 42*, 157 (1949).
49. Hacskaylo, Joseph. *J. Econ. Entomol. 50*, 280 (1957).
50. Hacskaylo, Joseph, and David R. Ergle. *Texas Agr. Expt. Sta. Bull. 821*, 1955.
51. Hamstead, Elwood O., and Edwin Gould. *J. Econ. Entomol. 50*, 109 (1957).
52. Haseman, L. *J. Econ. Entomol. 39*, 8 (1946).

53. Henderson, C. F., and J. K. Holloway. *J. Econ. Entomol. 35,* 683 (1942).
54. Henneberry, Thomas J., Floyd F. Smith, and Edgar A. Taylor. *The Effect of Plant Nutrition on Susceptibility of the Two-Spotted Spider Mite (Tetranychus telarius L.) to Malathion.* Presented at Entomological Society of America Meeting, 1957.
55. Hodge, Charles. *Physiol. Zool. 6,* 306 (1933).
56. Holloway, J. K., Chas. F. Henderson, and H. V. McBurnie. *J. Econ. Entomol. 35,* 348 (1942).
57. Houser, J. S., and L. L. Huber. *J. Econ. Entomol. 22,* 171 (1929).
58. Huber, L. L., C. R. Neiswander, and R. M. Salter. *Ohio Agr. Expt. Sta. Bull. 429,* 1928.
59. Huffaker, Carl B., and Carl H. Spitzer, Jr. *J. Econ. Entomol. 43,* 819 (1950).
60. Hurd-Karrer, A. M. *J. Agr. Research 54,* 601 (1937).
61. Hurd-Karrer, A. M., and F. W. Poos. *Science 84,* 252 (1936).
62. Ibbotson, Alan, and J. S. Kennedy. *Ann. Appl. Biol. 37,* 680 (1950).
63. ———. *Ann. Appl. Biol. 38,* 65 (1951).
64. Isely, D. *Univ. Ark. Agr. Expt. Sta. Bull. 320,* 1935.
65. ———. *Univ. Ark. Agr. Expt. Sta. Bull. 462,* 1946.
66. Jeppson, L. R., C. A. Fleschner, M. J. Jesser, and J. O. Complin. *J. Econ. Entomol. 50,* 293 (1957).
67. Jeppson, L. R., M. J. Jesser, and J. O. Complin. *J. Econ. Entomol. 46,* 10 (1953).
68. Jones, L. W. *Utah Agr. Expt. Sta. Bull. 390,* 1956.
69. Kennedy, J. S., and C. O. Booth. *Ann. Appl. Biol. 37,* 451 (1950).
70. ———. *Ann. Appl. Biol. 38,* 25 (1951).
71. ———. *Ann. Appl. Biol. 41,* 88 (1954).
72. Kennedy, J. S., and T. E. Mittler. *Nature 171,* 528 (1953).
73. Kennedy, J. S., Alan Ibbotson, and C. O. Booth. *Ann. Appl. Biol. 37,* 651 (1950).
74. Kiefer, H. H. Personal communication, 1957.
75. Klostermeyer, E. C. *J. Econ. Entomol. 43,* 427 (1950).
76. Klostermeyer, E. C., and W. B. Rasmussen. *J. Econ. Entomol. 46,* 910 (1953).
77. Lees, A. D. *Ann. Appl. Biol. 40,* 449 (1953).
78. Legay, J. M. *Ann. Rev. Entomol. 3,* 75 (1958).
79. Lienk, S. E., P. J. Chapman, and O. F. Curtis, Jr. *J. Econ. Entomol. 49,* 350 (1956).
80. Lipke, H., and G. Frankel. *Ann. Rev. Entomol. 1,* 17 (1956).

81. Luckmann, Wm. H. *The Effect of the Morphology and Physiology of the Corn Plant on the Survival and Control of the European Corn Borer.* Ph.D. Thesis, University of Illinois, Urbana, Ill., 1956.
82. Maltais, J. B. *Can. Entomologist 91,* 336 (1959).
83. McGarr, R. L. *J. Econ. Entomol. 35,* 482 (1942).
84. ———. *J. Econ. Entomol. 36,* 640 (1943).
85. Meyer, B. S., and D. B. Anderson. *Plant Physiology.* 2nd ed. D. Van Nostrand Co., Princeton, N. J., 1952.
86. Miller, Erston V. *The Chemistry of Plants.* Reinhold Publishing Corporation, New York, 1957.
87. Mittler, T. E. *Nature, 172,* 207 (1953).
88. Morgan, C. V. G., and N. H. Anderson. *Can. J. Plant Sci. 37,* 423 (1957).
89. Morgan, C. V. G., N. H. Anderson, and J. E. Swales. *Can. J. Plant Sci. 38,* 94 (1958).
90. Morris, V. H., C. R. Neiswander, and J. D. Sayre. *Plant Physiol. 16,* 197 (1941).
91. Neiswander, C. R., and V. H. Morris. *J. Econ. Entomol. 33,* 517 (1940).
92. Painter, R. H. *Insect Resistance in Crop Plants.* The Macmillan Company, New York, 1951.
93. Reinhard, H. J. *Texas Agr. Expt. Sta. Bull. 353,* 1927.
94. Rodriguez, J. G. *Ann. Entomol. Soc. Am. 44,* 511 (1951).
95. ———. *J. Econ. Entomol. 51,* 369 (1958).
96. Rodriguez, J. G., and R. B. Neiswander. *J. Econ. Entomol. 42,* 56 (1949).
97. Rodriguez, J. G., and L. D. Rodriguez. *Ann. Entomol. Soc. Am. 45,* 331 (1952).
98. Rodriguez, J. G., H. H. Chen, and Walter T. Smith, Jr. *J. Econ. Entomol. 50,* 587 (1957).
99. Schoene, W. J. *J. Econ. Entomol. 34,* 271 (1941).
100. Shifflette, Harry H. *Investigations Concerning the Appearance of Wings in Aphis gossypii* Glover (Aphididae). M.S. Thesis, L.S.U., 1957.
101. Shull, A. F. *Biol. Revs. Biol. Proc. Cambridge Phil. Soc. 4,* 218 (1929).
102. Simkover, H. G., and R. D. Shenefelt. *J. Econ. Entomol. 44,* 426 (1951).
103. Smith, D. S., and F. E. Northcott. *Can. J. Zool. 29,* 297 (1951).
104. Smith, E. H., and R. W. Harris. *J. Econ. Entomol. 45,* 607 (1952).
105. Smith, Nathan R., and Marie E. Wenzel. *Soil Science Soc. Am. 1947,* 227.

106. Snetsinger, Robt. E. Personal communication, 1957.
107. Snyder, K. D. *Ann. Entomol. Soc. Am.* 47, 603 (1954).
108. Squire, F. A. *Bull. Entomol. Research 30,* 475 (1939).
109. ———. *Bull. Entomol. Research 31,* 1 (1940).
110. Tauber, O. C., C. J. Drake, and G. C. Decker. *Iowa State Coll. J. Sci. 19,* 343 (1945).
111. Taylor, L. F., J. W. Apple, and K. C. Berger. *J. Econ. Entomol.* 45, 843 (1952).
112. Thompson, W. L. *J. Econ. Entomol.* 32, 782 (1939).
113. ———. *Fla. Agr. Expt. Sta. Rept. 1939-40,* 158 (1941).
114. ———. *J. Econ. Entomol.* 35, 351 (1942).
115. Thorsteinson, A. J. *Proc. Tenth Intern. Congr. Entomol.* (1956) 2, 599 (1958).
116. ———. *Entomologia Experimentalis et Applicata 1,* 23 (1958).
117. Todd, Frank E., and Ormond Bretherick. *J. Econ. Entomol.* 35, 312 (1942).
118. Trager, W. *Biol. Revs. Cambridge Phil. Soc.* 22, 148 (1947).
119. ———. *Insect Physiology,* K. D. Roeder, Editor. John Wiley and Sons, New York, 1953, p. 350.
120. Uvarov, B. P. *Trans. Entomol. Soc. London,* Dec. 31, 1928.
121. Webster, J. E., and V. G. Heller. *Okla. Agr. Expt. Sta. Tech. Bull. T-12,* 1942.
122. Webster, J. E., F. Davies, and J. Sieglinger. *Okla. Agr. Expt. Sta. Tech. Bull. T-49,* 1954.
123. Webster, J. E., J. Sieglinger, and F. Davies. *Okla. Agr. Expt. Sta. Tech. Bull. T-30,* 1948.
124. Wharton, G. W. Personal communication, 1957.
125. Wilson, H. A. *West Va. Univ. Agr. Expt. Sta. Bull. 366T,* 1954.
126. Wolfenbarger, D. O. *J. Econ. Entomol.* 41, 818 (1948).
127. Wollerman, E. H., Jr. *Development of the Southern Armyworm Relative to the Variation in Nitrogen Supplied to the Host Plant.* Doctoral dissertation, The Ohio State University, Columbus, O., 1949.
128. Zeid, Mahmoud M. I., and L. K. Cutkomp. *J. Econ. Entomol.* 44, 898 (1951).

Control of Screwworm Fly by Atomic Radiation[*]

E. F. KNIPLING

U. S. Department of Agriculture,
Agricultural Research Service,
Beltsville, Maryland

An understanding of the life history, habits, and population dynamics of the screwworm fly, together with knowledge of the effects of atomic irradiation on genetic material in insects, has led to a new promising way to control or eliminate the screwworm fly in certain areas. The screwworm fly, *Callitroga hominivorax* (Cqrl.), is a destructive parasite of livestock in the southern areas of the United States. The method of control involves the release among the wild population of male flies that have been made sexually sterile by exposure to gamma rays. This paper is an account of the research that has led to this unique method of insect control.

Biology and Economic Importance

The screwworm fly is about three times as large as the common house fly. It deposits its eggs on wounds of warm-blooded animals. After 12 to 24 hours, about 200 tiny larvae hatch from each egg mass. The larvae feed on the tissues of the host for about five days. When fully grown, they are over ½ inch in length and about ⅛ inch in width. They then leave the wound to pupate in the soil. After eight days to several weeks, depending on prevailing temperatures, adult flies emerge. Mating takes place on about the third day, and eggs are deposited about one week after the emergence of the fly. The complete generation from egg to egg during summer months ranges from three to four weeks.

[*]This paper with slight differences, was published in *The Scientific Monthly*, Vol. 85, October 1957.

Screwworm flies disperse widely by flight; they have been shown to disperse at least 9 miles (8). A related species, *Phormia regina* Meig., is capable of flying at least 28 miles (10).

After an animal is infested, the wound becomes increasingly attractive for oviposition. Consequently, multiple infestations result, and several thousand larvae may be present in the wounds. Unless such infested animals are found and treated promptly, they will be killed in a week to ten days. Death of the host is caused by consumption of tissues by the larvae and shock resulting from the loss of blood and lymph from the infested wound.

This insect is the most destructive pest of livestock in the southwestern and southeastern states. Losses are most severe in domestic animals, particularly cattle, sheep, goats, swine, and horses. However, the pest also attacks deer, rabbits, coons, opossums, and other wild animals. Infestations may also occur in man, but fortunately rather infrequently. When they do occur, there may be serious consequences because the attack is most commonly in the nasal passage, and treatment to destroy the larvae is very difficult.

Entomologists in the United States Department of Agriculture have conducted research on the pest for many years. Much information has been obtained on the life history and ecology of the parasite and on methods of treating wounds to prevent infestations or to destroy the larvae in infested animals.

Several excellent wound treatments have been developed. The most effective material now in use by stockmen is a smear known as EQ-335. This composition, containing lindane and pine oil, will prevent infestations in wounds and will destroy larvae already present. The newly hatched larvae cannot penetrate sound skin. However, any break in the skin may lead to an infestation. The most common causes of wounds suitable for attack by screwworms include accidental injuries, shear cuts, tick bites, fighting, and surgical operations. In addition, newborn animals are particularly susceptible to screwworm attack in the navel before the navel-cord attachment site is healed.

Ranchers in screwworm areas must be constantly alert during the warmer months of the year, when screwworm flies are most

active, to find and treat infested animals before they are destroyed by the parasite. In many areas, particularly in the open ranges of the Southwest, livestock production would prove unprofitable if range riders were not employed to find and treat susceptible or infested animals.

The insect survives the winter in the southern parts of Texas, Arizona, and California. It is also a year-round parasite in much of Mexico and central and South America. It also overwinters in Florida. Each spring and summer it spreads northward several hundred miles from the overwintering areas. Through shipment of infested animals in the early spring, the parasite may also become well established in northern areas and cause severe losses before it is killed out by cold weather.

The total loss caused by the screwworm varies from year to year, but it is conservatively estimated that the average annual loss to the livestock industry amounts to $25 million.

Basis for Considering the Feasibility of Releasing Sterile Males

Proper livestock-management practices and wound treatments keep losses down, but they do not solve the screwworm problem. Other methods of control have been tried in order to reduce losses further, including extensive fly-trapping and community-wide animal-inspection programs. However, these methods have not proved practical. Not all infested domestic animals, especially on open ranges, can be found and treated. Even if all domestic animals are treated, the many wild animals that become infested serve as reservoirs for the parasite.

As pointed out by Lindquist (5), ecological studies have indicated that the number of flies even in areas of high infestation is very low in comparison with that of most insect species. Moreover, during winter months, the overwintering area is restricted and the fly population is greatly reduced. It has been estimated that the number of flies produced per week during the winter in Florida would be likely to average less than 100 per square mile. The low population density suggested the idea of controlling the insect by releasing more sexually sterile males than the number of fertile males that exist in the natural population.

It has been well established that sexual sterility can be induced in insects by exposure to x rays and gamma rays (Runner, 9; Muller, 7; and others). A method of rearing the parasite on an artificial medium consisting of ground meat and blood was developed by Melvin and Bushland (6). On the basis of these developments, a research program was undertaken to test the feasibility of employing sexually sterile males to control the screwworm. The decision to conduct this research was influenced by the encouragement and suggestions of H. J. Muller, noted geneticist, when I submitted the proposed program to him in 1950.

Laboratory Investigations

Exploration of the problem was undertaken by and under the direction of R. C. Bushland, entomologist with the United States Department of Agriculture at Kerrville, Texas. The findings in the laboratory, which have been published (2) may be briefly summarized as follows.

Studies with x rays, and later with gamma rays, from a radioactive cobalt-60 source provided by the Oak Ridge National Laboratory showed that exposure of screwworm pupae five to seven days old to approximately 2500 roentgens resulted in complete sterility of the male flies that subsequently emerged. A dosage of 5000 roentgens produced sterility in females. Exposure to gamma rays at dosages up to 20,000 roentgens did not seriously affect the vigor of the flies, although the average length of life was reduced somewhat. When sterile males were placed in cages with normal unirradiated females, mating took place and the females produced only sterile eggs. Further tests showed that such females continued to produce infertile eggs throughout their life span, which is normally about two to three weeks. Therefore, when a sterile male mates with a normal female, the effect is equivalent to destruction of the female.

The most encouraging feature of the laboratory studies was the demonstration that the sexual vigor of the irradiated males was not greatly reduced. Normal females were placed in cages together with irradiated and unirradiated males in various ratios

to test the sexual vigor of the males or discrimination on the part of the females, or both, in matings with the two kinds of males. The ratio of sterile to fertile egg masses was almost the same as the ratio of irradiated to unirradiated males in the caged population. For example, if ten normal females, ten normal males, and ninety irradiated males were present in a caged population, about 90 per cent of the females deposited sterile egg masses. Another point of practical significance was the indication that the presence of irradiated, sterile females did not adversely affect the results. Therefore, if a release program were undertaken, it would not be necessary to separate the females from the males, a costly undertaking.

Theoretical Possibilities

The laboratory investigations established that the basic principles for successful control of the screwworm by releasing sexually sterile males were sound. The population decline in each generation which theoretically might be expected from a release program in which sterile males initially outnumber fertile males is shown in Table I, as previously published (4). It is emphasized that these figures are theoretical, but if we assume

TABLE I. Theoretical Population Decline in Each Subsequent Generation When a Constant Number of Sterile Males Are Released Among a Natural Population of 1 Million Females

	Generation			
	1	2	3	4
Number of unmated females in area	1,000,000	333,333	47,619	1,107
Number of sexually sterile males released	2,000,000	2,000,000	2,000,000	2,000,000
Ratio of sterile to fertile males competing for each female	2:1	6:1	42:1	1,807:1
Assumed percentage of females mated to sterile males	66.7	85.7	97.7	99.95
Theoretical population decline of fertile females	333,333	47,619	1,107	Less than 1

a maximum effect of released sterile males, the population decline would be rapid and dramatic.

The example assumes that biotic factors are such that the population is stabilized at a constant level. In other words, an assumed fly population of 1 million females and the same number of males, in the absence of any control effort, would produce 1 million females and 1 million males to replace the parent population that dies out from old age, predation, and other causes. In this hypothetical case, the initial release rate of 2 million sterile males results in a ratio of two sterile males to one fertile male. It is further assumed that the released males compete fully with the normal males in mating with the normal females in the population. In such event, two-thirds of the reproductive capacity of the population will be destroyed. Then, if we assume a maximum population decline, the population of virgin females in the second generation will only be one-third of that in the first. Consequently, the continued release of males at the initial rate will result in a ratio of six sterile males to one fertile male. This will cause an even more rapid decline in the third generation. By the fourth generation, or in about four months, the screwworm population will be wiped out. It is recognized that, in considering the potentials of the sterile-male approach, we cannot necessarily expect a maximum population decline. However, theoretically, if the decline is no greater than 25 per cent of the theoretical maximum, eradication should still result in about six or seven generations.

Early Field Investigations

The laboratory findings and theoretical calculations were sufficiently favorable to indicate possibilities that the screwworm fly might be eradicated by release of a preponderance of sexually sterile males among the wild population. It was necessary, however, to test the procedure in field experiments before its feasibility could be determined. Success would be dependent on a number of important factors. Precise information was needed on the number of screwworm flies in the wild population. If the population density was too high, the cost

of rearing and releasing a dominating population of sterile males would be prohibitive. It was also necessary to establish that the reared and released, irradiated males would disperse and compete successfully with the wild males. Early field experiments were conducted by A. H. Baumhover, A. J. Graham, and others in the Entomology Research Branch.

Since personnel and facilities were limited, it seemed desirable to conduct such experiments on a small island. The only small, somewhat isolated islands harboring screwworms in the United States were a group off the west coast of Florida in the vicinity of Fort Myers.

A 15-square-mile island of Sanibel was chosen for these tests. This island is separated from the Florida mainland by a water barrier about 2 miles wide. Studies employing goats as host animals indicated that the screwworm population was at least as high as the average for the State of Florida during the winter months, and perhaps higher.

In order to obtain an estimate of the natural population on the island, screwworm flies from larvae reared on host animals that had been made highly radioactive with phosphorus-32 were released on the island. Egg masses deposited by these flies were sufficiently radioactive to be identified. The ratio of radioactive egg masses to those deposited by the natural population indicated that the natural population in each generation was probably less than 100 flies per square mile.

Sterile male screwworm flies were then released at the rate of 100 per square mile, per week. This rate of release resulted in a 4/1 ratio of sterile to fertile egg masses collected on host animals. Continued weekly releases for three months reduced the natural population to a low point, but eradication could not be demonstrated. There was good evidence that a few fertile females previously mated with fertile males migrated to the island from nearby islands and from the mainland. It was concluded that the success of the method could be demonstrated only by conducting an experiment on a small, completely isolated island that would not be within range of migrating flies from other areas.

Eradication Experiment on Curaçao

In 1954 an opportunity was presented to conduct an eradication experiment on the island of Curaçao in the Netherlands Antilles. This island harbored a high population of screwworms, which were causing heavy losses among goats and other domestic animals. The veterinary service on the island requested information on methods of control, and a cooperative program to attempt eradication was arranged by the United States Department of Agriculture and the Netherlands Antilles government. The nature and results of these investigations, reported by Baumhover et al. (1), are briefly summarized here.

The island has an area of 170 square miles. It is 40 miles from the nearest land, which practically precludes the migration of screwworm flies from other areas. Studies were conducted for several months to obtain information on the natural population density on the island. Host animals were exposed at eleven locations, and daily records were made of the number of egg masses deposited on them. Prior to the release of sterile males, over 99 per cent of the egg masses deposited were fertile. Sterile males were released on a portion of the island for several weeks at the rate of 100 per square mile per week. The ratio of sterile to fertile eggs collected indicated that it would be necessary to release several hundred sterile males each week to achieve a dominant population of sterile males.

The eradication effort was started on 9 August 1954. It was decided that about 400 sterile males would be released per square mile each week. The screwworm larvae were reared at the Orlando, Florida, laboratory. Pupae were exposed to a radioactive cobalt source described by Darden et al (3). The rate of exposure was 7500 roentgens. At this dosage, not only are both male and female flies sexually sterile, but the females are also incapable of producing eggs.

Irradiated pupae were placed in special paper-bag containers, transported by commercial airlines to Curaçao and released from a small aircraft. Releases were made twice each week. Fly drops were made at 1-mile intervals. Sterile females were also

liberated, since separation of the sexes was not practical. Susceptible host animals were located in eleven pens well distributed on the island. Eggs were collected daily, and the rate of sterility was determined. Since the sterile females released were incapable of producing eggs, egg masses collected were from females in the natural population.

Data showing the number of fertile and sterile egg masses collected on the host animals each week following the appearance of sterile egg masses are given in Table II.

TABLE II. Record of Fertility of Screwworm Fly Eggs and of Decline in Number of Egg Masses in Screwworm-Eradication Experiment on Curaçao

Weeks after start of experiment	Number of egg masses		Percentage of sterile egg masses
	Fertile	Sterile	
1	15	34	69
2	17	38	69
3	17	36	68
4	10	37	79
5	7	42	86
6	3	23	88
7	0	10	100
8	0	12	100
9	0	0	

The number of screwworm flies in the natural population could not be determined accurately, but it is believed that the release of 400 sterile males per square mile, per week resulted in a ratio of about three or four sterile males to one fertile male. During the first week, 69 per cent of the wild females deposited infertile eggs. As expected, this percentage remained about the same for three weeks. This is about the minimum time required to produce a new generation. By the fourth week there was a trend toward a higher percentage of sterile eggs. During the sixth week a marked decrease in wild population was indicated. During the seventh week, which may be regarded as the beginning of the third generation, the natural population had declined to such a low point that no fertile eggs were collected

in the sample taken. Some fertile eggs would probably have been taken if more animals had been exposed and if a larger number of egg masses had been collected. However, the population of sterile males was so high in proportion to the population of fertile males that the chances for a fertile mating were exceedingly slim. From the ninth to the thirteenth week no egg masses, either sterile or fertile, were collected. One small, infertile, atypical egg mass was taken in the fourteenth week, and another in the fifteenth week. These small egg masses may have been deposited by released females which by chance had received less than the expected 7500-roentgen dosage. It is also possible that, out of the many thousands of irradiated females released, some may have succeeded in regenerating egg-producing cells before they died. Thereafter, no eggs of any kind were collected, although susceptible host animals were exposed through the twentieth week.

In addition to data on fertility of egg masses, reports of infestations in the domestic animals were obtained from the live-stock owners. No screwworm attacks were reported in livestock after the ninth week; this confirmed the data secured on the experimental animals.

Early in January 1955, it was concluded that complete eradication had been achieved, and the experiment was terminated. According to egg-collection data and the absence of screwworm cases, virtual eradication was achieved during the third month, or after about three or four generations of exposure to the sterile males. However, releases of sterile males were continued for about two months longer to be certain of complete eradication. No screwworm cases on the island were reported up to February 1957.

It is interesting to note that the rate of population decline in the eradication experiment in general agreed with the theoretical calculations given in Table I. The theoretical figures predicted elimination by about the fourth generation, and actual elimination of the pest was probably achieved by this generation.

Possibilities of Further Application

The success of the eradication program on Curaçao has stimulated great interest by livestock growers in having the screwworm eradicated in the southeastern United States. The infestation in the Southeast now survives from year to year because of a favorable overwintering area in the Florida peninsula. The infestation in the Southeast did not exist until 1933, when it became established through shipment of infested livestock from the Southwest. It is believed that if the insect could be eliminated from the area, and if measures were taken to prevent reintroduction through shipment of infested livestock, the area would remain free of the pest. Screwworm flies from the Southwest are not likely to spread naturally as far as Florida in one season, and the insect normally does not survive the winter in the area between south Texas and the Florida peninsula.

Since completion of the eradication experiment on Curaçao, research by the United States Department of Agriculture's Entomology Research Branch has been intensified. The Florida livestock owners have been cooperating in this expanded program. The purpose of this research is to improve methods of rearing and detecting low populations of the insect to make them economically feasible for larger areas. The overwintering area for the Southeast infestation comprises about 50,000 square miles. An eradication program employing the same release rate as that on Curaçao will mean the release of 20 million sterile males per week. Since an equal number of females will be produced, and to allow for some breeding stock and some mortality in the pupal stage, it will be necessary to rear about 50 million screwworm flies per week. For a fly-rearing project of this size, approximately 75,000 pounds of meat will be needed each week. A large and special rearing plant will be required. A tentative plant design has already been prepared with the assistance of the United States Army Chemical Corps at Fort Detrick, Maryland. A fleet of about thirty small aircraft will be needed to distribute the flies. Special cobalt-60 sources will be necessary to irradiate the pupae. Much manpower will be required

to carry out the program. The release of sterile males should be continued for at least two years, if necessary. It is apparent that a program of this kind will be a huge undertaking.

The research personnel of the Department of Agriculture are confident that eradication can be achieved. The cost of such a program has not been accurately estimated, but it is believed that a two-year eradication program would cost about $9 million. Since the losses caused by the pest in the Southeast have been estimated at no less than $10 million each year, such a program appears to be justifiable from an economic standpoint. Adequate measures to prevent reintroduction of the pest from the Southwest through shipment of infested animals pose problems that need careful study. When the research program currently under way is completed, probably during 1957, the United States Department of Agriculture, the states having an interest in such a program, and the livestock industry will undoubtedly consider all aspects of the problem and decide whether or not to recommend that an eradication program be undertaken in the Southeast.

Use of Technique for Controlling Other Insects

Some thought has been given to the possibilities for controlling other insects by releasing sterile males (4). It is obvious that the method will not be economically feasible for most insects. Most species occur in such great numbers that it would be too costly to rear enough insects to release a dominant population of sterile males. Methods of rearing many insect species have not been developed. Many insects do not fly, or they have such a limited flight range that released males could not be distributed adequately to compete with the fertile males.

A number of other limiting factors exist among other insects. However, on the basis of current knowledge, the technique is worthy of study. For example, further research might show that the method could aid in the eradication of Mediterranean fruit fly infestations of the type now in Florida, which are now being eliminated by chemical methods. The Hawaii laboratory of the Entomology Research Branch has developed economical

methods of rearing this insect, and preliminary studies have shown the sterile-male technique to be sufficiently promising to warrant further consideration. Scientists in Africa have shown interest in the possible application of the technique for eliminating the tsetse fly from certain areas after first reducing the existing population to a low point through the use of other control measures.

Since most insects are present in large numbers, the successful use of sterile males to eliminate well-established infestations can be expected only after the natural population has been reduced to a point where a dominating sterile population can be released and maintained until elimination is achieved. The method might also prove useful as a means of eliminating a newly established infestation if a great preponderance of sterile males could be released initially and maintained before the population increases and spreads.

Much research will be required before the limitations and potentialities of the technique can be determined for any specific insect. Such research should include studies on mating habits of the insect and studies to determine whether sexual sterility can be achieved without adversely affecting the male's sexual vigor and length of life. Methods of rearing the species in large numbers and a practical way to release and distribute the insect must be developed. Such research should be encouraged on highly destructive species which conceivably might lend themselves to self-destruction by the unique sterile-male technique.

Added in proof: Since this paper was presented, a cooperative eradication program was initiated. The program was started early in 1958 under the supervision of the Animal Disease Eradication Division, Agricultural Research Service, U. S. Department of Agriculture, and the Florida Livestock Board. The program proved highly successful. Within a year virtually all natural screwworm activity ceased. In November 1959 the production and release of sterile flies was discontinued. Although inspectors are continuing surveys in Florida and other southeastern states, there is every reason to believe that eradication has been achieved.—E. F. K.

REFERENCES

1. Baumhover, A. H., *et al. J. Econ. Entomol. 48*:462 (1955).
2. Bushland, R. C., and D. E. Hopkins. *J. Econ. Entomol. 44*:725 (1951); *46,* 648 (1953).
3. Darden, E. B., Jr., E. Maeyens, 2nd, R. C. Bushland. *Nucleonics 12*(10):60 (1954).
4. Knipling, E. F. *J. Econ. Entomol. 48*:459 (1955).
5. Lindquist, A. W. *J. Econ. Entomol. 48*:467 (1955).
6. Melvin, R., and Bushland, R. C. *J. Econ. Entomol. 33*:850 (1940).
7. Muller, H. J. *Proc. Intern. Congr. Genetics, 5th Congr. Berlin,* 1927; *Z. induktive Abstammungs- u. Vererbungslehre Suppl. 1*:234, 1927.
8. Parish, H. E. *J. Econ. Entomol. 30*:740 (1937).
9. Runner, G. A. *J. Agr. Research 6*:383 (1916).
10. Yates, W. W., and A. W. Lindquist. *J. Econ. Entomol. 45*:547 (1952).

Parasites and Predators for Pest Control

CHARLES A. FLESCHNER

University of California,
Citrus Experiment Station, Riverside

The cases in which parasites and predators have been used to achieve pest control are so numerous that no attempt will be made to list them at this time. The purpose of this discussion is to present a broad, somewhat superficial historical sketch of the field as a whole, followed by a rather detailed account of a single project now in progress. Particular projects are cited because of their historical value, because of their highly successful outcome, or because they demonstrate certain principles of the biological method of pest control.

The fundamental basis for the utilization of beneficial insects in the control of various agricultural pests is in the equilibrium which exists between plant and animal populations in their undisturbed native habitats. Populations frequently are in equilibrium at very low densities. A given species of plant-feeding insect, for example, may be maintained at an extremely low population on certain host plants by its natural enemies. Man occasionally disrupts this equilibrium by transporting plants from place to place, often transporting their insect pests with them. The natural enemies of these pest insects, however, are less often included in this movement. The absence of controlling natural enemies may enable the pest species to become more destructive in the new area than it was in the place of origin. In such cases an effective natural balance may be reestablished through the introduction of enemies of the pest species from the native habitat.

Usually an introduced plant is desirable for one reason or another, so that the insects which feed on it are considered injurious, and the parasites and predators that feed on these

insects are, as a consequence, considered beneficial. However, if the plant is undesirable, or a weed, the plant-feeding insects are considered beneficial and the parasites and predators of the plant-feeding insects are considered injurious. Thus, a plant-feeding insect is judged either beneficial or injurious on the basis of its feeding habits. By the same token, parasites and predators are judged as beneficial if they prey on harmful insects, or as injurious if they prey on beneficial insects.

For the reasons given, most of the cases of agricultural pest control through the use of beneficial insects are concerned with the introduction and establishment of natural enemies of pests of foreign origin. Other methods of utilizing beneficial insects to control agricultural pests include the mass production and periodic release of native or established beneficial insects and the utilization of cultural methods designed to conserve or to augment native beneficial insects. Each of these methods of pest control through the use of parasites and predators will be considered in this paper.

A general review, worldwide in scope, which includes information on the use of parasites and predators for pest control, has been given by Sweetman in his book entitled *The Biological Control of Insects* (24). Several general reviews of the status of biological control in various countries are available, these being by Clausen (3) for the continental United States, Pemberton (20, 21) for Hawaii, O'Connor (19) for Fiji, Jenkins (16) for western Australia, Miller *et al.* (18) for New Zealand, and Kamal (17) for Egypt.

Translocation of Beneficial Insects for Insect Pest Control

The first written record of the movement of beneficial insects from place to place for the control of pests is that by Forskål, published in 1775, which has been discussed by Clausen (2). Forskål stated that in Yemen, which is situated in the southwest corner of Arabia, the date palms were attacked by ants which often destroyed the trees; to control these ants the growers each year brought down from the mountains colonies of a predaceous or beneficial species of ant and placed them in the palms to

control the destructive ants. The use of ants for the protection of orchards from insect pests is a practice of long standing in certain Asiatic countries. Even today the citrus growers of South China often place bamboo runways between trees to aid beneficial ants in their movement from tree to tree.

The international movement of beneficial insects for pest control began in 1873 with the shipment of the mite *Tyroglyphus phylloxerae* Riley from the United States to France for the control of the grape phylloxera. This was followed in 1874 by the introduction of the lady beetle *Coccinella undecimpunctata* (L.) into New Zealand from England for the control of aphids. The next recorded movement was that of *Apanteles glomeratus* (L.), a parasite of the cabbage worm, to the United States from England in 1883. Although these three efforts resulted in establishment of the parasites in their new environment, in no instance was complete economic control attained.

The first instance of complete and sustained economic control of an insect pest by a parasite or predator was the control of the cottony-cushion scale, *Icerya purchasi* Mask., a citrus pest in California, by the vedalia beetle, *Rodolia cardinalis* (Muls.).

The cottony-cushion scale was accidentally introduced into California from Australia about 1869. It was first found on a species of Australian acacia in a nursery at Menlo Park, near San Francisco. None of the natural enemies of this scale was introduced with it. Free of any effective natural check the scale spread rapidly over a large portion of the state. It was introduced on lemon trees from the nursery at Menlo Park into southern California prior to 1876 and soon it became a widespread primary pest of citrus. No control proved effective against it. By the early 1880's citrus crops were lost, trees were ruined, and properties were depreciated in value.

In 1888, C. V. Riley, Chief Entomologist of the United States Department of Agriculture, arranged for Albert Koebele to go to Australia in search of enemies of the cottony-cushion scale. Within several months, Koebele sent two species of insect enemies of the scale to California. These were the vedalia beetle and the parasite fly *Cryptochaetum iceryae* (Will.). Both spe-

cies became established, but the vedalia beetle proved to be the more effective of the two. Within a year, orchards receiving the first liberations of the vedalia were practically free of the scale, and within two years the cottony-cushion scale was of no economic importance in California.

The successful outcome of this project is now one of the milestones of biological control; it marks the true beginning of the sustained biological control movement. This initial success gave the practice of biological control such promise that this method of controlling pests soon spread throughout the world, resulting in many striking successes.

The following list includes ten species of entomophagous insects whose purposeful introduction into various parts of the world brought full commercial control of their hosts. It is significant that in each case only one species of natural enemy was necessary for control (8):

Anaphoidea nitens Gir., a parasitic wasp (egg parasite). Australia to the Union of South Africa to control the eucalyptus snout-beetle, *Gonipterus scutellatus* Gyll.

Apanteles solitarius (Ratz.), a parasitic wasp. Europe to Canada and parts of the United States to control satin moth, *Stilpnotia salicis* (L.), a pest of certain forest and shade trees.

Aphelinus mali (Hald.), a parasitic wasp. Eastern United States to New Zealand, Australia, and elsewhere, to control the woolly apple aphid, *Eriosoma lanigerum* (Hausm.), a pest of apple trees.

Cryptognatha nodiceps Mshll., a lady beetle. Trinidad to Fiji to control the coconut scale, *Aspidiotus destructor* Sign.

Cyrtorhinus mundulus Bredd., a predaceous bug. Fiji to Hawaii to control the sugarcane leafhopper, *Perkinsiella saccharicida* Kirk.

Eretmocerus serius Silv., a parasitic wasp. Malaya to Cuba to control the citrus blackfly, *Aleurocanthus woglumi* Ashby.

Prospaltella smithi Silv., a parasitic wasp. China to Japan to control the spiny blackfly, *Aleurocanthus spiniferus* Quaint., a pest of citrus.

Ptychomyia remota Aldr., a tachinid fly. Malaya to Fiji to control the coconut moth, *Levuana iridescens* B.B.

Rodolia cardinalis (Muls.), a lady beetle. Australia to California and to many other countries to control the cottony-cushion scale, *Icerya purchasi* Mask., a pest of citrus.

Tetracnemus pretiosus Timb., a parasitic wasp. Australia to California to control the citrophilus mealybug, *Pseudococcus gahani* Green, a pest of citrus.

Ten entomophagous insects whose purposeful introduction has brought about some degree of control of an agricultural pest are as follows:

Aphytis lepidosaphes Comp. Hong Kong to California to control *Lepidosaphes beckii* (Newm.)

Bathyplectes curculionis (Thoms.). Italy to western United States to control *Hypera postica* (Gyll.)

Blastothrix sericea (Dalm.) Europe to British Columbia to control *Eulecanium coryli* (L.)

Campsomeris marsinella modesta Sm. Philippines to Hawaii to control *Anomala orientalis* Waterh.

Comperiella bifasciata How. Japan to California to control *Aonidiella citrina* (Coq.)

Compsilura concinnata Meig. Europe to United States to control *Nygmia phaeorrhoea* (Donov.)

Habrolepis dalmani (Westw.). United States to New Zealand to control *Asterolecanium variolosum* (Ratz.)

Metaphycus helvolus (Comp.). South Africa to California to control *Saissetia oleae* (Bern.)

Opius oophilus Fall. Malaya to Hawaii to control *Dacus dorsalis* Hendel.

Prospaltella berlesei How. Eastern United States to Italy to control *Aulacaspis pentagona* (Targ.)

INTRODUCTION OF PARASITE OR PREDATOR OBTAINED FROM PEST SPECIES OTHER THAN THAT TO BE CONTROLLED

It has been demonstrated in several instances that parasites obtained from a host species other than that to be controlled may be successfully utilized. An example of this is the control of the coconut moth, *Levuana iridescens*, in Fiji, through the introduction of a tachinid fly, *Ptychomyia remota*, a parasite of *Artona catoxantha* Hmps., a moth of a different subfamily. This highly successful biological control project has been reported upon in detail by Tothill *et al.* (25). In this instance the native home of the coconut moth could not be ascertained. However, *Artona*, a different moth pest of the coconut palm,

was known to be controlled by parasites in Indo-Malaya. Consequently, two parasites of *Artona,* a tachinid and an ichneumonid, were introduced into the Fiji Islands from Indo-Malaya. The tachinid *Ptychomyia* proved to be a very effective parasite of the coconut moth in Fiji. Field control of the pest was accomplished in many areas within six months after release of the parasites, and economic control was general throughout the islands within two years.

IMPORTANCE OF BIOLOGICAL RACES OF PARASITES

The biological control program on the olive scale in California serves to illustrate the importance of biological races of parasites in pest control. Stocks of *Aphytis maculicornis* (Masi), imported in 1951 from the area extending from India through the Middle East to the Mediterranean, proved to be indistinguishable morphologically, yet studies by Hafez and Doutt (12) revealed the existence among them of three races that have been designated as the Indian, Persian, and Spanish forms, and which show distinct biological differences. Under field conditions in California the Persian form has proved to be the most effective.

There are many such instances in which a single species of parasite may be represented by two or more races which show marked biological differences. Hence, it is important that stocks of each species of parasite be obtained from various parts of its geographic range rather than from only a single source.

INTRODUCTION OF BENEFICIAL INSECTS FOR WEED CONTROL

As mentioned earlier, a plant-feeding insect is considered beneficial when it is used to control weeds. The first outstandingly successful biological control of weeds through the introduction of plant-feeding insects was the control of prickly pear (*Opuntia* spp.) in Australia.

Various species of prickly pear native to America were introduced into Australia free of their natural enemies. From about 1900 onward they spread very rapidly. The cost of checking the invasion of properties was too great a financial load for many

landowners; hence, as the prickly pear spread, more and more land became unoccupied and holdings and homesteads were deserted. When the invasion reached its peak in 1925, about sixty million acres were covered with prickly pear.

The Commonwealth Prickly Pear Board, an independent organization representing cooperative effort by the governments of the Commonwealth, Queensland, and New South Wales, was appointed in 1920 for the express purpose of attempting to control prickly pear by establishing in Australia the insect enemies and disease organisms that attacked these plants in their native home, the Americas (5). Though many species of cactus insect enemies were found in the Americas, relatively few were introduced into Australia.

The most effective introduced insect enemy of prickly pear was the moth *Cactoblastis cactorum* (Berg.), whose larvae feed on prickly pear. *C. cactorum* was introduced into Australia from Argentina in 1925. Eggs of this moth were mass-produced in large-scale rearing cages and distributed throughout the prickly pear territory. The control of the prickly pear by *C. cactorum* was spectacular. Practically all the former dense prickly pear country was reclaimed and brought back into production.

Although there have been relatively few cases of effective biological control of weeds to date, the economic gains realized so far have been rather striking. Perhaps the greatest achievement in the biological control of a weed pest since the control of prickly pear in Australia is that of the recent biological control of the Klamath weed in northern California and other parts of the Pacific Northwest.

Prior to 1944, biological control on the North American Continent was limited to attempts to control insect pests. In 1944, however, the Agricultural Research Administration of the United States Department of Agriculture approved a joint project of the Division of Biological Control of the University of California College of Agriculture and the Division of Foreign Parasite Introductions of the Bureau of Entomology and Plant Quarantine, having as its objective the biological control of the range pest known as the Klamath weed or St.-John's-wort

(*Hypericum perforatum* L.). This weed, a native of Europe, has been very destructive to some of the most valuable ranges in the Pacific Northwest. The same weed occurs as a serious pest in Australia, and prior to 1944 the Australian Commonwealth government had explorers searching in Europe for insects suitable for introduction into Australia for its control. When, in 1944, this effort gave considerable promise of a successful outcome, the joint project mentioned above was inaugurated, and arrangements were made with the Australian government to import into California some of the European beetles used successfully in Australia. After making starvation tests on plants not tested by the Australians, the release of two leaf-feeding beetles, *Chrysolina hyperici* and *C. gemellata,* was authorized by the Agricultural Research Administration (22). Later, the root-borer beetle, *Agrilus hyperici,* and the gallfly, *Zeuxidiplosis giardi,* were imported to the United States from southern France. All these insect enemies of the Klamath weed became established, and they have been responsible for the control of the weed over hundreds of thousands of acres of grazing land.

Since the factors that control naturally occurring plant populations operate largely through the principle of competition, anything that weakens a plant species even to a slight degree may have a marked influence on the population density of the species concerned. Thus in the case of the Klamath weed it was not necessary for the insects to kill an entire stand of the weed in order to control it, because as the plant-feeding insects weakened the weed, valuable forage plants were able to compete with it and eventually to replace it. This successful control of the Klamath weed by its insect enemies will no doubt be followed by attempts to control other weed pests, particularly those of ranges, by the biological method.

The biological control method as applied to weeds is greatly limited by the degree of specificity of plant-feeding insects and the extreme caution which must be exercised in the selection of insects to be introduced. This is, to some extent, counterbalanced by the fact that in many cases a relatively small amount

of injury caused by the insects may greatly reduce the competitive ability of the weed. Even though a good start has been made, this method of weed control is in its infancy. Expansion of research in this field can surely be expected to produce more successes of great practical importance.

Mass Production of Insects

Economic mass production of insects plays an important role in the use of parasites and predators for pest control. It is obviously advantageous to be able to raise and release newly introduced beneficial insects in large numbers. In addition, where native or established parasites or predators can be mass-reared cheaply enough, they may be utilized in a periodic release program for pest control.

In the mass culture of entomophagous insects the main problem is generally the production of food for the beneficial species. This may be accomplished by rearing host insects on suitable plants or plant parts, or by developing an artificial food medium for either the host insect or the parasite or predator.

The discovery, in 1916, that mealybugs and black scale could be reared successfully on potato sprouts marked the beginning of mass culture and periodic release of parasites and predators for pest control according to Smith and Armitage (23). Millions of parasites and predators of black scale and mealybug pests of citrus have been reared on host insects mass-produced on potato sprouts.

Some other plant parts that have been used successfully in the mass culture of host insects for parasite production are potato tubers and the fruits of squash and citron melons. These serve for the production of California red scale, *Aonidiella aurantii* (Mask.); San Jose scale, *Aspidiotus perniciosus* (Comst.); oleander scale, *Aspidiotus hederae* (Vall.), and many others. Ripe oranges, squash, and citron melons have been used in the mass culture of the six-spotted mite, *Eotetranychus sexmaculatus* (Riley), and the two-spotted spider mite, *Tetranychus telarius* (L.).

In a number of cases artificial media have been utilized suc-

cessfully in the mass culture of host insects, parasites, and predators. Hagen (13) found that egg deposition of the predator *Chrysopa californica* (Coq.) was greatly increased by adding an enzymatic hydrolysate of brewers' yeast to the honey solution fed to the adults. Using the same food supplement with host insects, Hagen and Finney (14) reported that fecundity of females of the oriental fruit fly was very greatly increased.

House and Traer (15) found that the larvae of the sacrophagid fly *Pseudosarcophaga affinis* Fall. parasitic in the spruce budworm, *Choristoneura fumiferana* (Clem.), could be reared on an artificial medium. They showed that a proper mixture of pork liver and fish was fully acceptable to the parasite larvae and that a much higher proportion reached maturity on this medium than on the normal insect host. This development permitted year-round production of the parasite in any desired quantity.

Although there are a number of such cases in which insects can be produced on artificial food media, it is felt that this method applied to the production of parasites and predators is still in the early pioneering stage. Undoubtedly the knowledge of insect nutrition utilized in this respect will play an ever increasing role in the use of parasites and predators for pest control.

Conservation and Augmentation of Native or Established Parasites and Predators

ECONOMIC IMPORTANCE OF NATIVE PARASITES AND PREDATORS

Parasites and predators of insect pests are present and exerting some influence on the population of pest species in practically every field and habitat where insect pests occur. These beneficial insects consistently control many insect pests which, in their absence, would cause serious economic loss. Of the total number of insect pest species throughout the world, very likely the vast majority are under satisfactory natural control. Other control measures, such as the use of insecticides, are necessary only in instances where the beneficial insects or other

natural-control factors fail to maintain pest species below the level of economic importance.

Results obtained from long-term field studies on the biological balance in California avocado groves will serve to illustrate the great economic importance of native parasites and predators.

Pest control treatment is seldom necessary in California avocado orchards. Each year only a fraction of one per cent of the total avocado acreage receives chemical pest control. Field studies now in progress have shown that despite seeming freedom from destructive pests, there are many insect and mite pests of potential economic importance present in avocado orchards throughout southern California, but that in general they are under almost perfect biological balance (10). Some of the potential pests, such as the long-tailed mealybug, *Pseudococcus adonicum* (L.); black scale, *Saissetia oleae* (Bern.); and soft (brown) scale, *Coccus hesperidum* (L.), are controlled by introduced parasites, but most of them are controlled by native parasites and predators. Numerous experiments have shown that, in any area, when parasites and predators are excluded from avocado trees, damaging populations of various mite and insect pests soon develop.

In one experiment reported by Fleschner (11), for a period of 84 days all parasites and predators were removed by hand from a portion of an avocado tree in an orchard in the coastal area of San Diego County. During this time the omnivorous looper, *Sabulodes caberata* Gn., the six-spotted mite, the long-tailed mealybug, the avocado brown mite, *Oligonychus punicae* (Hirst), and the latania scale developed to high populations on the portions of the tree from which the beneficial insects were removed. The first three of these developed to seriously damaging proportions.

In order to save the leaves on the experimental portion of this tree it became necessary to remove the larvae of the omnivorous looper. However, a careful study of the natural balance of the looper larvae at this time disclosed that over 90 per cent of the very young larvae were parasitized by one or the

other of two species of small wasps, *Apanteles caberatae* Mues. and *Meteorus tersus* Mues. These two native parasitic wasps were largely responsible for the excellent natural control of the loopers that was maintained in the rest of the orchard during these studies. Throughout this entire experimental period there were no observed pest problems on the rest of the test tree or on any other tree in the grove.

In this instance, predatory *Typhlodromus* mites, a small black lady beetle, *Stethorus picipes* Casey, and a small staphylinid beetle, *Oligota oviformis* (Casey), all natural predators, were primarily responsible for the control of the avocado brown mite and the six-spotted mite.

This simple experiment clearly demonstrated that, except for the protective action of native parasites and predators, the damage caused throughout the grove by the pests mentioned would have been truly disastrous.

Other such studies showed that when beneficial insects were removed by hand from certain castor-bean plants, the plants soon lost most of their leaves because of feeding damage of the two-spotted mite, while the surrounding plants remained relatively free of mites and showed practically no mite damage. Similarly, in several instances where predators of citrus red mites were removed by hand from certain citrus trees, these trees were much more seriously damaged by the mites than were surrounding trees to which the predators had access (9).

At Riverside, which is located in the interior avocado-growing area, *Amorbia* may quickly build up to seriously damaging populations when parasites and predators are excluded by the use of screen cages or cloth sleeve cages. Upon removal of such barriers excellent natural balance is attained in a surprisingly short period of time.

SOME CULTURAL METHODS THAT INFLUENCE BIOLOGICAL BALANCE IN AVOCADO ORCHARDS

Data obtained from a number of widely distributed avocado orchards have shown that the presence of ants, of certain types

of dust deposits, and of certain insecticides may markedly decrease the effectiveness of various parasites and predators.

Ants.   A number of species of honeydew-feeding ants play an important role in the biological balance of certain agricultural pests. The influence of ants in this respect lies in the fact that numerous species of honeydew-secreting insects are effectively controlled by their natural enemies when ants are absent, but not when ants are present. The ant, in gathering the honeydew supplied by such insects, tends more or less automatically to protect them from their natural enemies. This protective effect is not limited to the honeydew-producing species but is often extended to other phytophagous forms such as mites and diaspid scale insects, when such forms happen to be within the area of ant activity as shown by Flanders (7) and DeBach *et al.* (4).

In avocado orchards the Argentine ant, *Iridomyrmex humilis* Mayr, while gathering honeydew from colonies of long-tailed mealybugs, soft (brown) scale, and black scale, protects them from natural enemies, and thus is frequently responsible for the development of damaging populations of these pests. These same ants also disturb or kill natural enemies of other pest species in their vicinity and are therefore frequently responsible for increasing the populations of such non-honeydew-secreting pests as the six-spotted mite, avocado brown mite, and latania scale.

In one avocado orchard, young trees were being seriously damaged by high populations of soft (brown) scale attended by Argentine ants. After the ants were eliminated by a ground spray of chlordane, the natural enemies soon brought the scale pest under excellent biological control.

Repeated observations and field experiments have shown that control of Argentine ants in California avocado orchards will result in a more effective biological control.

Dust.   Bartlett (1), Flanders (6), and others have documented the fact that various types of dust deposits inhibit the activity of parasites and predators of phytophagous insects.

In avocado orchards pest problems have been known to be

created when the activities of natural enemies were inhibited by dust deposits produced by frequent disking of loose dry soil; by dust created during installation of large pipe lines; by ash deposits produced by nearby burning of rubbish; by dust deposits from frequently used field roads; by dust from an adjacent turkey ranch; and by dust produced during the development of a nearby housing project. When the sources of such dust deposits were eliminated, a properly corrected, satisfactory biological balance in the orchard was, in general, soon reestablished.

Almost any measure taken to prevent dust deposits from forming on the trees in avocado orchards has been helpful in maintaining an effective biological balance.

Insecticides. In order to test the effect of certain insecticides and acaricides on the biological balance in avocado orchards, two long-term experimental blocks were set up in previously untreated avocado orchards in the intermediate avocado-growing area of Santa Paula, California.

At the time these experiments were started, no insecticidal treatments had ever been applied to either of the avocado orchards and no pest had ever developed to economic proportions; a very low population of latania scale occurred throughout the orchards; occasional colonies of avocado brown mites could be found on dusty trees near a field road; in a half-day's search several caterpillars of *Amorbia* or omnivorous looper could be found.

Yearly applications of Aramite, Ovotran, parathion, malathion. light-medium oil, DDT, dieldrin, and wettable sulfur were made in plots of 16 trees each, in both orchards. By the end of the first year serious populations of avocado brown mite had developed in the DDT and dieldrin plots. By the end of the second year, damaging populations of *Amorbia*, omnivorous looper, and latania scale had developed in the dieldrin and sulfur plots.

The foregoing experiments clearly demonstrate that the ill-advised use of insecticides, through destruction of beneficial insects, may intensify pest problems in avocado orchards.

INTEGRATED PEST CONTROL

Studies now in progress are designed to develop means of controlling sporadic outbreaks of *Amorbia* or the omnivorous looper without upsetting the balance of other pest species in the orchard. These studies include the use of a selective insecticide or a spray application of an insect pathogen which would give emergency control of *Amorbia* or the omnivorous looper but have little or no detrimental effect on the efficiency of parasites and predators.

Integrated pest control programs offer great possibilities for expanding the use of parasites and predators in pest control work. In California, for example, introduced parasites, native predators, disease organisms, and selective insecticides are all utilized in an integrated program to control the spotted alfalfa aphid. In this instance it is estimated that parasites, predators, and insect pathogens saved the alfalfa growers about eight million dollars during 1957.

Conscientious efforts to conserve and augment beneficial insects through such cultural methods as have been discussed will undoubtedly result in ever increasing benefits derived from parasites and predators in pest control.

REFERENCES

1. Bartlett, B. R. The action of certain "inert" dust materials on parasitic hymenoptera. *J. Econ. Entomol.* 44(6):891-896 (1951).
2. Clausen, C. P. Insect parasitism and biological control. *Ann. Entomol. Soc. Am.* 29(2):201-223 (1936).
3. ——. Biological control of insect pests in the continental United States. *U. S. Dept. Agr. Tech. Bull. 1139*, June 1956.
4. DeBach, Paul, C. A. Fleschner, and E. J. Dietrick. A biological check method for evaluating the effectiveness of entomophagous insects. *J. Econ. Entomol.* 44(5):763-766 (1951).
5. Dodd, A. P. *The Biological Campaign against Prickly-Pear.* Published under the authority of the Commonwealth Prickly-pear Board of Government Printer, Brisbane, Queensland, October 1940.

6. Flanders, S. E. Dust as an inhibiting factor in the reproduction of insects. *J. Econ. Entomol.* 34(3):470-471 (1941).

7. ———. The role of the ant in the biological control of homopterous insects. *Can. Entomologist* 83(4):93-98 (1951).

8. ———. The organization of biological control and its historical development. *Mededeel. Landbowhogeschool en opzolkingsstations von de Staat te Gent.* 20(3): 257-270 (1955).

9. Fleschner, C. A. Host-plant resistance as a factor influencing population density of citrus red mites on orchard trees. *J. Econ. Entomol.* 45(4):687-695. 1952.

10. ———. Biological control of avocado pests. *Calif. Avocado Soc. Yearbook* 38:125-129 (1953-54).

11. ———. Natural balance of mite pests in an avocado grove. *Calif. Avocado Soc. Yearbook* 39:155-162 (1955).

12. Hafez, M., and R. L. Doutt. Biological evidence of sibling species in *Aphytis maculicornis* (Masi) (Hymenoptera, Aphelinidae). *Can. Entomologist* 86:90-96 (1954).

13. Hagen, K. S. Fecundity of *Chrysopa californica* as affected by synthetic foods. *J. Econ. Entomol.* 43(1):101 (1950).

14. Hagen, K. S., and G. L. Finney. A food supplement for effectively increasing the fecundity of certain tephritid species. *J. Econ. Entomol.* 43(5):735 (1950).

15. House, H. L., and M. G. Traer. An artificial food for rearing *Pseudosarcophaga affinis* Fall., a parasite of the spruce budworm, *Choristoneura fumiferana* (Clem.) *Ann. Rept. Entomol. Soc. Ontario* 79:50-53, 1948 (1949).

16. Jenkins, C. F. H. Biological control in western Australia. *J. Roy. Soc. W. Australia* 32:1-17, 1945-46 (1948).

17. Kamal, M. Biological control projects in Egypt, with a list of introduced parasites and predators. *Bull. soc. Fouad I Entomol.* 35:205-220 (1951).

18. Miller, D., A. F. Clark, and L. J. Dumbleton. Biological control of noxious insects and weeds in New Zealand. *New Zealand J. Sci. Technol.* 18:579-593 (1936).

19. O'Connor, B. A. Biological control of insects and plants in Fiji. *Proc. VII Pacific Sci. Congr., New Zealand* 4:278-293, 1949 (1953).

20. Pemberton, C. E. History of the Entomology Department Experiment Station H.S.P.A. *Hawaiian Planters' Record* 52(1): 53-90 (1948).

21. Pemberton, C. E. The biological control of insects in Hawaii. *Proc. VII Pacific Sci. Congr.* 4:220-223, 1949 (1953).

22. Smith, H. S. Biological control of weeds in the United States *Proc. Entomol. Soc. Wash.* 49 (6):169-170 (1947).

23. Smith, H. S., and H. M. Armitage. The biological control of mealybugs attacking citrus. *Calif. Agr. Expt. Sta. Bull.* 509, 1931.

24. Sweetman, H. L. *The Biological Control of Insects.* Comstock Publishing Society, Ithaca, N. Y., 1936.

25. Tothill, J. D., T. H. C. Taylor, and R. W. Paine. *The Coconut Moth in Fiji.* Imperial Bureau of Entomology, London, 1930.

Effects of Disease and Insect Control Practices on Biological Balance in Apple Orchards*

A. D. PICKETT

*Crop Insect Section, Science Service Laboratory,
Kentville, Nova Scotia*

In the last decade marked changes in pest control practices have occurred. The stimulus of World War II on research in organic chemistry triggered the introduction of a large number of new chemicals into the pesticide field with the result that practically any species of pest may now be effectively dealt with, at least on a short-term basis, by the application of a suitable pesticide. But, as in the field of human conflicts, the fact that our arsenals have never been so well equipped does little to minimize our increasing sense of insecurity. As Kennedy (1) has aptly pointed out, "The chemical pest controller of today is wonderfully armed, but he still bears a remarkable resemblance to young David with his flock in the Bible, fending off wild beasts by hurling things at them."

That many species of pests become tolerant to some pesticides is now well established. The control of certain species appears to have almost developed into a race between the chemist in developing new and effective pesticides and the pest in developing new genetic strains that are tolerant of the new materials. As this contest is proceeding at an accelerating pace it seems logical, for obvious reasons, that other means of control should be investigated.

To my way of thinking, the economic entomologist, if he is to make a lasting contribution to his profession, must be a student of population phenomena and concern himself with the factors

* Contribution No. 3751, Entomology Division, Science Service, Department of Agriculture, Ottawa, Canada.

affecting biological balances, an extremely interesting although at times a somewhat frustrating study. My present assignment is to deal with problems concerning imbalances in populations caused by the use of pesticides. An excellent summary of the world literature on this subject has been prepared recently by Ripper (5).

"Balance," as considered here, is that condition that would exist in the absence of artificial control; it concerns the relative densities of interacting species, not absolute densities.

It was pointed out by Nicholson (3) that the repeated use of an insecticide does not necessarily lower, over an extended period, the population level of the pest species against which it is directed. Our investigations in apple orchards in Nova Scotia indicate that two phenomena may be involved: resistance to the pesticide may develop and the natural control agents may be destroyed. Although other factors may at times intervene, they seem insignificant in the cases we have investigated. Another phenomenon that frequently follows the repeated use of pesticides, especially with perennial crops, is the increase to pest status of species not previously injurious.

Influence of Fungicides

It is nearly thirty years since I first observed the results of imbalance caused by fungicides. At that time in Nova Scotia most apple growers were using considerable quantities of sulfur in their spray schedules whereas a few used only copper fungicides. In the autumn of 1929 a survey of the pest situation in approximately fifty orchards in a rather small area revealed that all but two orchards had rather heavy infestations of the European red mite. These two had never been treated with sulfur. All the others had had sulfur in one form or another. It was not until 1943 that we had an opportunity to start investigations on this phenomenon.

The following are a few of the many instances of imbalances investigated in our laboratory. Outstanding are the investigations on the severe outbreaks of the oystershell scale, *Lepidosaphes ulmi* (L.), reported by Lord (2). These studies

showed conclusively that in Nova Scotia this scale is normally controlled by a parasitic chalcid, *Aphytis mytilaspidis* (LeB.), and a predacious mite, *Hemisarcoptes malus* (Shimer). Figure 1

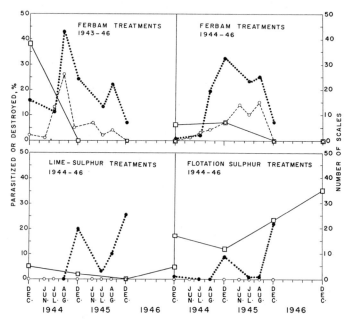

Fig. 1.   Percentage of scales parasitized by *Aphytis mytilaspidis* (dotted line) and destroyed by *Hemisarcoptes malus* (broken line), and numbers of mature scales per five terminals (solid line).

shows the variations in density of the scale and its two important natural control agents after treatments with three fungicides in replicated single row plots after several years of treatments with sulfur fungicides. These investigations made it possible to devise a spray schedule that corrected the imbalance between the scale and its natural control agents and changed the status of this insect from that of a major to an insignificant pest.

That a balance exists between populations of the European red mite, *Metatetranychus ulmi* (Koch), and those of its predators in orchards not treated with chemicals, and that this balance may be impaired by the use of certain fungicides,

whereas others tend to preserve it, is shown by Fig. 2. There were substantially greater fluctuations in density in the ferbam and sulfur than in the glyodin and phenylmercuric acetate

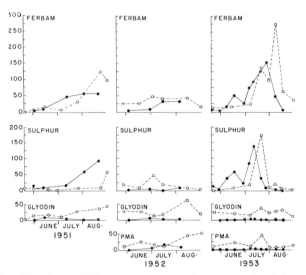

FIG. 2.   Numbers of the European red mite per leaf (solid line) and of predators per tapping tray (broken line) in an apple orchard after treatments with four fungicides for two or three consecutive years.

(PMA) plots. In the three plots treated in 1951, the mite populations were rather low in the spring, but by the time the spraying season was over, the predator complex had been disrupted sufficiently by ferbam and sulfur to allow substantial increases in phytophagous mites. This created conditions favorable to an influx of some of the larger predators which are not adversely influenced by ferbam or sulfur. These were mostly anthocorids and mirids, the mirid *Hyaloides harti* Kngt. being the most abundant. Since prey was available late in the season on these two plots, the predators deposited their eggs on these trees, and the 1952 generation was sufficient to reduce the phytophagous mite population to a low density early in the summer despite the fact that the fungicide treatments were continued throughout the spraying season. The scarcity of prey late in

1952 resulted in comparatively low predator densities in the spring of 1953, which allowed the mite populations to rise. This increase was followed rather closely by an increase in predators with a resultant decrease in mites to a low level. This condition is contrasted to that where glyodin or phenylmercuric acetate was used and the relatively smooth curves showing the population fluctuations. It should be mentioned here that glyodin is known to have some miticidal properties but that these are not sufficient to prevent mite populations from reaching high densities when the predator populations are reduced to practically zero through the use of a widely toxic pesticide such as DDT. Not enough work has been done with phenylmercuric acetate to determine its miticidal properties, but all the predators tested have shown a high degree of tolerance to it.

Investigations reported in 1949 (4) showed that the use of

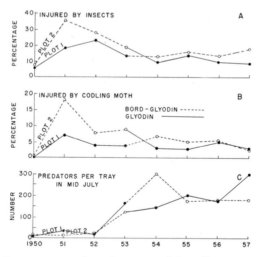

Fig. 3.   Percentages of apples injured by all insects and by the codling moth, and numbers of predators per tray, in mid-July, in two 5-acre plots of apple in successive years with slightly different fungicide treatments, the treatments having been reversed in 1954.

a sulfur fungicide in a spray schedule for five consecutive years resulted in twice as much damage from the codling moth as for bordeaux mixture. Further tests with other fungicides have

shown that only slight differences in the spray program may lead to substantial differences in codling moth damage. Figure 3 shows the results of treating two 5-acre plots in an orchard where the only difference in spray program was that one plot was treated with glyodin throughout and the other plot with two or three bordeaux applications early in the season, followed by three or four glyodin applications, and finally by a single light bordeaux application. After four years the treatments on the plots were reversed so that each plot had four years of each treatment. Figure 3 shows also the total insect damage to fruit and the numbers of predators per tapping tray in this orchard. There was an inverse relation between the numbers of predators and the insect damage, allowance being made for the lag in time required by the predators to become effective. It should be pointed out too that the figures for total predators taken are only very rough approximations. We know too little about the relative importance of the different species and the periods in which they are most effective.

Influence of Insecticides

More attention has been focused on the imbalances initiated in apple orchards by insecticides than on those caused by fungicides. The following are a few examples.

TABLE I. Phytophagous and Predacious Mites (Typhlodromids) per 100 Leaves Found on Apple Trees after Treatment with DDT or Ryania

Date of examination	DDT[a]		Ryania[a]	
	European red mite	Typhlodromids	European red mite	Typhlodromids
June 25	35	20	5	25
July 9	65	10	170	40
July 22	155	0	45	45
Aug. 6	695	0	25	120
Aug. 28	2030	0	25	50

[a] Sprays applied on June 29 and July 6 and 13, 1953.

Table I indicates the numbers of the European red mite and a group of predacious mites that prey on the former, in a plot

TABLE II

Treatment	July 16	July 17	July 22	July 31	Aug. 12
DDT	2	0	—	1	1
Ryania	37	63	17	13	43

TABLE III

Treatment	DDT	Ryania
Predacious thrips	9	239
Miridae	3	151
Coccinellidae	0	9
Pentatomidae	1	14
Hymenoptera	41	252
Spiders	15	98
Phytophagous and incidental species	914	2185

treated with DDT and another treated with ryania for control of the codling moth. In these plots predacious insects were also adversely affected by DDT as compared to ryania. This is shown in Table II by the average numbers taken per tapping tray during the four weeks following the final treatment. The total numbers of insects and spiders on a mature tree in each plot four days after the final treatment as determined by fumigation under a tree tent are given in Table III.

That codling moth populations increase more rapidly after applications of DDT than after ryania is shown from records taken during five consecutive years in the 5-acre plot mentioned before which was treated with ryania in 1953. The figures in Table IV are for average percentages of injured apples after

TABLE IV

Year	Insecticides	Stings	Deep entries
1950	DDT	1	1
1951	None	5	38
1952	Lead arsenate	21	32
1953	Ryania	7	0.2
1954	None	0.4	1.4

treatments with the various insecticides. These data in themselves would not be very convincing were it not for the fact

that they reflect so sharply the experiences of many fruit growers in Nova Scotia who have used both DDT and ryania for codling moth control. The extensive damage from the codling moth in 1952 after lead arsenate treatments indicates a relatively high degree of tolerance by the larvae to this insecticide.

These results suggest that it is important to avoid, insofar as is possible in commercial practice, the destruction of biological control agents. Economic entomologists and others concerned with pest control appear to have given scant attention to this aspect in designing spray schedules. Expediency frequently demands such prompt action to prevent serious economic losses that there is not time to study adequately the biotic factors; but to ignore them is unscientific and probably, in the long view, uneconomic. That this approach to the control of orchard pests is no longer an academic concept can be attested to by Nova Scotia fruit growers, the majority of whom have accepted the principle of biological balance and recognize it in planning their control programs.

REFERENCES

1. Kennedy, J. S. Insect population balance and chemical control of pests. *Chem. & Ind. 1953*:1329-1332.
2. Lord, F. T. The influence of spray programs on the fauna of apple orchards in Nova Scotia. II. Oystershell scale. *Can. Entomologist 72*:196-209 (1947).
3. Nicholson, A. J. Indirect effects of spray practice on pest populations. *7 Intern. Kongr. Entomol., Berlin, 1938 4*:3022-3028 (1939).
4. Pickett, A. D. A critique on insect chemical control methods. *Can. Entomologist 81*:67-76 (1950).
5. Ripper, W. E. Effect of pesticides on the balance of arthropod populations. *Ann. Rev. Entomol. 1*:403-438 (1956).

Disease Resistance in Animals

Nelson F. Waters

Agricultural Research Service,
United States Department of Agriculture,
East Lansing, Michigan

The greatest hazard in raising livestock anywhere in the world results from disease and parasites. In the United States alone livestock mortality can be estimated, conservatively, to approach one billion dollars annually. If we add to this the potential loss due to the unprofitable use of cropland and grassland, the cost of identifying, controlling, and combating disease, and the downgrading because of poor market quality due to sickness, then the total economic loss becomes staggering. Of equal concern is the constant danger of transmitting to man many of the diseases and parasites known to be present in livestock, domestic pets, and wild animals.

Genetic investigations on resistance to disease in the larger domestic animals, such as beef and dairy cattle, horses, swine, and sheep are nearly nonexistent, and this limitation is because of many practical and intrinsic difficulties. This is understandable because of the long generation time, restriction of family size, lack of facilities, and the economic worth of individual animals. For this reason, a search for methods of control and eradication of animal diseases and parasites has received the greatest attention and has had remarkable success.

Many of the diseases that affect domestic animals are caused by minute forms of life which include the bacteria, viruses, rickettsiae, and protozoa. We have accepted more or less the belief that the resistance and susceptibility of host animals are the deciding factors in determining evidence of disease. Certainly, host response is an important factor, but as we increase our knowledge of microorganisms, there comes a realization

209

that these minute parasites must be credited with an important, if not equal, part in disease control. It is well to realize that all the microorganisms are living animals and their existence is governed by the same biological laws that dictate life in the higher animals. The virus and bacteria, for example, have genetic potentialities and their action on the host is dependent on their individual genotypes. Therefore, in studying animal diseases, we must consider the interrelationship of the genes of the host and the genes of the pathogen.

The environmental variable must, likewise, be injected into any discussion of host-pathogen relationship, for we have long since accepted the fact that the environment plays an important part in determining the expression of nearly all genes and more frequently than not this environmental influence is most difficult to anticipate or control. Thus, in all genetic studies we recognize heredity and environment as separate components and realize that well-designed experiments should be so organized as to permit a measure of the influence of the environment as well as the contributions of the host and pathogen.

Resistance or Escape

Absence of disease manifestations in herds or flocks of animals does not necessarily mean innate resistance. Nearly, if not all, animals, both resistant and susceptible, have natural defense mechanisms that prevent or reduce the entrance of disease-causing agents into the body tissues. It is only when these natural barriers are broken down that the host animal is overcome. Likewise, any invasion by infecting agents into the body tissue permits an expression of the inherent ability of the host animal to resist disease.

Parasite vectors are equipped to pierce natural body barriers and deposit disease agents into a host animal. Rocky Mountain spotted fever, cattle tick fever, malaria, yellow fever, typhus, and tularemia are examples of diseases distributed by such vectors.

It is not always known whether resistant animals repel or eliminate the causative disease agent, thus preventing any prop-

agation, or whether immunization of the host prevents any measurable clinicopathological manifestation of disease. In either case the genetic constitution of the animal may be the deciding factor in expressing the degree of resistance or immunity.

High degrees of resistance to many infectious animal diseases involving a pathogen exist. For the most part, however, an expression of genetic resistance is polygenic, and rarely is it possible to demonstrate repeatedly complete genetic resistance or complete susceptibility. Frequently, the ability to demonstrate with sufficient numbers the genetic reaction of a host to a specific pathogen necessitates the artificial introduction of the pathogen at high dosages into the host. To be sure, this permits standardization of dosage promoting a uniform challenge, but it frequently differs from natural transmission and may be greatly influenced by the age of the host, and the route and dose of inoculum. For example, erythroblastic leukosis rarely occurs naturally among chickens but inoculation at an early age with a massive dose, either intraperitoneally or intravenously, will cause heavy losses among susceptible hosts.

Genes for Resistance

There are but few known examples in animals of single gene differences expressing resistance or susceptibility to disease. This inability to demonstrate single gene differences for complete resistance is not due to lack of experimentation. Numerous references involving degrees of resistance in animals appear in the literature. Gowen's (4) statement hardly can be improved upon that "Examples of host resistance are known for the whole range of pathogenic agents, bacteria, fungi, protozoa, helminths, viruses, and chemical poisons. In fact, so far as I am aware, no investigator who has adequately sought inherited host differences in disease response has failed to find them."

Sabin (19) demonstrated the complete resistance of Princeton Rockefeller Institute albino mice to 17 D strain of yellow fever virus, and thus provided an example of precise genetic response in host-pathogen relationship. Sabin demonstrated that PRI albino mice may show 100 per cent resistance to yel-

low fever, whereas Swiss mice are 100 per cent susceptible. Crosses between the PRI albino mice and Swiss mice suggest that resistance to 17 D strain yellow fever virus is dependent upon a single autosomal dominant factor for expression.

Investigations at the U. S. Regional Poultry Research Laboratory provide an example of an apparent autosomal dominant single gene pair capable of providing complete resistance to induced erythroblastic leukosis in chickens. Erythroblastosis is a malignant neoplasm of the bone marrow; the cell involved is the erythroblast which proliferates intrasinusoidally, with little or no differentiation, throughout the marrow tissue. In its terminal stages erythroblastosis is manifested by a leukemic state and leucostasis, resulting in a generalized acute passive hyperemia and death of the chicken usually prior to 100 days of age. Instances of naturally occurring erythroblastosis are rare; however, chickens inoculated at an early age will succumb or show no apparent effect, depending upon their genetic makeup. Studies of numerous matings of chickens have isolated 13 males, of 37 tested, which when mated to 107 different dams were capable of transmitting complete resistance to 733 progeny. Similarly, 68 dams transmitted complete resistance to their progeny, even though the sires with which they were mated did produce some affected progeny when mated to other dams.

The evidence that heredity is an important factor in resistance and susceptibility to disease has been adequately established. Lambert and Knox (12) demonstrated that selective breeding decreased perceptibly the mortality from fowl typhoid. Gowen and his co-workers at the Iowa Agricultural Experiment Station have made major contributions to our knowledge of genetic resistance to mouse and fowl typhoid.

Waters and Prickett (23) and Waters (21, 22) demonstrated that inbreeding and selection were successful in establishing six inbred lines of chickens showing various degrees of resistance and susceptibility to visceral lymphomatosis. In these experiments none of the chickens was inoculated, and exposure to infection was dependent entirely on naturally occurring visceral lymphomatosis. Hutt et al. (11) and Hutt and Cole (10)

established strains of chickens resistant and susceptible to fowl leukosis and, here also, exposure to infection was dependent on natural transmission.

Exhaustive studies on cancer in mice show definitely that the hereditary makeup of the mouse host influences the degree of resistance to nearly all types of tumors. Indeed, under controlled conditions, tumor incidence varies from complete absence to 100 per cent susceptibility. Despite this marked difference, it has not been possible to demonstrate that single gene differences are responsible for the presence or absence of tumors. There is evidence that genes expressing susceptibility to mouse tumors are influenced by other known genes. Numerous exciting factors including chemical, hormonal, radiation, temperature, and the presence of other pathogenic agents have some influence on tumor frequency in mice.

Numerous noninfectious pathological conditions are found in the animal kingdom. When such defects or abnormalities are found in domestic animals, it usually results in an economic loss. Many of these disorders may be classed as hereditary diseases in that the genes of the host animal alone, involving either one or few pairs of genes, are responsible for deviations from normal.

Crew (1) reported a pathological defect in Dexter cattle termed achondroplasia, which results in extremely short legs, together with a generalized syndrome of morphological disturbances throughout the body. This defect occurs with regularity in about one-quarter of the calves of the Dexter breed of cattle. Interestingly, such matings also produce the Kerry-type cattle having longer legs and narrower heads than the Dexter cattle. In the case of Dexter cattle we find the desirable type of short-legged, broad-headed individual only in a heterozygous condition, which consequently does not breed true.

Wriedt (24) and Mohr (17, 18) report the occurrence of achondroplasia in cattle that is less extreme in its manifestations and is recessive in nature. The occurrence of achondroplasia in cattle is not necessarily confined to any one particular

breed. This achondroplastic defect has been reported in dogs, pigeons, chickens, and many other animals, including man.

Genes for dwarfism in both beef and dairy cattle may be presumed to be widespread in cattle populations. Gregory and Carroll (7) reported the presence of dwarfism in several breeds and refer to earlier work on dwarfism by a number of investigators. Although most of the dwarf types are dependent on recessive genes for expression, such recessiveness may have its origin on different chromosomes and at different loci. Further, the evidence is suggestive that the dwarf syndrome, though superficially similar in expression, may not be the same in all breeds of cattle and is certainly not the same in different genera.

Lush *et al.* (14) reported the condition in goats wherein there is a failure of one or both testes to descend into the scrotum. Hadley and Warwick (8), McKenzie (15), and McPhee and Buckley (16) reported similar instances of cryptorchidism in livestock. This defect is inherited as a recessive, and is sex-limited in that it is only manifested in the male.

Numerous other defects in the larger animals have a genetic basis. Likewise, many lethal genes cause death at, or prior to, birth in mammals, or at hatching time in birds. Occurrence of lethals in domestic animals causes appreciable economic loss. The presence of lethals and semilethals in man, of which there are an appreciable number, is cause for much sorrow and anguish as well as great financial sacrifice. Some of the more common disorders are listed by Eaton (2), Lerner (13), Hutt (9), Gowen (5, 6), Sorsby (20), and Gates (3).

Our greatest battles against the diseases and parasites of domestic animals have been waged successfully by quarantine measures, testing for carriers of disease, control of animal parasites, and, when necessary, mass slaughter of infected animals. More recently the use of antisera, antibiotics, and other prophylactic means has held in check many of the diseases and parasites known to affect animals. Individual testing of animals for carriers of disease has become a standard practice. Bovine tuberculosis and brucellosis in cattle and swine, Salmonella pullorum of chickens and turkeys, and fowl typhoid are ex-

amples of standard testing procedures that have resulted in a drastic reduction of these diseases in herds and flocks. Control and eradication of diseases and parasites of livestock through the application of protective measures is not complete, and constant vigilance is necessary to hold the gains made while continuing the search for newer methods of control.

Nearly, if not all, animals would respond to genetic selection for resistance to disease if emphasis were directed toward this method of control. In most instances, however, such a genetic approach would not be economically sound in view of the proven control methods now practiced. Despite the paucity of genetic studies on disease resistance in the larger domestic animals, many genetic investigations involving small animals have contributed much to our knowledge of disease resistance. Further, many of the abnormalities and disorders of a non-infectious nature in animals are gene directed and a genetic approach is the only method of control.

REFERENCES

1. Crew, F. A. E. The significance of an achondroplasia-like condition met with in cattle. *Proc. Roy. Soc. (London)* B95:228-255 (1923).
2. Eaton, O. N. A summary of lethal characters in animals and man. *J. Heredity* 28:320-326 (1937).
3. Gates, R. R. *Human Genetics,* Vols. 1 and 2. The Macmillan Company, New York, 1946.
4. Gowen, John W. Contributions of genetics to understanding of animal disease. *J. Heredity* 28:233-240 (1937).
5. ————. Inheritance of immunity in animals. *Ann. Rev. Microbiol.* 2:215-254 (1948).
6. ————. Genetics and disease resistance. *Genetics in the 20th Century,* Chap. 19, pp. 401-429. The Macmillan Company, New York, 1951.
7. Gregory, P. W., and F. D. Carroll. Evidence for the same dwarf genes in Hereford, Aberdeen-Angus, and certain other breeds of cattle. *J. Heredity* 47:107-111 (1956).
8. Hadley, F. B., and B. L. Warwick. Inherited defects of livestock. *J. Am. Vet. Med. Assoc.* 70:492 (1927).

9. Hutt, F. B. *Genetics of the Fowl*. McGraw-Hill Book Co., New York, 1949.

10. Hutt, F. B., and R. K. Cole. On fleas, blood and the control of leucosis. *World's Poultry Sci. J.* 9:7-13 (1953).

11. Hutt, F. B., R. K. Cole, and J. H. Bruckner. A test of fowls bred for resistance. *Poultry Sci.* 24:564-571 (1945).

12. Lambert, W. V., and C. W. Knox. Selection for resistance to fowl typhoid in the chicken with reference to inheritance. *Iowa Agr. Expt. Sta., Research Bull.* 153:261-295 (1932).

13. Lerner, I. M. Lethal and sublethal characters in farm animals. A check-list and proposed numbering system. *J. Heredity* 35: 219-224 (1944).

14. Lush, J. L., J. M. Jones, and W. H. Dameron. The inheritance of Cryptorchidism in goats. *Tex. Agr. Expt. Sta. Bull. 407*, 1930.

15. McKenzie, F. F. Anatomy of cryptorchid boars. Cryptorchidism in swine. *Missouri Agr. Expt. Sta. Bull. 300*, 1931.

16. McPhee, H. C., and S. S. Buckley. Inheritance of cryptorchidism in swine. *J. Heredity* 25:295-304 (1934).

17. Mohr, O. L. Über Letalfacktoren, mit Berüksichtigung ihres Verhaltens bei Haustieren und beim Menschen. *Z. induktive Abstammungs- u. Vererbungslehre* 41:59 (1926).

18. Mohr, O. L. Letalfaklorum bei Haustieren. *Züchtungskunde 4*: 105 (1929).

19. Sabin, Albert B. Nature of inherited resistance to viruses affecting the nervous system. *Proc. Natl. Acad. Sci. U. S.* 38:540-546 (1952).

20. Sorsby, A., Editor. *Clinical Genetics*. The C. V. Mosby Co., St. Louis, Mo., 1953.

21. Waters, Nelson F. Etiological relationship of visceral and neural lymphomatosis. *Poultry Sci.* 33:365-373 (1954).

22. Waters, Nelson F. Avian lymphomatosis mortality among inbred line crosses. *Proc. World's Poultry Congr. 10th Congr.*, Edinburgh, 1954. Article 61.

23. Waters, Nelson F., and C. O. Prickett. Types of lymphomatosis among different inbred lines of chickens. *Poultry Sci.* 25:501-508 (1946).

24. Wreidt, C. Letale Faktoren. *Z. Tierzücht. Züchtungskiol.* 3: 223 (1925).

Breeding Field Crops for Resistance to Diseases

Ernest H. Stanford

University of California, Davis

A review of the value of breeding to control field crop diseases reveals both encouraging and discouraging results. On the negative side we find great losses sustained each year in many of our field crops, despite the efforts of plant breeders. In 1954 a committee of the United States Department of Agriculture estimated that the annual losses due to diseases of field crops, including forages, amounted to nearly 2.4 billion dollars. This estimate is based on the average values for the 1942-51 period.

Results from Plant Breeding

On the positive side we find some plant diseases under effective control by the use of resistant varieties and losses due to many other diseases much reduced. Accurate determinations of benefits derived from use of disease-resistant varieties are difficult to make. Coons (5) in 1952 estimated that disease-resistant varieties increased production by 10 per cent. If we apply these estimates to the total value of field and forage crops reported by the committee cited above, we obtain a figure of $691 million for the annual value of disease-resistant varieties. There can be no question that our dollars spent for plant breeding programs are bringing in good returns.

The emphasis on disease resistance in most plant breeding programs is brought out by reviewing the recently improved varieties of field crops registered by the American Society of Agronomy. A summary of the varieties registered from 1948 to 1957 is given in Table I.

Although this does not represent all the improved varieties introduced during the period, it shows the importance of dis-

TABLE I.   Field Crops Registered by the American Society
of Agronomy, 1948–57

Crops	Total no. varieties registered	Varieties having disease resistance
Cereals and flax	58	51
Cotton	2	2
Grain sorghum	23	13
Soybeans	14	4
Forage legumes	6	3
Forage grasses	14	9

ease resistance. Of the grand total, about 70 per cent of these varieties have disease resistance mentioned as one of their outstanding characteristics. It is interesting to note that the cereals, flax, and cotton have a particularly high percentage of disease-resistant varieties. Perhaps this is due to the fact that these crops have been cultivated intensively for many years and also that breeding programs have been underway for a longer period of time.

The use of disease-resistant varieties offers the ideal method of disease control where such varieties can be produced, since once the variety is in the hands of the grower there is no further cost except the minor expense of maintaining pure seed stocks. Unfortunately, there are limitations on the production of disease-resistant varieties. With some diseases nearly complete control is now possible; in other cases, disease resistance does much to reduce losses, but the varieties lack complete resistance. In still other cases, no source of resistance is known and none may be possible.

The milo disease may be cited as an example where nearly complete control of a disease seems possible. Milo disease, caused by *Periconia circinata,* a soil-borne pathogen, became widespread in the milo producing areas in the 1930's. Losses in badly infected fields ranged up to 100 per cent. Breeding programs were initiated in Kansas (18, 28) and California (16). A few resistant plants were found in most commercial varieties. Resistance appeared to be simply inherited, and the character was easily fixed in adapted varieties. Resistance to the disease

has been stable and the use of resistant varieties eliminates loss due to the disease.

Curly top of sugar beets represents a disease from which plant breeding has given a measure of protection to the grower, but not complete protection. This virus-caused disease is prevalent in the sugar beet areas west of the Rocky Mountains. For a time in the late twenties and early thirties it threatened to wipe out the sugar beet industry in these areas. In 1933 a disease-resistant variety, U. S. No. 1, was released, followed by other releases of improved varieties. Under severe conditions, curly top may still cause losses, but the level of resistance is adequate to make continued production of the crop feasible and profitable.

Resistant varieties have given farmers some protection from the cereal rusts. Varieties bred for resistance have given resistance for variable periods of time and frequently later have become susceptible to the disease on account of the change in the pathogenicity of the fungus producing the rust. Stakman (23) stated that in the past fifty years, wheat growers have had adequate protection against stem rust in twenty years, while losses have been reduced by the use of resistant varieties in other years.

Cotton root rot caused by *Phymatotrichum omnivorum* is a disease which attacks more than 2000 species of plants. In cotton it is particularly serious on certain soils of the Southwest. Losses in the state of Texas alone were estimated at 444,000 bales in 1928. A wide search for varieties or species of cotton having resistance has not given any positive results. This is not surprising in view of the broad range of host plants which the pathogen is capable of attacking. Any resistant plant, whether its resistance were morphological or chemical, would be required to differ widely from the normal patterns of growth or metabolism.

Alfalfa Breeders Use Many Methods

A brief review of the improvements made in alfalfa in a period of twenty-five years will illustrate advances made by

breeding in a relatively short period. While breeding for disease resistance in this country in cereal crops began as early as 1870, breeding in forage crops had its beginnings rather recently. Most alfalfa breeding programs started after 1925. In that year the cause of the bacterial wilt disease of alfalfa was identified by Jones (15). This disease soon spread to nearly all important alfalfa producing areas of the country. The severity of the disease, expressed by weakened plants and the rapid loss of stands in established fields, resulted in the initiation of breeding programs in a number of states. The first product of this effort, the wilt-resistant variety Ranger, was released in 1940 jointly by the United States Department of Agriculture and the Nebraska Agricultural Experiment Station. It was followed by other wilt-resistant varieties, Buffalo, Caliverde, Lahontan, and Vernal. By 1957, these varieties occupied well over half of the total alfalfa acreage in the United States.

An interesting sidelight was the effect of these improved alfalfa varieties on seed production. Five years after the release of the variety Ranger, the acreage planted to it was negligible because seed stocks were not available. Seed production was very low and uncertain in the principal consuming areas because of unfavorable climatic conditions. Under the sponsorship of the National Foundation Seed Stock Project extensive plantings were made in the Southwest under near ideal climatic conditions. Seed production of the single variety Ranger in 1956 was 40 million pounds, demonstrating for the first time that seed of an alfalfa variety could be produced in great volume outside its area of adaptation with assurance that all the inherent qualities of the variety would be maintained. This was made possible because the genetic identity of the variety was maintained by a strict system of certification involving identification of planting stocks, a limitation of one generation on seed grown outside of the areas of adaptation, and a series of inspections of fields and processing plants to prevent contamination and mixtures. We see then that the advent of a new disease was largely responsible for setting off of a chain reaction giving not only improved disease-resistant varieties but also a

more constant supply of high quality seed. Maintenance and increase of improved varieties are of vital importance if the breeder's efforts are not to be wasted.

While bacterial wilt has received the most attention, breeding for resistance to other diseases is becoming more and more important. Alfalfa is subject to some seventy-five diseases (8) caused by fungi, bacteria, viruses, and nematodes. Current breeding programs are directed toward developing varieties resistant to root and crown rots, foliar diseases, and nematodes.

Most of the new alfalfa varieties have been synthetics. That is, plants carrying the desired characteristics have been isolated from adapted varieties by clonal and progeny testing and the superior clones have been combined and allowed to interpollinate to produce the synthetics. This has been effective in cases where the adapted variety contained some plants carrying the desired resistance. Where the desired character was found only in a nonadapted variety, the backcross method has been effective in transferring resistance. This method makes possible a rapid program because it is not necessary to subject the variety to such a rigid evaluation program before release. Thus the variety Caliverde was developed in seven years by the backcross method.

The California alfalfa breeding program will be used to point out some additional features that may be of interest.

Breeding methods are adapted to fit the particular breeding problem. California Common 49 alfalfa, tolerant to the dwarf virus, was developed from the original California Common by selection, progeny testing, and resynthesis of selected clones (11). This method was selected when it was found that the variety carried a low percentage of tolerant plants and no better source of resistance was available. The Caliverde variety, resistant to bacterial wilt, leafspot, and mildew, was developed by backcrossing (25). No resistance to the wilt was found in California Common, hence it was necessary to transfer it, and backcrossing proved to be a rapid and effective way. Currently we are combining the disease resistance of Caliverde and California Common 49 into a single variety.

With varieties available to control bacterial wilt and the dwarf disease, the importance of some other diseases in depleting alfalfa stands comes into focus. While some of these diseases are more localized than wilt, their combined effect on the alfalfa production of the state is considerable. These diseases include *Rhizoctonia* root rot, *Phytophthora* root rot, *Fusarium* wilt and root and stem nematodes. Methods of inoculating and screening the plants for disease resistance were first worked out. A major part of this assignment fell to the Departments of Plant Pathology or Nematology. Their effective cooperation has been an important factor in the success of the program. The next step was the search for sources of the resistance to the disease. This began with our adapted varieties. If resistance occurs in even a low percentage of the plants, it is relatively simple to screen large numbers and recombine the resistant plants in a new synthetic, the procedure followed in the production of California Common 49 (11).

If resistance is not found in the adapted variety, varieties from other areas and foreign plant introductions must be tested for resistance. Such a procedure was followed in the search for satisfactory resistance to the root knot nematode. The hardy variety Vernal had satisfactory resistance. Crossing and back-crossing will be used to transfer this resistance to our improved Caliverde. The breeding programs for resistance to the various diseases mentioned above are at various stages in their advancement. Obviously the limitations of time and space make it impossible to screen sufficient numbers for resistance to all these diseases in a single generation, and hence the program must be carried on stepwise.

Keys to Success

Certain key factors are essential for the success of any breeding program. First is the necessity of effective methods of screening materials for disease resistance. In most cases, pathologists have provided satisfactory procedures for developing epiphytotics. However, the increasing complexity of breeding programs and the necessity of handling large volumes of ma-

terial often require even more efficient methods. A new procedure has been developed by Wheeler and Luke (31) for screening oats for resistance to Victoria blight. They found that the toxin produced by the pathogen, *Helminthosporium victorae* produced the same symptoms when sprayed on the germinating seedlings of the host plant as the pathogen itself. By producing large volumes of the toxin and spraying it on the germinating seedlings they were able to screen some 45 million seedlings for resistance to the blight. Several resistant plants were discovered by this procedure with the resistance apparently arising by natural mutation. The method was also effective when used on irradiated material.

Genes for resistance are the raw material with which the plant breeder works, and there is a constant need for new sources of resistance. The plant introduction program of the United States Department of Agriculture is filling an important need in this area (10). Foreign plant exploration, the Primary Plant Introduction Stations, and the seed storage facilities now being developed are essential to the success of the program. A more nearly complete cataloging of the genetic characteristics of the available stocks is important. A step in this direction has been made by the Food and Agriculture Organization of the United Nations with the cataloging of breeding materials for rice and wheat. This service should be extended to other crops.

Recently, irradiation technics have provided new genetic sources of disease resistance. These may be particularly useful where other sources of resistance to the pathogen or a specific biotype of it are not known, or where the resistance is in an otherwise undesirable stock. Some encouraging results have been reported for stem rust resistance in oats by Fry (7), Victoria blight resistance in oats by Konzak (17), resistance to race 15B of stem rust in wheat by Ausemus, Hsu and Sunderman (1), and resistance to leaf spot in peanuts by Gregory (9).

Related species have been an increasingly important source of genes for resistance in certain crops. Associated with interspecific crosses, particularly as the species become more divergent, are problems of embryo or seedling lethality, sterility, and

cytologically unstable derivatives. Notable advances have been made in overcoming these difficulties. Only a few of the successes in this area will be cited. The use of colchicine has made it easier to cross plants with differing chromosome numbers in a polyploid series (2). Embryo culture has made it possible to rear hybrid plants which are otherwise inviable (30). Grafting chlorophyll-deficient plants onto one of the parents has made it possible to raise these plants to maturity (22). The use of x-ray technics has made it possible to attach a small portion of an alien chromosome to one of the regular complements, and thus transfer to a nonhomologous chromosome a desirable gene without the undesirable traits associated with it (21).

Effective methods of manipulating the materials genetically to combine the disease resistance most efficiently with other desirable characteristics are, of course, of great importance. Pedigree selection has been the standard method for many years, with notable successes. The backcross method, effectively championed by F. N. Briggs, also has met with notable successes (3). Peterson (19) in surveying the breeding methods used to combat stem rust in wheat has reported an increasing use of the backcross method. The method of recurrent selection also finds application in cases where resistance is multigenic and the gene frequency is relatively low in the population. Jenkins *et al.* (12) has used this method successfully in improving the resistance of corn to leaf blight.

Shifting Pathogens

The problem of shifting physiologic races, outlined by Stakman and Christensen (24), is one of the most serious facing the plant breeder today. A number of workers have shown that the virulence of a pathogenic organism depends on genetic factors which are subject to the same processes of mutation and recombination that occur in their plant hosts and give rise to forms having different degrees of virulence. Thus varieties once resistant may become susceptible owing to a change in the prevalent races. The problem of shifting races is particularly impor-

tant with the rust and smut fungi. Stevens and Scott (26) have estimated that the average length of life of an oat variety in the corn belt is about five years, on account of the shift of races of rust. Thus it becomes a contest between the plant breeder and the pathogen to see which can develop new biotypes most rapidly.

Basic to the solution of the problem is a knowledge of the genes available for resistance to the disease in the host, a knowledge of the genes for virulence in the pathogen, and the relationships between the two genetic systems (23). A notable investigation of this type has been reported by Flor (6) working with flax rust, and a beginning has been made in bunt of wheat (4).

Several solutions have been suggested to the problem of shifting races of plant pathogens. Poehlman (20) has suggested the use of varieties having a moderate or intermediate type of resistance conferred by a group of genes, each contributing in only a minor way to the overall resistance of the plant. Presumably a number of mutations or gene recombinations in the pathogen would be necessary to break down completely the resistance of the host variety. Stevens (27) has proposed the rotation of resistant varieties having different sources of resistance. The rotation of the varieties would be geared to the observed buildup of virulent races of the pathogen. Jensen (13) has proposed the use of multiline varieties. Such a variety would be composed of a number of lines which were similar agronomically, but different in the genetic source of their disease resistance. Another suggestion is to combine these same sources of resistance in a single line. All the proposals except the last depend on the maintenance of an equilibrium between host and pathogen such that there may always be light losses from the disease, but that the losses would never reach serious proportions. The success of multiresistant lines depends on complete suppression of the pathogen. At present we know far too little about the dynamics of populations of the pathogen to decide which of these methods is best.

What Is Disease Resistance?

At present the plant breeder is selecting for resistance on the basis of plant reaction. He is breeding for resistance without knowing basically what he is breeding for within the plant. In a few cases resistance has been related to a particular chemical compound. Catechol (29) has been associated with resistance to onion smut and potato scab resistance has been shown to be related to the chlorogenic acid content of a layer of the tuber (14). For the most part reference to "physiologic resistance" or "mature plant resistance" is a way of avoiding the real problem of what makes the plant resistant. Perhaps buried with the secret of the true nature of resistance in the plant is the secret of breeding for a permanent resistance. Even if this is not possible, it would seem logical that if the plant breeder knew what he was breeding for, his chances of keeping ahead of the pathogen would be enhanced. The problem is not a simple one, or the answer would have been worked out long ago, but it is one for which we must find the answer.

REFERENCES

1. Ausemus, E. R., K. J. Hsu, and D. W. Sunderman. *Abstracts, American Society of Agronomy 1955*:48.
2. Brewbaker, J. L., and W. F. Keim. A fertile interspecific hybrid in *Trifolium* (4n *T. repens* L x 4n *T. nigrescens* Viv.) *Am. Naturalist* 87:323-326 (1953).
3. Briggs, F. N., and R. W. Allard. The current status of the backcross method of plant breeding. *Agron. J.* 45:131-138 (1953).
4. Briggs, F. N., and C. S. Holton. Reaction of wheat varieties with known genes for resistance to races of bunt, *Tilletia caries* and *T. foetida. Agron. J.* 42:483-486 (1950).
5. Coons, G. H. Breeding for resistance to disease. *Yearbook of Agriculture U. S. Dept. Agr. 1953*:174-192.
6. Flor, H. H. The complementary genic systems in flax and flax rust. *Advances in Genet.* 8:29-54 (1955).
7. Fry, K. J. Agronomic mutations in oats induced by x-ray treatment. *Agron. J.* 47:207-210 (1955).

8. Graumann, H. O., and C. H. Hanson. Growing Alfalfa. *Farmers Bulletin No. 1722.* U. S. Department of Agriculture, Washington, D.C., 1954.
9. Gregory, W. C. X-ray breeding of peanuts (*Arachis hypogea*) *Agron. J. 47*:396-399 (1955).
10. Hodge, W. H., and C. O. Erlanson. Plant introduction as a federal service to agriculture. *Advances in Agron. 7*:189-211 (1955).
11. Houston, B. R. Dwarf resistant alfalfa. *Calif. Agr. 3*:3 (1949).
12. Jenkins, Merle T., Alice L. Robert, and William R. Findley, Jr. Recurrent selection as a method for concentrating genes for resistance to *Helminthosporium turcicum* leaf blight in corn. *Agron. J. 46*:89-94 (1954).
13. Jensen, N. F. Inter-varietal diversification in oat breeding. *Agron. J. 44*:30-34 (1952).
14. Johnson, G., and L. A. Schaal. Relation of chlorogenic acid to scab resistance in potatoes. *Science 115*:627-629 (1952).
15. Jones, F. R. A new bacterial disease of alfalfa. *Phytopathology 15*:243-244 (1925).
16. Kendrick, J. B., and F. N. Briggs. Pythium root rot of milo and the development of resistant varieties. *Calif. Agr. Expt. Sta. Bull. 629,* 1939.
17. Konzak, C. F. Induction of mutations for disease resistance in cereals. *Brookhaven Symposia in Biol. 9*:157-176 (1956).
18. Melchers, L. E., and A. E. Lowe. The development of sorghums resistant to milo disease. *Kansas Agr. Expt. Tech. Bull. 55* (1943).
19. Peterson, R. F. Accomplishments of the pedigree and backcross methods in wheat breeding. Report of Third International Wheat Rust Conference 1957, pp. 5, 6.
20. Poehlman, J. M. Are our varieties of oats too resistant to disease? *Abstracts, American Society of Agronomy 1952*:15-16.
21. Sears, E. R. The transfer of leaf-rust resistance from *Aegilops umbellulata* to wheat. *Brookhaven Symposia in Biol. 9*:1-22 (1956).
22. Smith, W. K. Propagation of chlorophyll-deficient sweetclover hybrids as grafts. *J. Heredity 34*:135-140 (1943).
23. Stakman, E. C. Problems in preventing plant disease epidemics. *Am. J. Botany 44*:259-267 (1957).
24. Stakman, E. C., and J. J. Christensen. Problems of variability in Fungi. *Yearbook of Agriculture, U. S. Dept. Agr. 1953*: 35-62.
25. Stanford, E. H. Transfer of disease resistance to standard varieties. *Proc. 6th Intern. Grassland Congr. 1952*:1585-1590.

26. Stevens, N. E., and W. O. Scott. How long will present spring oat varieties last in the central corn belt? *Agron. J.* 42:307-309 (1950).
27. Stevens, R. B. Replanting "discarded" varieties as a means of disease control. *Science 110*:49 (1949).
28. Wagner, F. A. Reaction of sorghums to the root, crown and shoot rot of milo. *J. Am. Soc. Agron.* 28:645-654 (1936).
29. Walker, J. C., and M. A. Stahman. Chemical nature of disease resistance in plants. *Ann. Rev. Plant Physiol.* 6:351-366.
30. Webster, G. T. Interspecific hybridization of *Melilotus alba* x *M. officinalis* using embryo culture. *Agron. J.* 47:138-142 (1955).
31. Wheeler, H. E., and H. H. Luke. Mass screening for disease resistant mutants in oats. *Science 122*:1229 (1955).

Breeding Vegetable and Fruit Crops for Resistance to Disease

J. R. SHAY

Department of Botany and Plant Pathology,
Purdue University, Lafayette, Indiana

The usefulness of genetically controlled resistance in plants to combat disease has been well established over the past decades. Success in this area of agricultural research has contributed significantly to the present production strength of our agricultural economy. The economic advantages of the "built-in control" features of resistance over other methods such as fungicide protection and soil treatments are obvious. Examples of valuable disease-resistant varieties could be cited from all agricultural crops, but the record in the vegetable crops is especially noteworthy. A vegetable grower, by proper selection of varieties, can now control such destructive diseases as Fusarium wilt of cabbage, tomato, and watermelon; common mosaic of bean; celery leaf blights; spinach blight; cucumber scab; and many others. In most cases, he will not sacrifice quality or productivity of his crop for the disease control provided by the resistant variety. This reflects the care and long-range planning of the many competent research people who have devoted the greater part of their careers to this work; for in many cases, the original resistance source was a primitive species or variety with little or no horticultural merit.

Progress has been much slower in fruit crops than in vegetables. This is undoubtedly due to the longer time required for most fruit plants to pass from seed to fruiting. In the case of the tomato, for example, three generations may be produced in a single calendar year, whereas with strawberry, a single generation requires 1½ years, with peach 3 years, and with apple or pear, 5 to 7 years.

Plant pathologists and breeders began objective development of disease-resistant crop varieties shortly after the rediscovery of Mendel's law at the turn of the century. With a half century of this work now behind us, it is worthwhile to examine some of the experiences in vegetables and fruits to see what they might contribute to a critical evaluation of resistance as a method of plant disease control.

Early Successes

Workers prior to the 1920's dealt largely with the selection and propagation of resistant individuals from the available varieties. Successful examples of this work include Essary's selections of Fusarium wilt-resistant tomatoes (12) and Jones's Fusarium wilt-resistant cabbage (20). All these resistances are polygenic in their inheritance, and the degree of control provided ranges from partial to complete, depending largely upon time of infection and environmental conditions. During the late 1920's and the 1930's, a number of monogenically controlled resistances were described that provided field immunity under all conditions tested for such important diseases as Fusarium wilt of cabbage, pea and tomato; cantaloupe powdery mildew; tomato leaf mold, and many others. These discoveries gave tremendous impetus to disease resistance breeding of vegetables, not only because of the high level of resistance provided by these genes but also because of the simplicity of their use in breeding.

Will Resistance Hold Up?

Today, the one fault of disease resistance that is emphasized most strongly by critics (21) is the failure of developed varieties to remain resistant when subjected over the years to the multitude of pathogenic variants of the pathogen. This is a serious fault. Such occurrences not only destroy an established control procedure for the particular disease, resulting in immediate economic loss, but they also chill the enthusiasm of present and future disease resistance pathologists—a potential loss that may be many times greater.

How serious has this fault been in disease resistance varieties of vegetables and fruits, and what have we learned that will help us avoid it in the future? In Table I, a number of representative resistance cases are classified according to the causal agent, the "resistance life" of the variety, and the mode of resistance inheritance. In some of the cases listed, the resistance germ plasm has been in widespread commercial production for many years, but in others it has not yet been so widely tested.

An examination of the table shows that about half of the monogenic resistances to fungus pathogens have been short-lived. This frequency of control failures has contributed to the generalization that monogenically controlled resistance is undependable. Monogenic resistance has been notoriously undependable for long-term control of such fungus diseases as the plant rusts, the powdery mildews, and the downy mildews. These disease types are represented here by bean rust, cantaloupe powdery mildew, and potato late blight. In these cases, the generation time for reproduction of the pathogen is brief, the inoculum is produced in volume, and the spores are airborne—characteristics that provide for rapid adjustments in the genotypes of the prevailing population of the pathogen. Favored genotypes such as those capable of reproducing on a resistant host can rapidly become predominant in the population and the resistance is short-lived.

Restrictions in local and long-distance spread of the pathogen may lengthen greatly the period of use of monogenic resistance. It is known, for example, that a second strain called Race 2 of the Fusarium wilt pathogen of tomato exists (1) that can attack the monogenic resistance of the red currant tomato that is now being incorporated into new tomato varieties as a standard practice. The distribution of Race 2, however, appears to be so sharply limited that it has not yet caused damage. Since the Fusarium pathogen is soilborne with restricted dissemination potentialities, it is likely that the spread of Race 2 from its known areas will be very slow. Further, our experience indicates that the tomato Fusarial wilt pathogen is quite stable and specialized races are rare. Consequently, the red currant resist-

ance factor may be useful over a wide area for many years to come.

A full explanation, however, of the basic differences in behavior of those monogenic resistances that have been widely useful and those that have not cannot be found in the epidemiological characteristics of the disease. This is emphasized by the fact that a single disease, such as apple scab, may have monogenic resistances represented in both groups. The single gene resistance of a *Malus baccata* variety, Dolgo; seedlings of R12740-7A, a Russian apple; and a third variety, Geneva, are all successfully attacked by races of *Venturia inaequalis* of apparently limited distribution. On the other hand, a number of single-gene controlled resistances from the Asiatic species *Malus floribunda, M. atrosanguinea,* and others, have not yet shown susceptibility (33). Clones of these species have been maintained in a number of mixed plantings in the United States since their introduction more than fifty years ago under conditions highly favorable for the development of the disease.

One is led to the conclusion that the explanation for the true differences are to be found in (*a*) the nature of the host resistance barriers presented by the different monogenic resistances and (*b*) the inherent limits of pathogenicity variation of the pathogen. We will discuss these points further, but first let us turn to the experiences with polygenically controlled resistances to fungus diseases.

Monogenic versus Polygenic Inheritance

Here we note that for a number of the monogenic "problem" cases, there has been favorable experience in the use of polygenic resistance. This is true for cantaloupe powdery mildew and potato late blight. No differential strains of the pathogen have arisen to these resistances or to polygenically controlled resistance of a number of other diseases. One of the few well-known cases of physiologic specialization to polygenically controlled resistance is strawberry red stele (28). This disease is caused by *Phytophthora fragariae,* a relative of the potato late blight fungus. But unlike the late blight fungus, it is soilborne

and is sharply restricted in its dissemination by natural means. Here then, is a disease in which race problems have become quite severe even though the pathogen is not adapted for efficient air distribution of its spores.

Field immunity in which no reproduction of the pathogen occurs has often been held to be more desirable than field resistance, in which some reproduction or sporulation takes place. The reasoning has been that a host permitting some development would be a more effective screen for virulent mutants. In Table I, the field reactions of the various resistances are given so this point can be examined. The cases considered here do not support this thesis.

More information is available on the mode of inheritance of resistance to fungus diseases than to diseases caused by bacterial, viral, or nematode agencies. This accounts for the relatively few entries in these categories in Table I. The taxonomy of the plant parasitic nematodes has undergone major changes during the past eight years. Recognition that the former single root-knot species is comprised of several species explains certain occurrences of severe disease development on resistant varieties. For example, the Shalil and Yunnan peach varieties described as resistant to root-knot (23, 41) were later found to be susceptible in certain locations (10). When the nematodes were examined in detail it was determined that the peach stocks were resistant to *Meloidogyne incognita* but susceptible to *M. javanicus*. Until all such instances of reported susceptibility of root-knot resistances are examined for nematode species identification, it is not possible to classify them accurately in the categories used here.

A preponderance of the resistances to viruses has been useful for rather long periods. The resistance of the spinach varieties Old Dominion and Virginia Savoy (35) has been in use for many years. Fulton (13) collected a strain of the virus to which these varieties were susceptible, but it has not become sufficiently widespread to reduce the usefulness of the resistance. In contrast to the fungus disease resistances, there does not appear to be any great differences in the "resistance life"

of monogenic and polygenic resistances to the virus diseases considered here.

Information on inheritance of resistance to bacterial diseases of fruits and vegetables is scant and reflects the neglect of this important group of plant diseases by plant pathologists during the past thirty years. It is interesting that few bona fide cases of physiologic specialization in plant pathogenic bacteria can be cited. Whether this is true or is due to inadequate study is not known.

Returning again to the fungus pathogens, one might ask why breeders and pathologists have continued to place emphasis on monogenic resistance when polygenic resistance seems to offer more security against race specialization. There are two main reasons. In the first place, monogenic resistance is much easier and less costly to use in breeding; in segregating progenies, resistant and susceptible classes are discrete, and close linkage with undesirable characters is rather rare. Secondly, the level of resistance is usually higher. Many of the monogenic resistances confer field immunity and no supplemental control measures are necessary. With many of the polygenically controlled resistances, disease control is not complete, and must be supplemented by other measures.

The differences in hazards as judged by these past experiences with monogenic and polygenic resistances are influencing many disease resistance pathologists and breeders to place more and more emphasis on polygenic resistance along with disease escape and disease tolerance. As mentioned, these characters are much more difficult to work with—larger populations must be handled, more generations usually must be grown, and screening for individuals with these attributes in their greatest degree usually demands more precisely controlled disease test conditions. Providing these will cost more money and require more professional and technical staff than we have invested in our breeding programs in the past.

Genetics of Pathogens

We must expand studies aimed toward understanding the genetic nature and pathogenic limits of the wild type popula-

tions of the major fungus pathogens. Recent experiments with
wheat stem rust (44) and leaf rust pathogens (42) indicate
that the parasexual mechanism described by Pontecorvo *et al.*
(26) in *Aspergillus nidulans* may be fully operative in these
important economic species. Isolates of each of these rust pathogens with genetic markers, when mixed and inoculated on
selected wheat varieties, have given rise to new races in which
the genetic characters of the component races of the mixture
have been recombined. The origin of these new races is readily
explained only on the basis of some type of fusion of somatic
nuclei with subsequent recombination of genes and reduction
in number of chromosomes. Elucidation of this process may
change our concept of the natural population characteristics of
these pathogens. An astronomical number of rust fungus recom-
binants could result each season from this vegetative process in
the vast amounts of rusted wheat tissue that is present over the
great wheat areas of this country. This probably means that
any resistance for which virulence genes exist in the rust species
will be short-lived when incorporated in widely planted varieties and the process of selection of races from the natural population is begun.

There seems to be no relief from this hazard so long as we
must continue in ignorance of the mechanisms by which our
various resistance genes intercede in the infection process. If
we could have knowledge of the chemical and physical modes
of action of resistance genes, we would hope to accumulate
sufficient information to be able to predict the lasting qualities
of the various resistances available to us for any given disease.
This would remove much of the empiricism of our present
procedures.

On the basis of these evidences from the past, the future
course in disease resistance research and development seems
quite clear—intensified effort toward finding or inducing host
resistance factors presently unknown; expansion of present programs to permit evaluation and use of known resistances that
have been considered too difficult to manipulate; increased
study of the pathogenicity characteristics of populations of the
causal agents; and greater emphasis on the chemical and phys-

ical modes of action of the various genes for resistance in the host and for virulence in the pathogen. The results of the past give assurance that such a course will enable man to continue with more successes than failures to adapt plants for his specialized needs.

TABLE I. Classification of Representative Vegetable and Fruit Disease Resistance Cases According to Causal Agent, Mode of Inheritance, and Field Experience

Disease	Original source of resistance	Pathogen	Field reaction	Authority
I. Fungus Diseases				
Monogenically[a] controlled resistance				
a. Proven susceptible to races of prevalence				
1. Potato late blight	*Solanum demissum*	*Phytophthora infestans*	Immune	Black (7)
2. Lettuce downy mildew	European varieties	*Bremia lactucae*	Immune	Jagger and Whitaker (18)
3. Bean powdery mildew	Several varieties	*Erysiphe polygoni*	Immune	Dundas (11)
4. Cantaloupe powdery mildew	Indian varieties	*Erysiphe cichoracearum*	Immune	Jagger et al. (19)
5. Bean rust	Several varieties	*Uromyces phaseoli typica*	Immune	Zaumeyer and Harter (45)
6. Apple scab	*Malus baccata*	*Venturia inaequalis*	Immune	Shay and Williams (33)
7. Tomato leaf mold	*Lycopersicon pimpinelli-folium*	*Cladosporium fulvum*	Immune	Bailey (4)
8. Bean anthracnose	Several varieties	*Colletotrichum lindemuthianum*	Immune	Burkholder (9)
b. Remaining resistant to prevalent races				
1. Spinach downy mildew[b]	Iranian variety	*Peronospora effusa*	Immune	Smith (36)
2. Cucumber scab	Longfellow variety	*Cladosporium cucumerinum*	Immune	Bailey (5)
3. Tomato leaf spot	*Lycopersicon hirsutum*	*Septoria lycopersici*	Resistant	Lincoln and Cummins (22)

[a] Resistances that have been found to be controlled by more than one factor pair are classified here as polygenic.
[b] In 1958, a race of *Peronospora effusa* developed extensively in California on this source of resistance [Frank W. Zink and Paul G. Smith. A second physiologic race of spinach downy mildew. *Plant Disease Reptr.* 42:818 (1958)].

TABLE I (Continued)

Disease	Original source of resistance	Pathogen	Field reaction	Authority
4. Tomato gray leaf spot	L. pimpinellifolium	Stemphylium solani	Immune	Hendrix and Frazier (16)
5. Tomato fusarium wilt	L. pimpinellifolium	F. oxysporum f. lycopersici	Immune	Bohn and Tucker (8)
6. Cabbage fusarium wilt	American varieties	F. oxysporum f. conglutinans	Immune	Walker (43)
7. Cedar-apple rust	Several apple varieties	Gymnosporangium juniperi-virginianae	Immune	Moore (24)
8. Apple scab	Asiatic species of Malus	Venturia inaequalis	Immune	Shay and Williams (33)
Polygenically[a] controlled resistance				
a. Proven susceptible to races of prevalence				
1. Strawberry red stele	Aberdeen and other varieties	Phytophthora fragariae	Resistant	Reid (28)
b. Remaining resistant to prevalent races				
1. Potato late blight	Selections of Solanum demissum and other species	Phytophthora infestans	Resistant	Niederhauser et al. (25)
2. Apple scab	Antonovka	Venturia inaequalis	Immune	Schmidt (30)
3. Cabbage fusarium wilt	American varieties	F. oxysporum f. conglutinans	Resistant	Jones and Gilman (20)

238

II. Nematode Diseases

Monogenically[a] controlled resistance
- a. Proven susceptible to races of prevalence
  - None
- b. Remaining resistant to prevalent races
  1. Tomato root knot — *Lycopersicon peruvianum* — *Meloidogyne* spp. — Resistant — Barham and Winstead (6)
  2. Pepper root knot — Santanka x S variety — *Meloidogyne* spp. — Resistant — Hare (14)

Polygenically[a] controlled resistance
- a. Proven susceptible to races of prevalence
  - None
- b. Remaining resistant to prevalent races
  1. Lima bean root knot — Hopi 5989 and Westan — *Meloidogyne* spp. — Resistant — Allard (3)
  2. Peach root knot — Shalil and Yunnan varieties — *Meloidogyne incognita* — Resistant — Havis *et al.* (15)

[a] Resistances that have been found to be controlled by more than one factor pair are classified here as polygenic.

TABLE I (Continued)

III. Virus Diseases

Disease	Original source of resistance	Pathogen	Field reaction	Authority
Monogenically[a] controlled resistance				
a. Proven susceptible to races of prevalence				
1. Tomato spotted wilt	Argentine variety	Spotted wilt virus	Resistant	Smith and Gardner (37)
b. Remaining resistant to prevalent races				
1. Bean mosaic	Corbett Refugee	Bean virus 1	Resistant	Ali (2)
2. Bean pod mottle	Several varieties	Bean pod mottle virus	Immune	Thomas and Zaumeyer (39)
3. Bean southern mosaic	Several varieties	Bean mosaic virus 4	Immune	Zaumeyer and Harter (46)
4. Pepper mosaic	Tabasco variety	Tobacco mosaic virus	Immune	Holmes (17)
5. Spinach blight	Old Dominion; Va. Savoy	Cucumber virus 1	Immune	Smith
Polygenically[a] controlled resistance				
a. Proven susceptible to races of prevalence				
1. Tomato spotted wilt	Lycopersicon pimpinelli-folium	Spotted wilt virus	Resistant	Smith and Gardner (37)
b. Remaining resistant to prevalent races				
1. Cabbage mosaic	Selections from varieties	Cabbage viruses A and B	Resistant	Pound and Walker (27)
2. Cucumber mosaic	Oriental varieties	Cucumber virus 1	Resistant	Shifriss et al. (34)
3. Lima bean mosaic	Fordhook and others	Cucumber virus 1	Resistant	Thomas et al. (40)
4. Bean curly top	Several varieties	Curly top virus	Resistant	Schultz and Dean (31)
5. Potato latent mosaic	S41956 variety	Potato virus	Immune	Stevenson et al. (38)

Monogenically[a] controlled resistance
  a. Proven susceptible to
    races of prevalence
    None
  b. Remaining resistant
    to prevalent races
    1. Bean halo blight   Several dry bean varieties *Pseudomonas phaseolicola*   Resistant Schuster (32)

Polygenically[a] controlled resistance
  a. Proven susceptible to
    races of prevalence
    None
  b. Remaining resistant
    to prevalent races
    1. Pear fireblight   Selections from *Pyrus* spp. *Erwinia amylovora*   Resistant Reimer (29)

[a] Resistances that have been found to be controlled by more than one factor pair are classified here as polygenic.

REFERENCES

1. Alexander, L. J., and C. M. Tucker. Physiologic specialization in the tomato wilt fungus *Fusarium oxysporum f. lycopersici*. *J. Agr. Research* 70:303-313 (1945).
2. Ali, Mohamed A. Genetics of resistance to the common bean mosaic virus (Bean Virus 1) in the bean (*Phaseolus vulgaris L.*). *Phytopathology* 40:69-79 (1950).
3. Allard, R. W. Sources of root-knot nematode resistance in lima beans. *Phytopathology* 44:1-4 (1954).
4. Bailey, C. L. Studies in racial trends and constancy in *Cladosporium fulvum* Cooke. *Can. J. Research* C28:535-656 (1950).
5. Bailey, R. M. Progress in breeding cucumbers resistant to scab (*Cladosporium cucumerinum*) *Can. J. Research* 36:645-646 (1939).
6. Barham, W. S., and N. N. Winstead. Inheritance of resistance to root knot in tomatoes. *Proc. Am. Soc. Hort. Sci.* 69:372-377 (1957).
7. Black, W. Inheritance of resistance to blight (*Phytophthora infestans*) in potatoes; inter-relationships of genes and strains. *Proc. Roy. Soc. Endinburgh* B64:312-352 (1952).
8. Bohn, G. W., and C. M. Tucker. Studies on Fusarium wilt of the tomato. I. Immunity in *Lycopersicon pimpinellifolium* Mill. and its inheritance in hybrids. *Missouri Agr. Expt. Sta. Research Bull. 311*, 1940.
9. Burkholder, W. H. The production of an anthracnose-resistant white marrow bean. *Phytopathology* 8:353-359 (1918).
10. Christie, J. R., and Leon Havis. Relative susceptibility of certain peach stocks to races of the root-knot nematode. *Plant Disease Reptr.* 32:510-514 (1948).
11. Dundas, B. Further studies on the inheritance of resistance to powdery mildew of beans. *Hilgardia* 13:551-565 (1941).
12. Essary, S. H. Notes on tomato diseases with results of selection for resistance. *Tenn. Agr. Expt. Sta. Bull. 95*, 1912.
13. Fulton, J. P. Studies on strains of cucumber virus 1 from spinach. *Phytopathology* 40:729-736 (1950).
14. Hare, W. W. Inheritance of resistance to root-knot nematodes in pepper. *Phytopathology* 47:455-459 (1957).
15. Havis, Leon, B. G. Chitwood, V. E. Prince, G. S. Cobb, and A. L. Taylor. Susceptibility of some peach rootstocks to root-knot nematodes. *Plant Disease Reptr.* 34:74-77 (1950).

16. Hendrix, J. W., and W. A. Frazier. Studies on the inheritance of Stemphylium resistance in tomatoes. *Hawaii Agr. Expt. Sta. Tech. Bull. 8*, 1949.
17. Holmes, F. D. Inheritance of ability to localize tobacco mosaic virus. *Phytopathology 24*:984-1002 (1934).
18. Jagger, I. C., and T. W. Whitaker. The inheritance of immunity from mildew (*Bremia lactucae*) in lettuce. *Phytopathology 34*:427-433 (1940).
19. Jagger, I. C., T. W. Whitaker, and D. R. Porter. Inheritance in *Cucumis melo* of resistance to powdery mildew (*Erysiphe cichoracearum*) (Abs.) *Phytopathology 28*:671 (1938).
20. Jones, L. R., and J. C. Gilman. The control of cabbage yellows through disease resistance. *Wisconsin Agr. Expt. Sta. Bull. 38*, 1915.
21. Lewis, D. The genetical approach to plant breeding. *Advance. Science 12*:291-295 (1955).
22. Lincoln, R. E., and G. B. Cummins. Septoria blight resistance in the tomato. *Phytopathology 39*:647-655 (1949).
23. Long, J. C., and W. E. Whitehouse. Variations in root-knot nematode infection of various lines of peach progenies at Chico, Calif. *Proc. Am. Soc. Hort. Sci. 43*:119-123 (1943).
24. Moore, Robert C. A study of the inheritance of susceptibility and resistance to cedar-apple rust. *Proc. Am. Soc. Hort. Sci. 37*:242-244 (1940).
25. Niederhauser, John S., Javier Cervantes, and Leopoldo Servin. Late blight in Mexico and its implications. *Phytopathology 44*:406-408 (1954).
26. Pontecorvo, G., Elizabeth Tarr Gloar, and E. Forbes. Analysis of mitotic recombination in *Aspergillus nidulans*. *J. Genet. 52*:226-237 (1954).
27. Pound, G. S., and J. C. Walker. Mosaic resistance in cabbage. *Phytopathology 41*:1083-1090 (1951).
28. Reid, Robert D. Breeding strawberries resistant to red core root rot. *Plant Disease Reptr. 36*:395-405 (1952).
29. Reimer, F. C. Development of blight resistant French pear rootstocks. *Oregon Agr. Expt. Sta. Bull. 485*, 1950.
30. Schmidt, M. *Venturia inaequalis* (Cooke) Adech. VIII Weitere Untersuchungen zur zuchtung scharfwiderstandsfahiger Apfelsorten. (Erste Mitteilung) *Zuchter 10*:280-291 (1938).
31. Schultz, H. K., and L. L. Dean. Inheritance of curly top disease reaction in *Phaseolus vulgaris J. Am. Soc. Agron. 39*:47-51 (1947).
32. Schuster, M. L. A genetic study of halo blight in *Phaseolus vulgaris*. *Phytopathology 40*:604-612 (1950).

33. Shay, J. R., and E. B. Williams. Identification of three physiologic races of *Venturia inaequalis. Phytopathology 46*:190-193 (1956).

34. Shifriss, Oved, C. H. Myers, and Chas. Chupp. Resistance to mosaic virus in the cucumber. *Phytopathology 32*:733-784 (1942).

35. Smith, L. B. Breeding mosaic resistant spinach and notes on malnutrition. *Virginia Truck Expt. Sta. Bull. 31-32*:137-160 (1920).

36. Smith, Paul G. Downy mildew immunity in spinach. *Phytopathology 40*:65-68 (1950).

37. Smith, P. G., and M. W. Gardner. Resistance in tomato to the spotted-wilt virus. *Phytopathology 41*:257-260 (1951).

38. Stevenson, F. J., E. S. Schultz, and C. F. Clark. Inheritance of immunity from virus X (latent mosaic) in the potato. *Phytopathology 29*:362-365 (1939).

39. Thomas, H. Rex, and W. J. Zaumeyer. Inheritance of symptom expression of pod mottle virus. *Phytopathology 40*:1007-1010 (1950).

40. Thomas, H. Rex, W. J. Zaumeyer, and Hans Jorgensen. Inheritance of resistance to lima bean mosaic virus in the lima bean. *Phytopathology 41*:231-234 (1951).

41. Tufts, Warren P. Nematode resistance of certain peach seedlings. *Proc. Am. Soc. Hort. Sci. 26*:98-100 (1929).

42. Vakili, Nader G., and Ralph M. Caldwell. Recombination of spore color and pathogenicity between uredial clones of *Puccinia recondita f. sp. tritici.* (Abs.) *Phytopathology 47*:536 (1957).

43. Walker, J. C. Inheritance of Fusarium resistance in cabbage. *J. Agr. Research 40*:721-745 (1930).

44. Watson, I. A. Further studies on the production of new races from mixtures of races of *Puccinia graminis* var. *tritici* on wheat seedlings. *Phytopathology 47*:510-512 (1957).

45. Zaumeyer, W. J., and L. L. Harter. Inheritance of resistance to six physiologic races of bean rust. *J. Agr. Research 63*:599-622 (1941).

46. ———. Inheritance of symptom expression of bean mosaic virus 4. *J. Agr. Research 67*:295-300 (1943).

Breeding Plants for Resistance to Insect Pests[*]

REGINALD H. PAINTER

Department of Entomology, Kansas State University, Manhattan

The general title of this symposium *Biological and Chemical Control of Plant and Animal Pests* correctly emphasizes the fact that all available means must be used in control of injurious insects. Chemical control usually has received major emphasis because of the discoveries of new organic insecticides. The virtues and powers of these new insecticides have been publicized by the advertising staffs of the large companies producing them. This is as it should be both because of their great effectiveness and also because, before the mid-1940's, we did not know how much damage insects could do. Plants often could not be grown free from insect damage before the discovery of DDT and similar insecticides. Chemical control must continue to be, generally, our first line of defense against mass insect attack.

Another advance, less well known but far less expensive to growers, has been the development of insect-resistant crop varieties. Such varieties have sometimes been used when all other methods of control have failed. No chemical control of the wheat stem sawfly has been economically possible, but despite the presence of the insect, the use of sawfly-resistant Rescue and Chinook spring wheats permits the profitable growing of wheat on 1.8 million acres in Canada and more than 600,000 acres in north central United States.

Plants less damaged or less infested than others under comparable environmental conditions have been called resistant. The resistance must be shown to be inherited and usable in plant breeding.

[*] Contribution No. 706, Department of Entomology, Kansas Agricultural Experiment Station, Manhattan, Kansas.

Although workers have observed differences in insect infestation and damage between species and varieties of plants for as long as the science of applied entomology has been studied, only recently has systematic use been made of this knowledge of plant-insect relationships.

For over thirty-one years an organized experiment station project has been conducted at Kansas State University on the "Resistance of Crop Plants to Insects," the first project of its kind in any United States experiment station that has been continued to the present day. It is cooperative between the Departments of Entomology and Agronomy and the United States Department of Agriculture. Largely as a result of this project, the Kansas Agricultural Experiment Station has to date approved for distribution eleven crop varieties resistant to various insects, including varieties of sorghums, alfalfa, corn hybrids, barley, and wheat. Sometimes the finding of these resistant strains has come through the routine testing of the insect reaction of breeding material being studied by the plant breeder; at other times it has resulted from a prolonged search for sources of resistance followed by a planned breeding program. In breeding insect-resistant crops we are actually making use of our knowledge of evolution.

The practical use of insect resistance involves the study of genetics and ecology and their interactions. The results of the use of insect-resistant varieties have often increased yields at lower cost to farmers and sometimes decreased insect populations. This paper will deal mostly with the practical side of resistance and will use numerous examples, especially from Kansas. For many of the examples cited, discussion with full bibliographies will be found in reviews by Painter (9, 10). A few additional references will be given.

One of the first questions asked regarding an insect-resistant crop is how permanent will it be. It is not always possible to answer this question but there are some notable examples of permanence. The earliest record of an insect-resistant variety which we can identify at the present time is that of the Winter Majetin apple, reported to be resistant to the woolly apple

aphid *Eriosoma lanigerum* (Hausm.) in 1831. According to most recent reports that apple variety is still resistant to this aphid. Another interesting example is that of the resistance of sorghums to grasshoppers, *Melanoplus* spp. C. V. Riley, in 1877, first reported that sorghums were more resistant to grasshoppers than corn. This contrast is still true (Fig. 1). When Riley saw

FIG. 1.   This difference in the damage done by grasshoppers to corn (left) and sorghum (right) has been seen in each grasshopper outbreak since 1877.

this case of resistance, sorghums were a novelty, very few acres of them being grown. Yet in 1957 with over 8 million acres of sorghums grown in Kansas, the American grasshoppers had not "learned" to eat sorghums, although during this period of about eighty years these insects had every opportunity to do so. These examples of two very different kinds of insects might be repeated in a number of instances where less time was involved.

This observation on sorghum and grasshoppers leads to more confidence in examples of grasshopper resistance in corn and other crops. Kansas hybrid 2234 has considerably more resistance to grasshoppers than many other hybrids of corn, but not as much as sorghums. This hybrid is currently grown by a good many Kansas farmers. In our study of the resistance of corn to grasshoppers we have found that, in general, inbreds selected

from Kansas varieties were more resistant than inbreds selected from eastern corns. Therefore, apparently, there has been natural selection for grasshopper resistance over the years when the Indians and early settlers grew corn in this area. The use of grasshopper-resistant corn may not lower populations of grasshoppers materially but it certainly may decrease the number of times when other controls of these insects are needed. This would be an important consideration in reducing the cost of production in areas where the injury of corn by grasshoppers is frequent.

The study of the corn earworm *Heliothis zea* (Boddie), which began in Kansas about 1919, gave early evidence of the presence of resistance in different varieties of corn. For many years the study of resistance of corn to the earworm has consisted of a testing program involving the varieties, inbreds, and hybrids being studied by the corn breeder for other characteristics. This method of search for insect resistance limits the possibility of finding high-level resistance to the materials that are being studied currently in the corn breeding program. In Kansas most ears of most varieties are infested to some extent by the earworm. Therefore a method was worked out by which all the ears produced in any plot of an inbred or hybrid were arbitrarily classified for the amount of damage done by the insect. This served to separate the better lines from the poorer ones. In some lines the larvae even ate much of the cobs. This is true of line 187-2, a commonly used inbred which has many highly regarded characteristics. In contrast, a few lines have only a few kernels injured on each ear. Information on the degree of injury by the earworm has been considered by the corn breeder in deciding which inbreds to use in hybrids.

After about ten years, an opportunity came to measure the results of the earworm testing program. In 1939 when the first corn performance test was conducted in Kansas, all forty of the Kansas Agricultural Experiment Station double-cross hybrids in the test had less earworm injury than any single out-of-state hybrid or commercial hybrid. Similar results were recorded the next two years. Recently efforts have been directed toward finding a higher level of resistance.

At the present time in the southern part of the southeastern United States several hybrid corns are being grown that carry resistance to earworm and rice weevil. At least one of these (Dixie 18) showed 83 per cent less damage than the corns it replaced. In the Rio Grande Valley, Calumet sweet corn, which is somewhat resistant to the earworm, with limited insecticide applications, has given satisfactory control which could not be achieved by the use of either resistant variety or insecticide alone. A number of other cases are known where the host affects the ease of control with chemicals (3, 9, 10, 13). Thus the combination of resistant varieties and reduced chemical control is a promising field for study.

Differences in the resistance of sorghum varieties to chinch bugs, *Blissus leucopterus* (Say), have been known for a long time. Actually these differences were already a part of the varietal characteristics of the varieties when they were first imported from Africa and Asia. The recent production of hybrid sorghums comparable to hybrid corn has renewed interest in the resistance of sorghum to chinch bugs. Especially is this true as the hybrid sorghums are grown farther east where the chinch bugs are ordinarily a problem. The sorghum varieties Dwarf Yellow Milo and Atlas have been used as susceptible and resistant checks respectively in our plantings for the study of chinch bug resistance. In Table I there are records of the percentage of plants killed by the insects in these two varieties in plots in 1930 and in 1956. Although twenty-six years separated the two sets of data taken, they were essentially similar. Atlas was first distributed to Kansas farmers as a new variety in 1928. In the quarter of a century or more since Atlas was first distributed, chinch bugs have not "learned" to injure it more than they did when it was originally distributed, although in the meantime that variety has become the leading sorgo in the Middle West.

In the field, differences in resistance ordinarily are based on differences in the percentage of plants killed by chinch bugs. Other data presented in Table I indicate some of the reasons why there is this difference between the two varieties. In the first place, there is a striking difference in the number of eggs laid by females when fed on the plants of the two varieties. This

characteristic, the effect of the plant on the insect, is known as antibiosis and often occurs in resistant plants. In addition, a difference occurs in the number of bugs attracted to plants of the two varieties. This is spoken of as preference and may occur simply because the insects do not perceive the resistant plants

TABLE I. Relationship of Chinch Bugs, *Blissus leucopterus* (Say), to Atlas Sorgo and Dwarf Yellow Milo, 1930, 1936, and 1956

Characteristic	Atlas	Milo	Component
Per cent plants killed Lawton, Okla., 1930[a]	20	100	Combined, including tolerance
Per cent plants killed Manhattan, Kans., 1956[b]	0	91	
No. eggs laid (10 days) Lawton, Okla., 1936[c]	1	118	Antibiosis
No. eggs laid (25 days) Manhattan, Kans., 1956[b]	4	207	
Per cent bugs attracted to plants Lawton, Okla., 1936[c]	20	80	Preference
Average no. hours seedlings lived Lawton, Okla., 1936[c]	125	78	Tolerance

[a] Snelling *et al.* (15).
[b] Sifuentes (14).
[c] Dahms *et al.*, 1936.

as well as they do the susceptible ones. In the laboratory it can also be shown that the susceptible plants will not live as long under a chinch bug attack as will the resistant ones. This analysis in the laboratory which shows some of the reasons why there is a difference in the percentage of plants killed in the field also shows that there is more than a single basis for the differences as seen in the field. Resistance is made up of one or more of the three components, preference, tolerance, and antibiosis. In the resistance to chinch bugs, all three are factors. In the resistance of corn to grasshoppers and of the Colorado potato beetle to certain species of *Solanum*, it is mainly preference and nonpreference. In the resistance to the European corn borer, *Pyrausta nubilalis* (Hbn.), in corn, tolerance and antibiosis have been the main factors that have been studied, but it is known that there is also a difference in preference. In the resistance

Fig. 2. Resistance of Dicktoo barley to greenbugs compared with the commonly grown Reno barley under greenhouse conditions. The difference is principally but not entirely, the result of tolerance.

to the hessian fly in wheat, antibiosis has been the principal component that has been studied. Green bug, *Toxoptera graminum* (Rond.), resistance in wheat and barley (Fig. 2) consists mostly of tolerance.

Factors affecting the progeny of insects feeding on resistant plants appear to be complex. In Table II there is reported the

TABLE II.   Number of Young Produced per Female in 10 Days by Two
Biotypes of Corn Leaf Aphid, *Rhopalosiphum maidis* (Fitch),
Compared with Plant Liquid Taken in by Individual
Aphids in 3 Hours (12)

Biotypes and character	White Martin		Sudan 428-1
Fecundity			
KS-1	12.5	*	1.2
	ns		*
KS-2	15.4	*	7.3
Per Cent Body Weight Gained or Lost in 3 Hours Feeding			
KS-1	+11.84	*	−2.55
	ns		*
KS-2	+ 8.98	ns	+5.96

* differences significant at 5 per cent level.
ns = differences not significant.

study of the fecundity and percentage of body weight gain or loss after three hours feeding by two different biotypes of the corn leaf aphid, *Rhopalosiphum maidis* (Fitch). These biotypes are strains of a single aphid species that do not differ in any visible structure but do differ in various physiological characters. Both biotypes reproduce quite well on White Martin sorghum but differ remarkably in their reproduction on the sudan selection. There is no difference in the amount of food taken in by the two biotypes from White Martin nor by biotype KS-2 on either of the two hosts. In contrast, a big difference in the amount of plant liquid taken up by KS-1 on the two hosts suggests that this may be the principal cause in the difference in fecundity. On the other hand, the difference in fecundity of KS-2 on the same two hosts is apparently not related to the quantity but rather to the quality of the material taken up by

the aphid. These two biotypes of a single species therefore differ in their relation to two varieties of a single species of host.

A number of corn hybrids carrying varying degrees of resistance to the European corn borer have been developed for use in the central United States. The corn borer entered the central United States in Ohio where the program for breeding borer-resistant hybrids has been under way for the longest period. Perhaps 98 per cent of the field corn sown in Ohio carries some resistance. G. H. Stringfield, corn breeder in Ohio, has stated, "The corn borer hazard has been reduced to a minor problem on those farms that use these [resistant] hybrids." T. H. Parks, formerly extension entomologist in Ohio, stated that the growing of certain adapted resistant varieties "makes the use of insecticides unnecessary" against the European corn borer in field corn (10).

Because of the work of Beck, Bottger, Dicke, Holdaway, their co-workers, and others, reviewed by Painter (9, 10), perhaps more is known of the basis of corn borer resistance than of many other insect-plant relationships:

COMPONENTS OF RESISTANCE TO EUROPEAN CORN BORER

1. Tolerance of some corn inbreds.
2. Nonpreference for oviposition.
3. Antibiosis (effect of plant on larvae) concerned with:
   a. Morphology of plant.
   b. Stage of growth of larvae.
   c. Stage of growth of plant.
   d. Concentration of sugar in tissues.
   e. Relative concentration of three resistance factors, in various tissues comprising chemicals whose structure and characteristics are partly known.

Inbreds and hybrids differ in preference shown for them by moths in oviposition and in tolerance to the tunneling larvae. Most of the resistance measured has been the effect on first instar larvae when feeding in the whorl (antibiosis). Here and elsewhere in the plant three chemically defined substances that

have an effect on the larvae are partly known. As indicated, selection of plants by chemical test for one of these resistance factors would probably give poor results because other components of resistance would be missed.

So far a full understanding of the causes of resistance has not been necessary for the use of insect resistance. Information on the components and bases of resistance may or may not be of help in the practical problems of selecting insect-resistant plants. Probably many cases of resistance are too complex. Certainly such information will be of use in understanding resistance and plant-insect relations in general and of much value in specialized cases of resistance. Perhaps knowledge of the bases of resistance may lead us to new and useful insect repellents or even new insecticidal compounds. Studies of the causes of resistance should be made by following "leads" which appear during the development of resistant varieties. Such studies cannot be expeditiously made during the search for resistance.

The resistance of wheat to the hessian fly *Phytophaga destructor* (Say) has been a particularly successful example of the use of insect resistance both to increase yield, decreasing the cost of production, and to decrease the population of the fly. For more than fifty years after the spread of the hessian fly into Kansas in the 1880's this insect frequently did more than a million dollars worth of damage per year to the Kansas wheat crop. Quite often fields of wheat in central Kansas had to be plowed up because they were not worth harvesting because of such injury. Since the middle of the 1940's at the time of the introduction of the hessian fly-resistant Pawnee variety, this kind of loss from this insect has been quite unnecessary.

. The statement has sometimes been made that an insect-resistant variety might be resistant to the insect but probably was no good otherwise. This is emphatically not true of Pawnee which was one of the most improved winter wheat varieties ever distributed to farmers. The wheat variety Tenmarq was one of the highest yielding varieties available for growing in Kansas when Pawnee was released. The records available at the time of the distribution of Pawnee to farmers indicated that it had a 17 per cent advantage in yield over Tenmarq in the

absence of hessian fly. Its advantage in yield over many of the other varieties grown was quite a bit larger. In the presence of the hessian fly, Pawnee yielded far more than did other varieties currently grown. This led to its rapid acceptance by farmers. Pawnee was released to Kansas farmers in 1943 and to Nebraska farmers a year earlier. By 1947 it had become the leading variety in acreage in Kansas and by 1949 was the leading variety in acreage in the United States. To the present time it has retained that position.

Not only was the yield of Pawnee good but also the increasing acreage of Pawnee had a drastic effect on the fly population. Pawnee was introduced at a time when the hessian fly was building up to outbreak proportions and when conditions in the field were exceptionally favorable for the development of the insect. In spite of these favorable conditions, in the presence of the resistant variety, the general population of the hessian fly decreased rather rapidly. During the early 1950's drought conditions, unfavorable to the fly, occurred extensively in Kansas. This drought further reduced the populations of the insect. In recent seasons it has been almost impossible to find the hessian fly in central Kansas where in previous years many fields of wheat had been destroyed (Fig. 3).

Pawnee carries a rather high tolerance to the hessian fly but it is highly resistant to only a part of the hessian fly population. This fact led to the search for more factors for resistance to incorporate into commercial wheats. Several thousand wheat strains have been tested and about 6 per cent have been shown to carry high resistance. Meanwhile an analysis of the genetic factors concerned in the antibiotic resistance of wheat to the hessian fly has shown that at least five pairs of factors were present; there is evidence that two or three more are also present. All these genetic factors involve antibiosis and no genetic analysis has been made of tolerance or preference which is known also to be present. Several different experiment stations have been concerned in this analysis and in use of resistance derived from different sources in breeding commercial wheats resistant to the hessian fly.

A related study concerns the presence of races of hessian fly

FIG. 3. A row of plants of Turkey wheat (center) severely in-jured by hessian fly and leaf rust, compared with two Marquillo hybrids that were relatively uninjured, Manhattan, Kansas, fall, 1942. It has been necessary to discontinue such field tests because the widespread use of fly-resistant wheat varieties has reduced hessian fly population to the point where infested stubble for such tests was no longer available from Kansas farmers' fields.

which differ in their ability to infest different varieties of wheat. The presence of these races has been the primary reason for the geographic limitation on resistance of Pawnee. The early work on this subject was done at Kansas State College but lately more detailed study has been made in Indiana. Laboratory studies show that there is a lock and key relationship between genetic factors for resistance and the different races of fly. Each race seems primarily to be able to feed on varieties of wheat carrying a particular genetic factor for resistance but not on

varieties of wheat carrying some of the other factors. Thus the means for combating the presence of races of fly are even now in the wheat breeding nurseries and in a few cases are being grown in farmers' fields. The races of hessian fly able to breed on the more resistant wheats were selected and so far as known exist only in the laboratory (4). It is possible that they may develop and be able to live in nature but so far have not done so.

One of the varieties of wheat carrying resistance to several races of fly is Ponca, which was released to Kansas and Oklahoma farmers in 1951. In addition to high resistance to the hessian fly, Ponca carries high seedling resistance to leaf rust and is a fine milling and baking wheat with a yield about comparable to Pawnee. Ponca has had an average of about 4 per cent of the plants infested compared with an average of 80 per cent in Tenmarq in the same tests. Ponca derives its hessian fly resistance from *Triticum durum* used in an interspecific cross made many years ago between Marquis bread wheat and the macaroni wheat, the genes for resistance being present in the spring variety Marquillo, one parent of Ponca (Fig. 3).

Ponca was grown on 14.2 per cent of the Kansas wheat acreage in 1956, mostly in southeast Kansas where Pawnee is more susceptible to hessian fly. There, in some counties up to 78 per cent of the acreage was in Ponca. In other counties in the eastern two-thirds of Kansas where the hessian fly was a problem, 54 to 75 per cent of the acreage commonly was sown to Pawnee or Ponca.

Agricultural scientists in other states besides those in the hard red winter wheat growing area have been working toward incorporating hessian fly resistance into varieties adapted to their particular regions. A list of the wheats bred for resistance to hessian fly is given in Table III. The Kawvale variety has been replaced in its area of adaptation by Pawnee and Ponca. Dual, Russell, and Todd, which derive their resistance from the spring wheat Illinois No. 1W38 have been released too recently to assess their full value in fly control, but at least Dual appears to have met with favorable reception from farmers, and its resistance to hessian fly in the field has been up to expectations.

TABLE III.   Wheats Bred for Resistance to Hessian Fly, *Phytophaga Destructor* (Say)

Name	Year distributed	State
Kawvale	1932	Kansas
Pawnee	1942, 1943	Nebraska, Kansas
Big Club 43	1944	California
Ponca	1951	Kansas, Oklahoma
Dual	1955	Indiana
Russell	1956	Wisconsin
Todd	1956	Kentucky

Big Club 43 which was released in California in 1944 derives its resistance from the old white winter wheat called Dawson and now occupies 98 per cent of the acreage formerly infested with fly in central California. Shortly after the release of Big Club 43, it was planted so extensively in the hessian fly infested area that the population of fly which previously had infested 50 to 100 per cent of the wheat plants was reduced to the level that study of this insect had to be discontinued for lack of insects. Recent reports indicate that it is still almost impossible to find hessian fly in the Montezuma Hills region of California where this variety is grown. Thus in California and in Kansas entomologists and plant breeders have worked themselves out of a job except as agronomists breed new susceptible wheat otherwise better than the present available hessian fly-resistant ones.

Some of the methods of breeding plants for resistance to insects may be illustrated by studies now underway in several states in breeding alfalfa for resistance to the spotted alfalfa aphid *Therioaphis* (*Pterocallidium*) *maculata* (Buckton) (Fig. 4). This destructive insect was probably introduced in 1953. It was discovered in 1954 in the southwestern United States and now is present or has been collected in more than thirty states. Its rate of spread has surpassed that of any other insect of which we have a record and is partly due to its reproduction since all the insects are females and give birth to living young at a high rate of speed. The kinds of damage include the killing of seedlings and often larger plants, the reduction of yield of

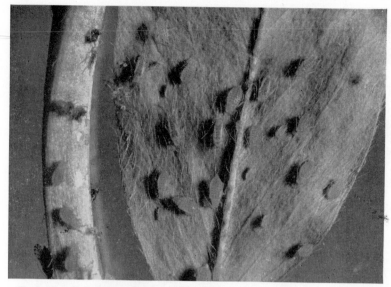

Fig. 4. The spotted alfalfa aphid was first discovered in the United States in 1954 and now has been collected in thirty states.

seed and forage, the reduction of the value of forage for animal food, and the deposit of honeydew which sometimes is thick enough to cause sicklebars to break when the alfalfa is cut. Early in its spread, the spotted alfalfa aphid reached some of the nurseries in Arizona, California, and in Nevada where new varieties of alfalfa were being tested, and where it was found that the variety Lahontan was resistant to this aphid (Fig. 5). Lahontan which is adapted in Nevada, Arizona, and California was bred for resistance to wilt and to the stem nematode. The variety is derived from five clones, three of which are known now to be resistant to the spotted alfalfa aphid and two are more or less susceptible (8). All five clones are resistant to the nematode, and hence the resistance to nematode and aphid are probably not the result of the same mechanism. Lahontan is now grown on an increasing acreage in the Southwest where it has been quite satisfactory in resistance to the aphid. As the aphid spread farther east the variety New Mexico 16* was found

* Now called Zia.

FIG. 5. Severe injury to seedlings of buffalo alfalfa (right) compared with much less injury to Lahontan (left) by spotted alfalfa aphid Manhattan, Kansas, September 1956.

to be resistant in that area and has been released to New Mexico farmers. A third variety Moapa, which has been released by the United States Department of Agriculture and the experiment stations of Nevada and California, is derived from plants known to carry resistance to the aphid selected out of the variety African.

When the insect reached Kansas, workers at the Ft. Hays Branch Agricultural Experiment Station and at Manhattan began a search for sources of resistance that could be used in breeding an alfalfa variety adapted to that area (5, 6). In fields that had been severely injured by the aphid, a few plants that appeared to be resistant to the insect were dug and brought into the greenhouse for testing. Several appeared to have some tolerance to the aphid and on at least one of the plants the aphid appeared unable to maintain a population. In tests both in the greenhouse (Fig. 6) and in the field (Fig. 5), Lahontan was shown to have the same resistance that had been reported for the variety in California and Nevada. A good many varieties and foreign plant introductions have been tested for the presence of resistance (1, 7). Resistant plants from some varieties, especially Lahontan, have been crossed to susceptible, adapted alfalfa clones, and selections are being made in the progeny. The commonly grown alfalfa varieties, Buffalo and Kansas Common, are quite highly susceptible to the aphids, but in flats of Buffalo grown in the greenhouse an occasional surviving plant occurs after the remainder of the plants are killed by the aphid. These surviving plants are the basis of an attempt to select and propagate a spotted alfalfa aphid-resistant strain that would otherwise be like Buffalo. Altogether the Hays Branch Station and the main station at Manhattan have screened nearly a quarter of a million Buffalo plants to pick out a few which have a varying amount of resistance and which were then tested and retested for their ability to survive aphid infestation. After the poorer ones were discarded, the remaining plants were tested for their ability to support an aphid population (Fig. 7). The more resistant plants from both kinds of tests were set out in an isolated planting at Hays and allowed to interpollinate.

Fig. 6. The survival in the greenhouse of Lahontan alfalfa seedlings (row 8) after heavy attack by spotted alfalfa aphid in comparison with other named and unnamed varieties such as Ladak (5), Rhizoma (1), and Ranger (2).

FIG. 7.   Individual alfalfa plants under test for ability to support spotted alfalfa aphid populations. Five or ten aphids per plant are placed in each box with a leaf from the plant and the progeny produced recorded at the end of a week. The range of production has been from 0 to 6 or more aphids per female per day on different plants.

Seeds from each of the plants were then sown in flats for comparison with Lahontan and Buffalo. When heavily infested with spotted alfalfa aphids, seedlings dervied from these resistant plants survived infestation about as well as Lahontan and far better than ordinary Buffalo. Twenty-two of the best of these plants, selected on the basis of the tolerance of their seedlings and the ability of the original plants to suppress reproduction in the aphid, have been planted to make a twenty-two clone synthetic* which will be widely tested in Kansas and elsewhere. Preliminary tests indicate that this synthetic is as good or better than Lahontan in resistance to the aphid while it should have the other desirable characters and adaptation of Buffalo. Details concerning it will be published in the near future.

Thus three years after the discovery of the spotted alfalfa aphid in the United States, three resistant varieties are ready for farm use or are being used on farms. All three varieties ap-

* Recently distributed as Cody.

parently carry satisfactory resistance and adaptation in the areas for which they are recommended.

The methods used in breeding for resistance to the spotted alfalfa aphid have been:

1. A search for sources of resistance:
   a. In farmers' fields infested by the insects.
   b. In adapted varieties such as Buffalo.
   c. In foreign plant introductions.
2. The hybridization with improved adapted varieties followed by selection in segregating generations and the testing in comparison with fixed hybrids and other selections.

It should be emphasized that the methods of study of resistance must vary according to the components of resistance and habits of the insect being studied. The twenty-two clones from Buffalo alfalfa which are being used to breed a synthetic variety resistant to the spotted alfalfa aphid have successfully passed tests both for tolerance and antibiosis.

When insect reaction is not studied as a continuous part of the crop improvement program, plant breeders are likely to increase the insect control problems by the release of more susceptible varieties. In the search for sources of resistance to various insects it has frequently been observed that most of the foreign plant introductions studied were more susceptible to the insect than were varieties currently grown by farmers. This was true, for example, in the search for sources of resistance to the greenbug (11) where about two-thirds of the strains studied were more susceptible than the commonly grown wheat being used as a susceptible check. A knowledge of the insect reaction of varieties being studied in a crop improvement program is of great importance.

The following are the important characteristics of insect resistance as a pest control measure:

1. In contrast to chemical control, which is sudden and often rapidly decreasing in effect and often presents a toxic residue problem, resistance is cumulative and continuing and is without residue problems. The combined use of plant resistance and insecticides may therefore give greater than additive control and perhaps be longer lasting.

2. The breeding of insect-resistant varieties requires the continued cooperation of plant breeder and entomologist.

3. The production of a resistant crop plant variety requires ordinarily ten to fifteen years, although sometimes there are means of shortening this time.

4. The effect of a resistant variety has been to increase the yield or quality of the crop and often to decrease the insect population even in neighboring susceptible varieties.

5. The use of resistant varieties involves no direct cost to the user and perhaps adds the value of an otherwise improved variety. Where the margin of profit per acre is small the use of resistant varieties reduces the cost of production and increases stabilization. Where in agriculture will these benefits not be welcomed?

REFERENCES

1. Anon. Kansas surveys alfalfa varieties for aphid resistance. *What's New in Crops and Soils* 10:23 (1958).

2. Dahms, R. G., R. O. Snelling, and F. A. Fenton. Effect of several varieties of sorghum and other host plants on the biology of the chinch bug. *J. Econ. Entomol.* 29:1147-1153 (1936).

3. Dahms, R. G., and E. A. Wood, Jr. Evaluation of greenbug damage to small grains. *J. Econ. Entomol.* 50:443-446 (1957).

4. Gallun, R. L. Races of hessian fly. *J. Econ. Entomol.* 48:608-609 (1955).

5. Harvey, T. L., and H. L. Hackerott. Spotted alfalfa aphid. *Kansas Agr. Expt. Sta. Circ.* 345:21-24, 1956.

6. ———. Apparent resistance to the spotted alfalfa aphid selected from seedlings of susceptible alfalfa varieties. *J. Econ. Entomol.* 49:289-291 (1956).

7. Hackerott, H. L., T. L. Harvey, E. L. Sorensen, and Reginald H. Painter. Varietal differences in survival of alfalfa seedlings infested with spotted alfalfa aphids. *Agron. J.* 50:139-141 (1958).

8. Howe, W. L., and Oliver F. Smith. Resistance to the spotted alfalfa aphid in Lahontan alfalfa. *J. Econ. Entomol.* 50:320-324 (1957).

9. Painter, Reginald H. *Insect Resistance in Crop Plants.* The Macmillan Co., New York, 1951.

10. ———. Resistance of plants to insects. *Ann. Rev. Entomol.* 3: 267-290 (1958).

11. Painter, Reginald H., and Don C. Peters. Screening wheat varieties and hybrids for resistance to the greenbug. *J. Econ. Entomol.* 49:546-548 (1956).

12. Pathak, M. D., and Reginald H. Painter. Differential amounts of material taken up by four biotypes of corn leaf aphid from resistant and susceptible sorghums. *Ann. Entomol. Soc. Am.* 51:250-254 (1958).

13. Potter, C., and E. M. Gillham. Effect of host-plant on the resistance of *Acrythosiphon pisum* (Harris) to insecticides. *Bull. Entomol. Research* 48:317-322 (1957).

14. Sifuentes, Juan Antonio. The resistance of sorghum varieties and hybrids to chinch bugs, *Blissus leucopterus* (Say). Master's thesis Kansas State College, 1958.

15. Snelling, R. O., R. H. Painter, J. H. Parker, and W. M. Osborn. Resistance of sorghum to chinch bug. *U. S. Dept. Agr. Tech. Bull.* 585, 1937.

Index

Achondroplasia, 213
Airplane spraying, 11, 27
Airplane surveys, 26
Alfalfa, 131, 133, 219, 246, 259
   Lahonton, 259
   Ranger, 220
Alternaria solani, 56
Ambrosia beetles, 28
Animal Disease Laboratory, 13
Animal parasites
   losses from, 93
Antagonism, 127, 129, 130
Anthelmintic agents, 94
Anthelmintics
   antimony, 106
   arsenic compounds, 105, 106
   cadmium, 104
   carbamazines, 97
   chlorinated hydrocarbons, 103
   cyanacethydrazide, 106
   enheptin, 111
   fluorides, 102
   halogen compounds, 102
   hexachloroethane, 103
   hydrochlorides, 107
   mercury compounds, 106
   nicarbazin, 112
   nitrofurans, 111
   nitrophenide, 111
   phenothiazine, 94
   phthalofyne, 107
   piperazines, 97
   sulfa drugs, 109, 110
   tin, 106
   toluene, 108
   trithiadol, 113
Anthrax, 7

Antibiosis, 60, 250
Antibiotic agents, 49, 60, 108
Antibiotics
   actidione, 63
   agrimycin, 61
   anisomycin, 62
   hygromycin, 109
   phytoactin, 62
   phytostreptin, 62
   streptomycin, 61
   Terramycin, 61
Antimyiatics, 85, 86
Ants
   beneficial, 184
   imported fire, 12
Ants and biological balance, 195
Aphids, 88, 154, 157, 185, 252
Apple, 246
Apple scab, 232
Artificial culture of plants, 149
Artificial sweeteners, 45
Aspergillus niger, 57
Atomic radiation of screwworm
   fly, 169
Avocado, 131, 193

Bacillus popilliae, 143
Bacillus thuringiensis, 143, 145
Backcross breeding, 221, 224
Bacteria to control insects, 143
Bacterial diseases
   resistance to, 234
Bacterial wilt
   in alfalfa, 220
Balance and pest control, 202
Bark beetles, 24, 29
Barley, 246, 252

267

Extension work, 33

Fall webworm, 140, 143
FAO catalog of breeding stocks, 223
Federal Insecticide, Fungicide and Rodenticide Act, 39
Ferbam and insects, 203
Fireblight, 61
Flax rust, 225
Food additives, 45
Food, Drug, and Cosmetic Act, 40
Foot-and-mouth disease, 6
Forest diseases
    control, 17
    control by chemicals, 19
    losses due to, 15
Forest insects
    biological control, 31
    control, 23, 27
    losses caused by, 24
    surveys, 26
Forest management, 29
Form, host nutrition effects on, 161
Fowl leukosis, 213
Fowl plague, 5
Fowl typhoid
    resistance to, 212
Fruit fly
    Mediterranean, 4, 6, 7, 12
    Oriental, 4
Fungi
    control of insects by, 141
Fungicides, see also *Antibiotics*
    Bordeaux mixture, 206
    carbamates, 49, 59, 60
    chloranil, 55
    dichlone, 54
    efficiency of, 58
    gliotoxin, 61
    glyodin, 51, 65, 204
    imidazoline, 52

    karathane, 65
    maneb, 60
    mercury, 53
    nabam, 59
    pyrazoles, 52
    quinone, 49, 55
    silver, 53
    stability of, 59
    sulfur compounds, 53, 151, 202, 206
    thioureas, 52
    thiuram, 55
    triazines, 52, 56
    zineb, 59
Fungus spore membranes, 50
Fusarium oxysporum, 130
Fusarium solani, 132
Fusarium wilt, 230, 231

Genetic resistance
    of animals, 211
    of crops species, 217, 229, 264
    of forest species, 17, 31
Genetics of pathogens, 234
Glanders
    in horses, 5
Glyodin and insects, 204
Golden nematode, 4
Grafting, 224
Grape phylloxera and mites, 185
Grasshoppers, 11, 144, 159, 247
Green bug, 252
Green manures and potato scab, 131
Gypsy moth, 8, 140

Hall scale, 12
Heartrot
    in trees, 21
Heartworm
    in dogs, 98
Helminths, 97
Hemlock looper, 27